Roberta Latow has been an art dealer with galleries in Springfield, Massachusetts and New York City. She has also been an interior designer in the USA, Europe, Africa and the Middle East, travelling extensively to acquire arts, artefacts and handicrafts. Her sense of adventure and her experiences on her travels have enriched her writing; her fascination with heroic men and women; how and why they create the lives they do for themselves; the romantic and erotic core within – all these themes are endlessly interesting to her, and form the subjects and backgrounds of her novels.

'Her books are solidly about sex . . . it adds a frisson. It sets a hell of a standard' *The Sunday Times*

White Moon, Black Sea

Roberta Latow

HEADLINE

First published in Great Britain in 1988
by Futura Publications

Reprinted in this edition in 1994
by HEADLINE BOOK PUBLISHING

Grateful acknowledgement is made to the following for permission to
reprint previously published material: Chatto and Windus Ltd:
Excerpt from 'Perilous Things' by C.P. Cavafy from *The Complete
Poems of Cavafy*, translated by Rae Dalven. Reprinted by
permission.

10 9 8 7 6 5 4 3 2 1

ISBN 0 7472 4393 X

Typeset by
Letterpart Limited, Reigate, Surrey
Printed and bound in Great Britain by
HarperCollins Manufacturing, Glasgow

HEADLINE BOOK PUBLISHING
A division of Hodder Headline PLC
Headline House, 79 Great Titchfield Street, London W1P 7FN

For
Kenneth and Caroline Hawkins
good neighbours, fine friends

I shall not fear my passions like a coward.
I shall yield my body to sensual delights,
to enjoyments that one dreams about,
to the most audacious amorous desires,
to the wanton impulses of my blood, without
a single fear, for whenever I wish.

C.P. Cavafy

Chapter 1

An electrical storm gripped the aircraft, tossing the Boeing 707 from one fierce hand of wind to the other as if it were a slight, silvery toy. A loud crack of thunder tearing at his eardrums, Rashid Lala Mustapha watched through the small oval window as a bolt of lightning shot across the black sky, luridly illuminating the cabin. The aisles were littered with items that had broken free from the overhead racks: cardboard boxes tied with string, handwoven baskets with cloth stretched and sewn over the tops, hand luggage, bunches of flowers, coats, blankets, pillows. In a slow dance of chaos, the last and heaviest pieces left on the shelves plummeted on to passengers' heads and shoulders and tumbled to a restless stop, only to bounce off the knee-deep clutter in the aisles.

Passengers were screaming and weeping in panic. Fear settled like a dense fog inside the plane, a pungent scent that filled the nostrils and put the soul on guard.

Rashid did not travel alone, but with a man he had met secretly only hours before, a man named Nikos who was a big handsome native of Crete, and so sure of himself that he had instantly won Rashid's confidence. Nikos had made him feel certain the prize he

1

had sought in vain for so long would be his at last. Now this paragon of self-confidence was weeping and screaming along with all the others on the aircraft. Tears streamed down his ghost-white face, a hand over his mouth trying to hold back sickness. Rashid was furious. He managed to get a paper bag to the man just as the aircraft rolled once more to one side.

Passengers who were beyond thinking the least bit rationally released their seat belts and scrabbled through the mess to retrieve their possessions. The air pockets pulled them down and knocked them into the seats. The noise was deafening, yet there wasn't a steward to be seen, nor a calming word from the intercom.

The wind changed direction and pounded against the other side of the plane as it lurched forward. The hysterical passengers still in the aisles were knocked down, hurled against the seats.

'There's more to come,' Rashid muttered to himself. 'More thunder and lightning and God knows what.' It didn't matter, he thought, although he was not ready to die – especially not now, when he was on the brink of retrieving what he fiercely believed was rightfully his. Dicing with danger, riding on the edge, hand-in-hand with the devil or God, it was all the same to him. He would beat those two at their game.

The cabin was suddenly plunged into darkness as a bolt of lightning struck the plane. Then, eerily, it glowed inside and out from the light generated by another huge bolt. Rashid registered a vision of humanity that both disgusted him and reinforced his calm and fearlessness in the face of chaos . . . and death.

In less than three minutes the plane was travelling

2

on an even keel, air pockets gone and the blackened sky growing lighter. The rain was letting up, but within there was no calm. Havoc. Screaming and shouting mingled with the sharp stink of vomit, stale hot air and heavy doses of body odour. The passengers, mostly Greeks, were still so hysterical they were oblivious to having ridden out the storm.

A near disaster in the air was a first for Rashid. There were always firsts in Rashid's life. He thrived on them. He looked out of the window, away from the mess around him, and saw the sky growing lighter still. There, off in the distance, was the sun, a red ball suspended in dusky light.

He spoke to Nikos, his new-found friend, his supposed protector, the man who had been sent to see that he and his plain paper-wrapped parcel of dollar banknotes were safely delivered to the island.

'Look. It's over. It has been for minutes now. For Christ's sake, man, look out of the window. We're safe. Pull yourself together.'

Nikos was still white, still frozen with terror. Rashid stared at him for several seconds, horrified by the fear in the man's eyes: the danger was behind them, yet it continued to possess him. Grabbing Nikos by the lapels of his jacket, Rashid shook him violently. Should he slap him across the face to bring him to his senses? He raised his hand and then lowered it, remembering that the men of Crete never forget a humiliation. Instead he let the man go, and said, 'Nikos, we are safe, and you have a job to do. You must deliver me and my parcel to Mr Mavrodakis.'

The mention of Mavrodakis had an immediate effect on Nikos. Understanding glimmered in his eyes.

A voice boomed through the din over the intercom.

3

The pilot was shouting in Greek for calm. He repeated his demand many times before the noise in the plane began to abate. At last there was relative calm, punctuated by loud complaints accompanied by elbow pushing and whimpering as passengers salvaged their possessions.

Rashid and Mavrodakis's emissary were the only ones seated when the signs flashed on, asking the passengers of the afternoon Athens–Khania flight to prepare for landing. The clouds, now white, parted, and at last there it was: the coastline of Crete rising rugged and impressive out of the sparkling Aegean. The plane began its descent with its passengers still scrambling around in the aisles amongst the debris.

Rashid, like the Greeks, always called Crete 'the big island'. Big it surely looked, and unmalleable, with its mountain ranges in the far distance. Rashid had a great affection for Crete and its people in whom he detected a nobler strain than in other Greeks. He liked that, as much as any Turk could like anything Greek.

The plane was now flying low over Souda Bay towards the airport. Rashid smiled to himself, remembering there was nearly always a storm around Crete before landing, whether by plane or ship, and the reaction of the Greeks to it invariably punctured his vision of their nobility. It was one of the reasons he never travelled on commercial transportation except when, as now, he travelled in secret and as inconspicuously as possible.

No clouds now. The sky was a deep, Greek blue, and he felt the thrill he always felt as the plane flew easily over his Crete, the Crete of his ancestors, notorious Ottomans who, during the Turkish occupation, had ruled it with bloodied hands. They were robber princes who ruthlessly stole the best from the people along the coast from Rethymnon past Khania to the tip of the island. When the Turkish occupation was over, the world believed that the Lala Mustaphas had relinquished the land. Just a handful of people knew otherwise. Christos Mavrodakis was one of those people.

A smooth touchdown, doors open at last, a rush of hot air through the plane and the angry Greeks with their broken property pushed their way down onto the tarmac and across to the tiny airport terminal. Rashid and Nikos were the last to leave the plane.

Two men met them at the foot of the stairs. Nikos, the whiff of vomit still on him, put up a macho front for them. The Cretans, clumsily protective, walked their visitors briskly to an old black Buick waiting on the edge of the tarmac.

Down hot, dusty roads, over rough terrain stubbled with silvery-green olive trees, the driver went at suicidal speed as if bent on killing everyone in his path and in the car.

The oppressively high temperature and humidity seemed to bother Rashid not at all. He rode in the back of the car, cool in spite of the heat. The closer they came to Christos Mavrodakis's villa, the more he savoured every sight and sound of the journey. His quest was nearly over, all the years of intrigue, plots, and plans that had miscarried would belong soon to the past. He could think of nothing but the imminent repossession of the Oujie lands and estates in Turkey and Crete that were rightfully his.

He cared not at all that he was deceiving, cheating, stealing from Mirella Wingfield Corey, the woman he also loved. He had deliberately hunted her down as soon as he'd learned about her inheritance in order to seduce her and use her to get back the Oujie legacy to retrieve what her great-grandmother had stolen from his family. Why should Mirella object, since she and he were not emotionally but erotically deeply in love, and committed to each other in that love? He would expect her to recognise that what he did had to do with honour – family honour and not their relationship.

The car swerved off the main highway onto a narrow road and sped onward, spraying gravel in its wake. The occasional olive tree and dry scrubby landscape merged into miles of well-tended olive groves that extended right to the top of the mountain. The driver honked the Buick's horn as he negotiated a steep curve in the road and approached a pair of rusting sheet iron gates set into a high, crumbling, whitewashed wall. Dogs began to bark. A fat black cat with one eye missing, a hind leg shorter than the other three, and an ear half eaten away, rose from one of the pilasters, stretched lazily, hunched her back and hissed menacingly at the approaching car. Two handsome young men, as tough looking as the beaten-up cat, rose from rickety, weatherworn wooden chairs tilted against the pilasters flanking the gate. They wore open-necked, cotton plaid shirts and faded jeans tucked into shabby white traditional Cretan boots. Expensive-looking rifles in hand, they strutted towards the car that halted in its own dust cloud ten feet from the gates.

As soon as they greeted the men in the front seat, they slung their rifles over their shoulders and shook hands with them, then checked the back seat before shaking hands with Rashid and Nikos. Their faces broke into smiles for Rashid. They had done several jobs for Mavrodakis that had involved Rashid, and they liked him and admired not only his way with women, but also the ruthless and sometimes dangerous deals they had watched him pull off. They had seen the macho Rashid in action, and he was everything a Cretan admired in a man.

They all spoke in Greek and laughed when Rashid said, 'My God, she is still alive, your Salome! Each time I arrive, I expect to find that cat has not survived her last fight. But the old warrior is always here, minus another piece of herself.'

In a gesture typically Greek, one of the guards waved his hand in a series of circles, and said, 'Ah, that one. The fearless one, the one with not nine but ninety-nine lives. Pttu.' He spat on the ground and bent forward and tooted the horn. All eyes were on Salome as she sprang the ten feet from the pilaster through the air, her body flattened, legs splayed, fur flying, one eye glaring, the sewn one squinting. She landed with a soft thump on the hood of the car.

The great iron doors were slowly swung open from the inside as Salome attacked the windshield of the Buick with her paws, making fearsome hissing sounds. The driver shot the car forward. The cat swerved off the hood and up into the air to crash-land into an enormous hibiscus bush in full bloom, just inside the gate. Dead, never. The fight was on. She went for the Doberman Pinschers held back on leads by the two guards who worked the inside of the gate.

Rashid watched the pitched battle through the rear window of the car as it drove through a surprisingly different landscape now: lilac, rhododendron, camellia, gardenia, hibiscus, no longer bushes but overgrown trees. In this romantic Mediterranean botanical paradise wisteria mingled with bougainvillea and jasmine and trumpet vines in dazzling patches of colour that snaked over the decaying garden walls. The tendrils of the vines wrapped voluptuously over everything in the garden, even the seventy-foot date palms, royal palms aged beyond fruitfulness but queens of the garden still. Lemon and orange trees, heavy with fruit, and huge fig trees, oozing plump, purple ripeness, added to the lushness of Christos Mavrodakis's Eden. In six acres of overgrown, wonderful gardens, only the pistachio trees lining a winding road, regimented and at attention like a guard of honour, appeared to be well pruned and cared for. The dusty, rutted dirt road with its proud sentries bearing clusters of the delicious pistachio nuts led to a surprisingly large and beautiful neo-classical villa. Once the colour of terracotta, now faded to a soft, warm pink, the forty-room villa evoked a charm that indeed craved guarding from the intrusion of a modern plastic world.

Rashid met Christos on the stairs leading up to the house. They shook hands and then clasped each other warmly.

'How was the flight?'

'How was the flight!' The two men repeated the phrase in one voice and identical mocking tones, then laughed. It was a familiar joke between them, and the first thing every Cretan asked a new arrival to the island.

'Here is the package,' Rashid said abruptly.

'I did not believe you would bring it, Rashid. I thought you would back out of the deal at the end.'

'How extraordinary of you to think that. What ever gave you such an idea?' asked Rashid, apparently baffled by Christos's remark.

The men looked at each other and the question

loomed large between them. At last Christos snapped his fingers and called out, 'Yannis'. A white-haired, elderly man appeared immediately at the head of the stairs, stopped for a second and hurried down to greet Rashid.

Christos took the heavy, brown paper parcel from Rashid's hands and gave it to Yannis, then turned back to Rashid and asked, 'A drink? Tea? Coffee? Something to refresh you before we settle our business?'

'Good idea, Christos.'

'Bravo. Come, let's walk a bit. We'll go to the summerhouse.'

A woman watched them from an upstairs balcony, standing in the shadows, tall and majestic, an exotic beauty dressed all in white. She wore a Dior silk suit with nipped-in waist and a skirt cut on the bias that hung to the middle of the calf. Wide strips of silk, cotton and chiffon were cleverly entwined and wound around her head in a dramatic turban worn over the sheerest of veils pulled close over her face and under her chin. Tucked under her arm was a large, slim, envelope handbag of the softest leather, and her feet were shod in simple Ferragamo court shoes. On her ears were large, square-cut diamond earrings, and a platinum dog collar studded with matching diamonds clasped her long, sensuous neck. Her fingers sparkled with more stones exquisitely cut in various sizes and shapes. Her dramatic presence was like a fire that burned in an igloo of pure snow and clear ice.

She watched the men – Rashid, her master, and Christos Mavrodakis, his lifelong friend, her tormentor – as they walked along a path swathed through the jungle of luscious scents and blossoms towards the ramshackle summerhouse. She watched and she waited to be summoned by Rashid. They would be going home to Istanbul. She to Oda Lala's, the bordello where she lived waiting for Rashid's commands and her stolen hours with her lover, the American black man, Moses. Rashid to his life and home in Istanbul and to Mirella Wingfield Corey, the most important woman in his life.

Her gaze followed Rashid, his jacket now removed and slung over one shoulder. He reached up and picked an overly ripe purple fig from a huge sprawling tree weighed down with its fruit. He broke it open with his thumbs and, pressing the sweet flesh to his lips, sucked it into his mouth. She could see his pleasure in the taste of the fruit. He dropped the skin on the path and walking over it he plucked another from the neighbouring tree. 'My beautiful, decadent Rashid, my destiny,' she murmured.

Christos was walking, his hands behind his back, next to Rashid, and was saying, 'The others in the syndicate never doubted that you would go through with this takeover. Only *I* doubted it. But then, only I had ever seen you with Mirella, and how different you were then. Only *I* had witnessed that night at Oda Lala's when she was ready to enslave herself to you, and you, at the very last minute, released her. I was so certain then that at last someone had real power over you, that at last someone had broken you, Rashid. You wanted her for more than your sexual slave, or her inheritance. You didn't want to throw her away like the other females in your life whom you enjoy ruining. I even laughed to myself to think it had been a woman, a woman who possessed so much of the lands and their archaeological sites that you believe to be rightfully yours.

'How wrong could I be? Ever since we were children you have never ceased to surprise me. Nothing has changed; the surprises continue. You let her go. You allowed her to leave you for Adam Corey. I don't know how you could have done that. I could not. I believed you to have the coldest heart of any man alive, until I saw your face at her wedding when you walked her down the aisle on your arm and gave her away to Adam. I knew then. It was written all over your face, it burned in your eyes: You had never let her go. You possess that woman just as much as her husband does. You play the game of love with her; you are obsessed with each other.'

The men stepped into the dilapidated summer-house, an octagonal wooden affair of peeling, faded turquoise-colored paint and broken windows, topped off by an onion-domed roof of tarnished copper that had over the years been repaired with lead. They sat down in a pair of high-backed, wicker rocking chairs placed next to a round table covered in crisp white damask. It was laden with marvellous sweets from Turkey and Greece, Italy and Paris. In the centre was an ornate silver samovar. An old Cretan peasant woman stood off to one side at a small table on which a gas flame glowed ready for her to make fresh Turkish coffee. Nikos, Rashid's companion on the flight, stood at another table ready to serve anything alcoholic they wanted.

Rashid and Christos had been speaking in English. Now, Christos switched into Turkish, which the two attendants had no knowledge of. He picked up a *Fiora Panaforte Margherita*, the delicious Italian sweet from Siena that is rather like a half-inch thick pancake mixed with candied orange, lemon, and melon rind,

11

and solid with sugared almonds covered in a dusting of plain white flour. He broke off a piece and handed it to his cousin Rashid.

'There was a time about a year ago,' Christos went on, 'that the syndicate were beginning to worry about how deep your involvement went with the heiress Mirella. All those jewels you were buying her and they were picking up the tab for. But you came through, just before they were about to order you to deliver those corporate holdings we wanted. You had little choice then, you were in too deep to us. And you did understand that we would have killed her, if we had to, to get what we wanted.

'But this time is entirely different. We fronted for you, happily bought heavily for you, lied and cheated and used up a great many favours owed us to get you what you asked. We take care of our own, you know that. We felt we owed it to you because, when Mirella Wingfield sold you the corporate holdings we wanted, you made us one of the richest investment syndicates in the world and gave several of us the political power we desired.'

'Not so very different, Christos. You may take care of your own, but always at a price. True, you and the others were not cut in for a piece of these property deals, but each of you did get a twelve million dollars golden handshake and front money.'

'That's true, but to be expected. After all, in our place you would have done the same. Favours for friends are good. They are even better when preceded by the thank-you gift. And now, here you are, delivering the last present. I thought Mirella meant more to you than a hundred-year-old vendetta. You will lose her over this latest betrayal of yours. She holds lands

12

and sites in Turkey and here in Crete equivalent to the size of a small American state. Unknowingly she handed them over to phoney archaeological trusts and charitable organisations, the art and music foundations you secretly created in order to defraud her. What choice will she have? Especially since you insist upon announcing to the world that you alone have acquired them in a successful takeover that has righted an injustice to your family.'

'You never did understand women, Christos. Especially not women sexually devoted to a man. In time she will forgive me. If she doesn't, it will have been her loss not mine. You know what I demand of women. Total submission has always been the goal, the heart of a relationship for me. And leading a woman down that path is the sexual adventure I delight in. Mirella has kept me enthralled. She's one of the most fascinating women in the world, and I played an enormous part in making her that. You have to remember I was there, on the spot, from the time she inherited her great-grandmother's estate. I helped her to change from a sexually repressed woman, a mere high-powered American executive at the UN, to one of the most sensuous, free-spirited, glamorous and wealthy women in the world. She left me to marry Adam Corey for true love, whatever that may be, but she returns to me for another kind of love, an unadulterated sexual love. She'll never leave me again. She is no less bound to me than she is to her husband. I am as sure of that as I am of anything in this world. Adam is a famous lover of women, and I know he holds Mirella as much by sexual love as by the affection they share. But he hasn't the temperament to love only erotically. I do, and that's how I am able to keep Mirella, no matter

13

how many times I betray her.

'Ah, I begin to see. You were the last one to be paid off, Christos. You are the one to turn over all the deeds involved in the takeover. And so you thought, "This is his last chance. Rashid may renege on the deal and keep us all as front men and offer us shares, just so as he can save his secret love." That's why you demanded I give you Humayun for a week before the transfer and final payment. It was to keep her as a kind of hostage until I followed through. Or to make sure I followed through. It was a little extra insurance against non-delivery of your twelve million. And you chose Humayun because only you know how deep my involvement is with her. Tut, tut. Bad, Christos. That was bad. You didn't need a hostage. You know how ruthless I can be. I would never give up my quest, not for any woman.'

'Not *only* as a kind of hostage, Rashid. I did enjoy Humayun. She is the most sexually accomplished, inventive and obedient woman I have ever encountered. In fact, I want to keep her. Name your price.'

'You know better than that, Christos. I'll never set Humayun free, ever. Don't be greedy. Have I ever denied her to you? I can't remember a time when I have. Nor will there be a time when I will. And what, after all, would be the point? You would only lock her away and become more cruel towards her with every sexual encounter and orgasm you achieve together. You'll never settle the conflict that tortures you. It isn't as if you are a bisexual who can't make up his mind. You are and have always been, mentally and sexually, a homosexual. Boys are what you want. You can never have enough of them. You hate Humayun and you hate yourself. Why? Because she is a woman, but you cannot resist her.

Whatever it is you want from her gets right under your homosexual skin. All you would do if I did sell her to you is torture her to death. Your problem, Christos, is that you have never recovered from the shock of discovering that it's a woman who is the most debauched, depraved sexual turn-on in your life. A woman who is your sexual outlet, the only person who joyously will do anything, even to the death, to deliver you into sexual oblivion.'

Christos's face clouded. Rashid watched the vein just under the skin at his temple pulsate. He studied his cousin's handsome, but cruelly decadent face. Visions of Humayun, stripped, and confronting a group of handsome young men came to mind. Confused memories of sick and corrupt sexual delights that carried an erotic intensity far beyond wantonness. Suddenly Rashid was filled with a prurient passion. He wanted Humayun and he wanted her now, right here in his cousin's summerhouse. His craving for sexual delight was so great that under normal circumstances he would have had Humayun brought to him at once. But these were not normal circumstances. His quest was nearly at its end and that overrode everything else in his life.

Rashid squatted down before his cousin. They gazed into each other's eyes. Rashid patted Christos on the shoulder, then gently on the cheek.

'Christos, you, Humayun and I have had amazing sexual adventures together. There will be more, there will always be more for the three of us. I'll see to it for you, as I always have. Oda Lala's door is always open to you, and Humayun is under orders to deny you nothing. The three of us will know greater ecstasy than we have ever had, I promise. But I cannot sell

Humayun to you. She belongs to me. Now let's have some coffee.'

Rashid's words seemed to dissolve Christos's anger and disappointment. A light returned to his eyes, but no joy.

When he spoke his voice was hard, but not empty of affection. Relieved, Rashid listened to Christos say, 'There is a devil in you. But I find also a real generosity. That is what corrupts me.'

Rashid and Christos rose and clasped each other in a hug, and nothing more was said about the matter. He listened to his cousin give instructions to the old woman to make coffee, black, thick and sweet, and to bring tumblers of ice-cold water, the Greek and Turkish complement to all the sugar and fruit in their pastries. He watched Christos slice the cakes and tarts and other rich delicacies, spoon out Greek preserves in their thick sugary syrup on to small white plates for them to sample.

All the while Rashid kept thinking how like Christos it was to drop a one-liner that cut straight to the truth. Not a condemnation but a statement that told it the way it was and, at the same time, announced that the subject was closed.

Christos had always fascinated Rashid. It was the strange mix in him: tantalised by boys, in love with beauty and elegance, yet often restrained by his passion for what was simple and lofty in Greek island life. A shrewd, agile mind; an intelligence never flaunted. In his reclusive and private world, he managed to wield enormous power with close acquaintances who were statesmen, artists, media celebrities. He was a valued trouble-shooter for them, hence the wealthy, erudite dilettante he was today, yet one who had not shed the friends he had made on the way up.

In spite of his celebrity, he was unavailable to international society because of his manic insistence on privacy. Reputedly a man of culture and generosity who could be hard, ruthless and shrewd, Christos remained shrouded in mystery. No one really knew him. The notoriety and gossip, the extravagant stories about his personal and public life, gave him no joy. Who could say what did – except perhaps, Rashid, his closest friend, and the men who shared his brief, indeterminate affairs?

Christos had two passions that nourished him. His love for young nubile boys and the conquering and educating of them; and the sharp, quick mind he enjoyed using to exploit situations to their fullest. Everything in life was dealt with passionately, in extroverted joy and affection. All surface and very little depth. He lived his life like a Greek tycoon, without display, and with the heart of a poet and the eye of an artist.

Rashid enjoyed the contrast in looks between Christos and himself. His cousin was still very handsome, short – only five feet eight inches tall, with wide shoulders and a chunky body. His rugged, perfectly proportioned face, with a squarish, slightly cleft, chin was framed by a shock of pure white hair worn just a bit too long, thick and straight, curling up at the nape of the neck. The snow-white hair, the always dark tan, the tough masculine face, were all dominated by a pair of bright blue, sensuous eyes. Lascivious eyes. The two cousins were very much alike in one thing, they were sexually hungry all the time. Both were notorious sexual seducers. But Christos chose young men, and

17

left a string of bewildered male lovers across the world.

These casualties of love afforded him the reputation among rich, cosmopolitan homosexuals and the lower-class, rough-trade boys they sometimes favoured, of a virile, highly sexed lover who was able to satisfy his men as much with his lovemaking as with his generous gifts, money and romance.

Where did his money come from? The host of bodyguards always around him; the mysterious callers who flew in and out of his financial empire based on the mountain of olive groves in Crete; his Athens office building in Syntagma Square; the family villa in Sounion; the large roof garden flat he kept at the Grande Bretagne; signalled an illegal international crime syndication, but his excellent political and police connections challenged the assumption.

It always amused Rashid that with a converted Greek *caique* sailing the Greek Islands, a schooner moored in Cap Ferrat below his twenty-room villa there, an apartment in the Palais Royal in Paris, and permanent suites reserved for him at Claridges in London and the Pierre in New York, Christos never conducted business except when in Greece. All who wanted to deal had to do as Rashid was doing, conduct it in Christos's own territory. Rashid was convinced that it was true Christos held an advantage over his business associates because, by the time they had been through the trials and tribulations of the Athens airport, or of getting to Crete, they were compliant, and wanted only to deal and get out of the country as fast as possible.

That had been the pattern Rashid had adopted in the last twenty years. But it had not always been that way. There had been a time when he would have stayed with Christos for days and sometimes weeks enjoying his hospitality. And there had even been a time during Rashid's Oxford years when he maintained one of his family's period houses in the old port of Khania where he entertained his university friends and enjoyed the company of the foreign colony there. He thought about that as he mounted the stairs of the villa with Christos at his side. Suddenly a picture flashed through his mind: Humayun and himself, in their younger days, their first week together in Khania. His desire for her returned, only to be quickly put aside. Hunting down another portion of the Oujie legacy possessed him more.

Chapter 2

Rashid had no idea how he expected to feel at the moment of his triumph. He had never fantasised about it. He was excited, aware of all the adrenaline pumping in his body. But that was not unusual for Rashid, just part of deal making. When he entered the library with Christos to complete his takeover, Mirella was the last thing on his mind.

The comfortable coolness of the room after the heat in the garden cast a spell of rightness over Rashid. Orientalist paintings – Gerome, Lewis, David Roberts and the prize, an Ingres – adorned the walls between bookshelves that held one of the finest collections of rare books on Greece and Turkey. White marble busts of ancient Greeks and Turks, set on shiny black marble columns under dusty kenitia palms set in China pots on an enormous silk Isphahan carpet of great age seemed to be awaiting the return to the family of more of their lost heritage. Queen Anne wing chairs and cream silk draperies embroidered with vines, blossoms and singing birds, and Georgian furniture completed the room.

Christos walked to the windows. One by one he pushed open the shutters so that the still bright late afternoon sun streaked across the carpet and the room sprang to life. Like the garden, the room was dishevelled, carrying its own kind of grand chic in its disarray. If the curtains were frayed, hanging in ribbons in some places, it hardly mattered because they were more grand than worn, more museum worthy than not. And suddenly pride came into it. It was culturally proud and powerful. The two men and their purpose added tension and excitement.

Christos and Rashid sat opposite one another separated by a handsome mahogany George III partner's desk. Christos glanced first at his watch and then at a sheet of paper lying on the desk. The phone began to ring. He ignored it, his eyes fixed on Rashid's face. He thought he actually saw Rashid flinch as the phone cut into the quiet of the room.

'Your golden fleece, Rashid?' he said, as he reached down and picked up a dark purple kidskin box by its handle. He stood, smiled and handed it across the desk to Rashid, who rose to receive it.

Both men sat down again and Rashid returned the smile. A light danced in his dark brown eyes. 'Could be,' he said, 'I hope so. But let's wait for the telephone calls.' He looked at his watch and added. 'Well, one of the banks is calling on time.'

'Your integrity was never in question, Rashid. Only your involvement with Mirella. But I think a cool head rules that heart of yours. Take the box now, and enjoy your triumph. Here's the key.'

He tossed a gold key to Rashid, who caught it in mid air with one hand. Christos picked up the telephone.

Rashid listened to his cousin's conversation, his left hand on the box, his right clenched around the gold key. He made no move to use it.

'Ah, Mr Phenneger. And is the sun shining in

Lausanne? How does it find you, sir? Well, I trust?'
There was a long pause while the banker on the other
end of the line spoke. Then Christos continued. 'I see.
Well, thank you for being so prompt in confirming its
arrival. I hope to see you soon, sir. Goodbye.'

Christos replaced the receiver, chose a Mont Blanc
fountain pen and ticked off several items on the white
paper in front of him.

'The million in dollars,' he said, 'and the deeds to
your house in Khania and all your other property in
Crete, you brought with you in the brown paper
parcel. That checks out. Now Phenneger confirms a
deposit in my account for six million dollars worth of
gold bullion.' He looked up and was surprised to see
that Rashid had not opened the box. He was about to
say something when the second call came through. It
was from a banker in Zug.

'Confirmed, five million in uncut industrial diamonds,' Christos said and made another tick on his
list. 'That does it, Rashid, I'm satisfied. Now, for
God's sake, man, aren't you going to open the box? Or
don't you like the colour I chose for you?'

'Very smart, Christos. I will open the box.'

Christos watched Rashid going over the contents of
the purple box. He felt the force of Rashid's obsession
with the Oujie legacy concentrated in the tiny movements of his fingers. The ancient power over Turkey of
Rashid's family was being restored to his grasp.

Christos had no such obsessions, either private or
public, and certainly none about family. So a second
private deal with Rashid was easy. He had consented
to act as chairman for the syndicate backing Rashid's
scheme to swindle Mirella of another part of the Oujie
legacy. Their private deal had suited them both.

Their mothers had been sisters, high-born Turkish women of impeccable Ottoman lineage. Whereas Rashid's mother had married into an even more princely Ottoman family, her sister, Christos's mother, married out of her faith and into an enormously rich and cultured Greek family from Istanbul.

Christos's paternal great-grandfather had foreseen the persecution of the Greeks in Istanbul as inevitable. So he moved his family into Greece. This explained the mix of Turkish and Greek among Christos's holdings. When it became clear to Christos that Rashid wanted to own as much prime Turkish property as possible, he approached his cousin about a trade off – all Christos's property in Turkey for Rashid's in Greece.

For each man, this was the end of a long road to greater power in the country of his choice. Had Rashid fully sensed the significance of the contents of the purple box? Could he register the singular power and importance they conferred on him in his beloved homeland? Once, long ago, Mirella's ancestor, Kadin Roxelana Oujie, had been loved beyond reason by a sultan. His passion had enabled her to oust Rashid's forefathers. She had passed the power that had been theirs to Mirella. Now, by cunning, Rashid was about to steal back that power from Mirella.

It was all there. Every document Rashid needed. He replaced them in the box. The lock clicked shut. He set the key carefully alongside the others on his keyring. Then Rashid sat back in the wing chair and heaved a sigh. He began to chuckle to himself, and then relaxed into a deep interior laughter that finally brought tears to his eyes. Some time passed before Christos placed a goblet of cold water before Rashid and a hand on his shoulder.

'And what now, Rashid?'

A scent of lilac and jasmine, and she was there. The two men rose from their chairs, their eyes riveted on the lady in white whose very presence changed the atmosphere in the library. She walked directly to Rashid, stood before him and submissively lowered her head. He raised her hand and then lowered his lips to kiss the long slender fingers in a courtly manner. That was the way they always greeted each other in public. In private it was a different matter. At those times she would drop elegantly to one knee and kiss his hands, first one, then the other, address him as master, and never raise her eyes to his until he allowed it by word or gesture. She would usually be naked except for a diaphanous scarf or the odd jewel, worn not to cover but to excite.

Rashid reacted at once to her presence. She was one of his most prized possessions. Rarely had he wanted her more than he did upon seeing her at this moment. He was gripped by the power of a raunchy sexuality that showed through her junoesque beauty cocooned in the whiteness of her ensemble. Her regal bearing and the desire he read in her eyes possessed him, as they had so often during the many years she had been his sexual slave.

She had captured the erotic hearts of numerous men in those years. And still she was dazzling the two men in the room, making them oblivious to all but their sexual desire for her.

He held his golden fleece, the purple box, and its contents in one hand, and Humayun in the other. His first words to her were, 'Are you ready to leave?'

She did not speak, but merely nodded, affirming her

readiness. He smiled at her and charmed her by kissing her hand again.

'Good. I have a surprise for you. A change of plan.' Then he turned to his cousin and said, 'Christos, I have decided to accept your invitation. Until the morning then.' He stretched his hand across the desk to shake Christos's and was aware of a look in his cousin's eye that asked to be included not in the morning but now. Rashid ignored it.

'Rashid, I'd like to give Humayun a gift to thank her for her company this past week, if that's agreeable to you,' Christos asked, knowing very well it would be, because that was the form. A gift to this remarkable woman was a way to say thank you to Rashid without offending his generosity in sharing his sexual goddess. It was the form, and it had made Humayun a very wealthy woman in her own right. One of Rashid's great joys was the sexual intrigues they created together at his behest in which many men had acquiesced.

What happened next took Rashid rather by surprise. He had nodded his consent to his cousin, who then went around the desk to Humayun and presented her with a dark blue leather jeweller's box, one that would hold a necklace of some importance. Rashid stepped back a few paces from Humayun as a courtesy to his cousin. Christos and Humayun gazed into each other's eyes. It was not a happy or loving look that passed between them. Then Christos said, 'Wear these for me the next time, and, I hope, for yourself and no one else.' Then he offered her the jewellery case.

She hesitated, and a kind of anger seemed to emanate from her. She placed her hand on the case, and for a minute Rashid thought she was going to push it away. It would have been an outrageous rejection of Christos and Rashid alike, an aggressive act on Humayun's part, completely out of character, and meriting severe punishment. Then, much to the relief of the three of them, the moment of anger passed and she accepted the case, saying, 'Until the next time, then.' Nothing more, not a word or a gesture to express what she was feeling. There was neither a note of promise in her voice, nor one of indifference for that matter. There was a kind of thrilling silence, an inscrutability about Humayun that was part of her powerful erotic beauty.

Those few words, and Rashid could actually see desire for her in Christos's face. Desire and excitement. There was something else: a kind of decadence and even a spasm of hatred for his being so vulnerable to a sexuality so evidently feminine. Not so for Rashid. He loved and adored female sexuality, and he quickly swept her away and into the old battered Buick that had brought him to the villa. He watched the driver and Nikos, the bodyguard, as they devoured her with their eyes while they stood at the open doors of the automobile when Christos and Rashid exchanged a few last words.

And then they were off down the drive. Quite suddenly now for Rashid, Humayun had displaced Mirella, and even his amazing success in acquiring what he had sought so long and so desperately. He hardly saw the garden as they sped through it. He had eyes only for Humayun. So he missed seeing Salome leap onto the roof of the car. He heard only the huge thump and then a yowl as the cat rebounded through the air and landed somewhere, doubtless upright and unperturbed.

As they passed through the gates, he waved to the four guards who were about to pull them closed. Then he turned his full attention to Humayun. First, and without a word, he removed her turban and veil. Her golden-red hair tumbled around her shoulders. He took her face in both hands and revelled in the beauty of her cream-coloured skin and clever, seductive green eyes. Yet again he was captivated by the raw sensuousness of her looks. Her face was alluring with its proud patrician nose. He ran his finger down it and along the high cheekbones, held the finely pointed chin between his fingers and drew her face to his, placing a deep and sensuous kiss upon her lips. He wanted to feel the swell of her large voluptuous breasts in his hands, to mouth their tantalising nipples and the large halo around them decorated with henna dyed arabesques, to lay his cheek against her lovely, seductive mound where her pubic hair had been replaced by more of the reddish arabesques.

His heart felt full of her. He touched her hair and then raised her hand and kissed it. Humayun sensed a different kind of closeness with Rashid today that they had not shared for a very long time. A kind of loving that had happened to them only once during the first week they were together, when his father had given her to Rashid for life as a sexual gift. She had been paid well by the elder Lala Mustapha to see that his son would always be kept sexually happy and assured. Nothing had been said about love.

The years rolled back with every kiss Rashid gave her now, and she tried to keep her balance through those kisses as the old Buick swung down the mountain of olive groves. Mental balance no less than physical, because there was Moses now to consider. It was a losing battle. She was slipping back into her love

28

for Rashid, in defiance of all her newer instincts.

'I don't think I tell you often enough that you are the most beautiful and exciting woman in the world.'

'No, you don't,' she answered him with a dazzlingly sexy smile on her lips. 'In fact, you rarely tell me anything as flattering as that.'

'Oh, surely I do?'

'Perhaps the first week we spent together. Many, many times then. But that was a very long time ago.'

'But you have known?'

'Oh, yes, I have known.'

'That's all right then?'

She did not answer, but gave him another of her exquisite smiles. He raised both her hands in his and turned them over to kiss the palms and lick them with an eager tongue. She closed her eyes in ecstasy, so sensitive was she to his every touch. He looked up and whispered huskily, so the men in the front seat would not hear, 'I want you so much, all to myself, and I will have you that way soon, very soon.'

'Oh, yes, please,' she answered as she opened her eyes.

'Don't you want to know where we are going?'

She nodded eagerly.

'To Khania. I have sold my house in the old port to Christos, and we are going to spend the last night there together. Just you and I and the servants will be there. Does that please you?'

'I spent the happiest days of my life in that house and in Khania, Rashid. So many times I have wanted to return. Yes, it pleases me very much.'

'Do you remember how we met?' asked Rashid. 'They way I remember, as if it were yesterday? How I wasn't home when my father arrived with you. I stayed away deliberately. I had seen my father and you together several times, and from the very first wanted to snatch you away from him. He was so old, and you so young and fresh and beautiful. I could hardly believe you were to be mine. I wanted you, and yet I didn't want you, because I knew you would change my life. I would no longer be as free with my friends. They would never understand our relationship. Remember how I made you promise you would never speak of it to anyone? But it has been good. Happy, no?'

'Yes, from the very first,' she answered.

Rashid kissed her again. Both were aware that there was something very different about them and the way they were relating to each other today here in Crete. Something had radically changed Rashid. Was it that for the first time sentimentality had entered their relationship? It made Humayun feel awkward, but she was helpless to pull herself from the past.

'It was such an odd day for me too, that day we met,' she said, 'I had been your father's concubine since I was thirteen, and he had been good to me, so good that all I wanted to do was please him. I spent all my days and nights learning the art of lovemaking, just to give him pleasure – only to be told I was being educated in the world of erotica solely to become your sexual slave. When we arrived we found you away from home, he left me there anyway, like any old parcel, and with barely a word of farewell, just a warning to please you, or bear the consequences.

'That was the first time I realised I was no more than a chattel. And so, while waiting for you, I made up my mind to be the most remarkable possession you would ever own. Hours went by, and I decided to go out for a walk, and to look for you and give myself to you.'

The surprise in Rashid's face did not go unnoticed by her. Of course, it had to be there. She had rarely spoken so directly to him in all their years together. Was it her affair with Moses that gave her the courage now? Or was it these few moments of loving and caring, the memories, and Crete that opened her to him now?

'I couldn't find you,' she continued. 'It was midday and oh, so very hot. I headed back to your house. Somehow I became lost in the maze of winding back streets that flattened out at the back of the port. I was tired and hungry. I can remember that vividly. I passed several sailors in a doorway who were laughing and talking. One called out to me in Greek.

'I turned down another street and farther on I saw three Island men coming towards me. They were tall, big, handsome with their dark moustaches and broad smiles. They were shepherds down from the mountains in their village dress, with black scarves and little fringes tied around their heads. Their trousers were tucked into dusty, but shiny high black boots. They wore black shirts, black sashes around their waists and one had a white cape thrown over his shoulders. The other two had sheepskin jackets, I think, over their shirts. I was amazed by the way the three of them were striding toward me in the tiny street with its white houses and small wooden doors.

'I thought, "Oh this is Crete, proud and strong, rugged and male." I half hoped as they walked towards me that they would carry me off to some remote village in the mountains overlooking the sea. They were surely the kind of men women dream of being captured by. To me they looked more like Cretan mountain pirates than shepherds, and they made me think of the famous Cretan feuds that wiped out families, the murders of passion, the vendettas passed down from generation to generation that I had heard stories about. I had my little moment of fantasy that you would rescue me from them, fall in love with me, and I would be enslaved to a romantic hero.'

Rashid put his arm around Humayun as the car swerved off the gravel road and on to the tarmac of the main road to Khania. She turned in the seat, better to face him, and his fingers grazed her cheek with such tenderness that she placed her hand over his, holding it there for a second, not wanting to lose the moment. She was suddenly embarrassed by the intimacy, and removed Rashid's hand from her cheek and held it in her lap as she continued, 'I had to pass by the men, but they blocked my way. The one in the centre ate me up with what seemed to be liquid black eyes. He gabbled in Greek to me, but I said nothing, afraid to let them know I spoke only Turkish. I remember giving them my most charming smile and making gestures that told them I couldn't understand. But it made no difference. He went on talking to me and the three of them kept laughing as I tried to get around them. The man in the centre picked me up with two hands around my waist. He lifted me high off the ground and, before I could even protest or wave my arms around, pretending to be a lady in distress, he twirled me over his shoulder and put me down behind him. The three men laughed heartily while they moved away and never looked back at me. I stood there alone in the dusty street watching them swagger away from me.

'Now that I am reminded of that little scene, I find it hard to remember whether I was more disappointed or amazed that they didn't kidnap me. I remember the morning walk, and the men, and the incense that lingered with me after I looked into a small white church. Visions of Byzantium, virile, rugged men, violent passions, sex, the sea and the landscape, whirled around in my head, and I fell under the spell of Crete, the first place where I had ever really been outside on my own. There was no freedom from the bordello in Istanbul where your father kept me.'

'And that's when I found you.'

'Yes, I was still wandering through the streets trying to find my way back to the old port, and I bumped right into you. You appeared as if by magic. I knew at once it was you, and was disarmed by your handsomeness, the sensuality on you like perfume. I was flushed, and angry with myself for being lost and having to ask you to take me home.'

Rashid laughed and kissed her on the lips, not once but twice, and said, 'By my life, I remember that. We stood there looking at each other. I thought to myself, she is mine. I tried to hold back my joy but remember feeling a little twisted smile break through. I knew at once who you were, because there was not a single woman in Khania as startlingly beautiful as you. I wanted to chastise you for not remaining in the house, but the best I could do was ask you if you were lost.'

'Not quite, Rashid. Your first words to me were a declaration. You said, "You are lost." I answered, "Yes, I am, and hungry." And then you declared, "Never do this again. Never wander away from the house without asking me. You would not dare to do that to my father, and I will not have you do it to me." Then you took me firmly by the arm, and together we walked under that hot sun towards the old port. You told me that you were taking me to a restaurant where

33

we were to meet your friends and, since there was a language barrier and no one there could speak Turkish, I need not worry about being with strangers. You were charming, kind, and interested in me. You wanted to know all about me. For the first time in my life someone wanted to know me. Humayun. I was so happy; you won me to your heart before we ever joined the foreign colony in Khania. They were all at lunch at that restaurant with the awning. That was the first time I had ever dined in public.'

Humayun began to smile at Rashid as she added, 'You said something to me before we joined the group seated at that long rectangular table. It was littered with plates of half-eaten food, I remember, and full bottles of wine and glasses. 'You said, "Remember, when in public like now, I will introduce you as a friend of the family. They would not understand your real role in my life. That's a secret we must keep to ourselves".'

There was a look of astonishment on Rashid's face when he asked, 'It was so long ago. A lot has happened since that day. But you still remember it all, don't you?'

'You, and that first lunch with the foreigners of Khania, changed my life. Am I going to forget that? They fascinated and you charmed. I fell in love for the first time in my life. We spent those first three idyllic days alone together except when we took a meal at midday with the group. None of it has dimmed for me. The evenings when you cooked for us in your house, and talked endlessly about yourself and your ambitions, your dreams, your love for the erotic – how uninhibited you seemed about that – all of it you wanted to share with me. You showed me the most passionate sexual side of yourself. I thrilled to it, rose

34

to it with my own. But, if we were wild in our sex, we were tender too. You taught me so much about the island, the people, the language, the customs. I was a most willing pupil. I sat at your feet in adoration. You taught me the basics of speaking well in Greek – so forcefully impressing on me how much you loved and respected the language, and resented it being misused. You spoke about writers and painting. And I fell hopelessly in love with you. Any woman would have.'

Rashid squeezed her hand reassuringly, rather than put love into words. Humayun had to turn away from him, so moved was she by the memories. They had brought a tear to her eye, which she would rather not have Rashid see. It was evening now, and the car rattled through the darkness towards the very place where their lives together began.

'I was so much a part of the foreign colony living in Khania then,' Rashid mused. 'I thought the ex-patriate poets, painters, writers and escapists were fascinating. I spent most of my time with them and Christos. Your arrival never drew me away from my love for the west, for westerners and their life style, but it did draw me back into the Turkish, the oriental side of my life. It reminded me that I was first of all an Ottoman, a muslim. I think it revived my love for that life of power and passion my ancestors thrived on. Decadent. Intriguing.'

Gently, with fingers on her cheek, he turned her face back towards his and continued, 'I too have memories. Maybe not as acute as yours, but they are there. Will you play the flute and sing for me tonight the way you did then? I was delighted and charmed. Yes, and I suppose even seduced by your company. And that has never changed. I remember how, when you had too much

35

wine, affection poured out from you to me. It just added to the excitement of my sexual excesses with you. Your obedience and loyalty, your courageous will to please me were always what made me want to be more gentle and more generous to you. It gave me so much pleasure to spend days on end teaching you languages, to swim in the sea, to appreciate everything beautiful, and people and what makes them create those things. And the joy behind every sexual door we nudged open. You were perfect material to mould into the extraordinary woman that you are now.'

He took her in his arms and kissed her with a great passion. Even as she slipped into the kiss with her body and her soul, her own inner promptings were telling her, 'Be cautious, Humayun. Once before you thought you and Rashid were growing together, were as one, building up a full relationship to be shared only by the two of you. For all the attention that he paid you then it was just a seduction. The same as for any newcomer in his life. You may not have known that then, because you were under his spell and waited, enchanted with a prince who took you, body and mind. But you must know it now.'

But imaginary voices of caution go unheard in moments of lust and love, even if they speak for a real love that is pure and honest, such as she was experiencing for the first time in her life with Moses. Moses. He simply vanished from her mind. She eased her arms around Rashid's neck and returned his kiss.

They left the car and hand in hand they walked around the crescent-shaped port of Khania. A few foreigners whom they had once known there and who remained still welcomed them warmly.

'They were wonderful times, those old days, when we were young and innocent,' Rashid said to Liz Cordell, a big-shouldered giant of a woman whom they had known well when she was in her late thirties. A quiet, sensible, hard-working illustrator of children's books, she was part of the incestuous group of ex-patriates who lived in and around the old port. They clung together, dined and gossiped madly together. They both dished and defended each other according to how they felt that day. To be critical and protective of each other was their way of survival in the small, egocentric, creative circle. She had been kind to everyone and very much liked by the people of Crete. In her little car she used to bump across country roads, over the mountains to every village where she made friends and sketches.

'Yes, wonderful. One moment you and Humayun were part of our lives, and then you were gone. We all wondered what happened to you. But the press filled us in, with the adventures of one jet-setting Turkish playboy. We thought you might return one day.'

Rashid insisted that she stop and share a bottle of wine in one of the cafes. She stopped but chose beer, and so the three of them drank beer. It was such a throw back, that courtesy of only drinking what one of the group could afford, a habit they all cultivated in the old days, with money an inconstant supply among the expatriates. But, if one of them had sold a book or a painting, then there was wine – whisky, even, for a long book, a large canvas.

It was true he had abandoned them and – worse – forgotten them, never given them a thought. Suddenly they were all there in his mind, and he was curious as to what had happened to them.

'I was thrilled in those days to be part of the group. I

liked so much the way you all lived. No one was ever offended if any one of us preferred our own company and wanted to dine alone, and when invitations were issued to dine in one of our houses, no one was ever vexed if he was excluded. Personal privacy was all important to each of us and we all respected that, and yet remained solidly a clan of friends.

'There was just one exception, that English playwright, his French wife with the two children, who very rarely joined the long table at the Kavouria. Odd man, he was. Rich and successful, he didn't like to see the poverty and struggles, the joys and disappointments of the other foreigners in Khania. I remember he particularly did not like Martin Bolder, or the fact that he wrote a brilliant literary first novel and little else. He saw him as a silver-tongued fascist who tried to seduce every man, woman and child to his way of thinking. They were always seen whisking important people from the airport to their house, and always dined at another restaurant in the port away from us other foreigners.'

'And he was always trying to cultivate a friendship with your cousin Christos, because he knew how wealthy and influential he was,' Liz added. 'You won't find him here, Rashid; he is long gone.'

'The one I liked was that grand old English aristocrat with the double-barrelled surname,' Rashid said. 'He sat in the shade by himself. Never joined the table. He was always cordial to the group. They'd stop one by one and talk to him for a few minutes. Drunk from morning until night, and drunk again the same way the next day and every day. But always somehow in control. He carried his shabby clothes and intellectual sloppiness with a panache that made one think he was much more profound and sensitive than the competent travelbooks he

38

wrote indicated. Charming, likeable, intelligent. An old-time homosexual of the Maugham, Coward, Auden ilk. He stayed tucked up in one of the rooms in the same hotel six months of the year, year after year. His liver must have given out long ago, no?'

'Yes, it gave up on him. He died here and is buried in the cemetery up on the hill above the port.'

Humayun listened to the pair talking about the others whom she had shared those happy days with. Now they were talking about a woman called Marcia Maine: a dumpy seventy-five year old Australian, revered if at all for a one-off opera hit. She had been in Khania for a very long time composing operas. Once a year, usually at Christmas, she invited them all for a drink. Her life was filled with visitors, invited guests who passed through Khania on their way somewhere else. The Australian musical world, along with avant-garde New York, waited vainly for her to repeat her success.

Humayun remembered the woman, and felt her presence and those happy days as if she and Rashid were living them all over again. She began to laugh and, slipping her arm through Rashid's, she asked Liz in an English much polished since last she had been in Khania, 'There was a very odd man from Hollywood, a sort of half-man, half-girl, Teddy. Yes, that was it Teddy Todd—'

Rashid interrupted her. 'Of course, Teddy Todd, that screaming queen.' Rashid laughed for the three of them. 'He was a joke. A Hollywood cameraman. Hadn't Joan Crawford stolen him from Hedy Lamarr, who in turn had hijacked him from Joan Bennett because he got their best angle every time? He had been coming to Khania long before any of us, and spent several months of the year here.'

Liz stopped laughing, took a drink of her beer and said, 'You two won't believe it. He is still here. Still dressed for Rodeo Drive at all times. Still pounding out his interminable memoirs. Still appearing each year with a wow of a boy just old enough to pass for his grandson. He still leaves right before Christmas every year for Beverly Hills and a little tuck here and there to keep his facelift in place. Remember how the other homosexual foreign residents tried to tell him to play down his queenliness and confine his voracious sexual appetite for Greek sailors to the port? Wasn't noticeably successful.'

'Teddy Todd. Do the Islanders still laugh at him but soak up his generosity, just as we all did?'

'Seen any leopards with their spots changed? He still holds a small court of his own at a table on the other side of the Kavouria restaurant, always in the sun. And even now, the odd time that we do go to the Kavouria, one by one we give up our tables in the shade and join him. There are other foreigners of the old days still living here, but they and the life they used to live are so different now. We have all changed so, all except Teddy. We keep to our houses most of the time except for shopping or the occasional afternoon sitting with friends from abroad. There is no longer a long table of us at the Kavouria. Now, when we do dine here in the port, it is usually at other, newer restaurants that play with an international cuisine.'

Liz Cordell began gathering up her basket of shopping and stood to say goodbye. She looked at them and said, 'You know, it really is lovely to see you both again. It's all so boring and bourgeois here now. I even bore myself asking "Where are all the interesting, talented people now? The crazies with dreams to fulfil, the creative and interesting Greeks. Where is the drama and the scandal we all thrived on? Oh for a younger version of Maude and William Murphy to arrive here again. Remember them? She was just like a charwoman, he an ancient little prince of a man. An old and famous roué in the Paris of the Twenties where he ran with the bohemians of the day. Hemingway, Miller, Fitzgerald all put bits of him into print. Still with a twinkle in his eye for the ladies and a pinch for the young girls. Still the roué at a very old age, with a nagging Maude to care for him, pick up slippers, sweep the ash from his collar and chide his obsessions with women and fucking.

'Still after forty years, writing the great pornographic novel. Poor, with rich and famous friends he never imposed on. He was as much a delight as Maude was a boring, worrying, bitter nag. Any time she heard him air his lust, she'd sit up and holler, "You disgusting old man, shut up. No one wants to hear your filth. Why do you go on so?" '

Liz laughed a little and continued, 'Remember when she would catch him kissing and petting a young girl, she would beat him about the chest and pull him away as if he were a senile old fool or a child? Sweet, filthy, cunt-mad Willie, who all his life never wanted to do anything but fuck, who wanted to experience all that was possible sexually. And poor, dumpy Maude, with her common features, tatty grey hair, heavy moustache and those dreadful wrinkles that appear on the upper lip of some old women. Where did they pick each other up?

'Poor old Maude. She wore herself out trying to make ends meet for them. Abused him for still wanting to fuck her and every woman alive. They were regulars at the long table at noontime meals, unless their allowance ran out. I really liked the old boy. I wish she could have been nicer to him.'

Humayun had liked him too, even if he was always touching her thighs under the table and whispering things in her ears that it was better not to understand. 'What happened to them?' she asked.

'Oh, the Murphys left the same year as you did. They were trying a new place – Ibiza – after some scandal which resulted in their papers not being renewed.'

The three kissed each other on the cheeks, and Liz said as they parted, 'You were our prize young dilettante in those days, Rashid. Slotted in as a perfect contrast to Larry Wardman and Malcolm Phipps and Martin Bolder and Ian Weston. What happened to us all, and where'd you all go to live and play out your dreams?'

'What happened to us, Liz, is we grew up and became successful. Where did we go? We're still circling the world looking for Khanias that might work for us.'

Rashid and Humayun sat in silence for a few minutes after Liz left. The past was there with them, but the past was the past. They both felt it without having to speak of it. Humayun was aware that Rashid could not take his gaze off her.

'You are one of the Khanias that still works for me, Humayun. Let's go.'

They surprised the owners of the Kavouria, the taverna that had been their favourite place to eat in the old days, who threw their arms around them in a glorious welcome. After coffee at a tiny table set on the cobblestones overlooking the water, with a fine view of the restored period mosque built during the Turkish occupation by one of Rashid's ancestors, they walked the few steps to Rashid's house. Each caught up in nostalgia for Khania, they were as two young lovers on holiday.

Chapter 3

They had hardly slept, just dozed off between sexual trysts, and, as was always the way with them, the excitement doubled and trebled with every sexual act and orgasm. More, they always wanted more, and it had to be different and more thrilling. Both were masters at getting what they wanted, and here it was, morning, and, though they were sitting on the balcony and could look over the sea, with a breakfast of champagne, fresh figs and omelettes stuffed with wild mushrooms and slivers of crisp bacon, wild honey and sweet butter on freshly baked bread, it only sharpened their taste buds for more of each other. Lust was upon them like a morning dew, and all thought of anything else was far from their minds.

It was never over for them. Rashid showed himself as sensitive, creative, sensual and complex. And he wanted her, Humayun, all over again. She felt exactly the same way herself. He stood up and tenderly drew her to him. Slowly he stripped her of the diaphanous black silk shawl she had wrapped herself in. He was careful not to touch her skin as he undressed her. He kissed her lips lightly with great gentleness.

When he had her completely naked, he ran his

fingers through her long, golden-red hair several times and then, putting his hand on her shoulder, he turned her around, his eyes boring deep inside her as he surveyed every inch of her body.

She stood there now with her exotic sexual master, who touched his lips tenderly upon hers, yearning to be taken by him yet again. To feel him penetrate her with a wild passion was the least of her erotic desires. In a low, husky voice, he ordered her to stand there as she was and be very still. Humayun was trembling with desire for him. Her breasts were sensitive, begging to be touched. She wanted Rashid to plunder them with his hands, to suck them. She wanted to feel the fierceness of his teeth upon her beseechingly protruding nipples. She sighed, filled with the urge to be drained of her passion for him.

He never took his eyes from her body. They kept roving over it slowly, and as he looked, he opened his silk robe and let it fall where he stood. Now it was her turn to look. Her eyes were fixed on his long, thick penis resting against his thigh. He watched her watching him, and saw a lasciviousness in her eyes that told him what she wanted.

He finally touched her, held her face in his hands and then ran them caressingly down her long, slender neck and where it tapered into her wide-shouldered, tall, lean body dominated by firm, magnificently full breasts. She shivered with anticipation as he clasped her narrow waist. Slim hipped from the front, she carried full and voluptuously round, tight buttocks.

He adored her, recognised the greed in her eyes for his long thick phallus, and knew how much she wanted him. He was merciless in taking her, but not before he had lain her on the breakfast table and plied her with

44

strawberries dipped in honey and cream, and sucked them slowly from her vagina, all the time nibbling on her clitoris. The heat of the sun, the sound of the sea, only added to the sensuous morning.

Now he stood naked and rampant before her, waiting but not giving her what she wanted. She finally reached out to take his throbbing penis in her hands, and with all the right words began to goad him into a near frenzy for her. He pushed her down on her knees and, lifting her beautiful face up, he ordered her to open her mouth. Her sucking drew him to the edge of sexual ecstasy, his words of instigation were hardly necessary. He pressed his hands down on the top of her head and all but gagged her with himself, commanding and controlling the way she served him. And this most extraordinarily submissive and feminine beauty delivered herself freely to the violence of his passion for her.

And now he would give her what she wanted, what they both wanted, penis and cunt fucking together to achieve an endless stream of orgasms to draw them out of the world and into an oblivion of sex.

Rashid returned to the bed with two small glasses of Metaxas four-star brandy. He looked down on Humayun, who was lying on her back, one arm folded over her eyes, her hair streaming out across the pillow. She was naked, her knees were close together, bent at an angle to the top half of her body. She looked to Rashid like a voluptuous broken doll. What was it that impelled him to this breaking of her?

He smiled while looking down at her, and an excitement went through him, for he *had* broken her. Putting the two glasses of brandy on the side table next to the bed he sat down on the edge next to her. He stroked her hair several times and then took her arm away from her eyes. He bent down and, turning her face to him, kissed her tenderly, gently on her bruised lips.

'Have a glass of brandy with me, Humayun, and then you must dress. Christos has been waiting for us in the port.' He handed her the glass. To her he seemed so different now from the man who had taken her violently all through the night and the morning.

Humayun sat up with knees tight together against her chest, hiding her nakedness, and sipped her brandy. She was aware that a dimension she had always sought in loving Rashid did exist. No matter how tenuous it was. This strange interlude, returning to Crete and to his house where it all began, had proved that to her. She could be more to him than an obedient sexual servant. Now the knowledge had entered them both. For her this was a joy, a finding of what had long eluded her. Would it change the life they shared, this confirmation of the bond linking them in the role each played for the other?

In her heart she could only want this strange, unexpected interlude to go on forever. But she had shed the illusions she had once held about Rashid. She knew he would transform himself confusingly from lover to sexual master, as he had done in this very house so many years before. She had been shocked then. No such thing could happen now. Their positions had been defined, and they had lived happily with them ever since.

Rashid sat down next to her. She locked her gaze to his. He gathered her in his arms and slid her on to his lap, caressing her nakedness. They remained silent, savouring their brandy. Humayun was aware of contentment. It declared itself to her in his every gesture, the way he held her in his arms. She could see it in his face, sense the beat of it in his heart, the flow of it from his skin. She knew deep in her soul that, wonderful as it was between them, that serene joy enveloping him had little to do with her. Yet how could she be offended? It was enough for her that he was happy and content, and that they were what they were to each other.

Finally, he spoke. 'I don't expect we shall ever return to Khania. Do you?'

'Maybe not together, and not in our bodies, but I know I shall. My soul will wander under the sun in this old port of Khania, this house, and haunt this sea. How can it ever forget the beauty of Crete, the love and passion and happiness it found here with you? Oh, yes. My heart and my soul will roam here for eternity.'

They looked into each other's eyes and Humayun was delighted to see in Rashid's that the outside world had not yet come completely between them. She took her moment. She placed her arms around his neck and gave him a kiss that ignited a flame of passion in them both. This was where their love lay, in a shared erotic life. She wanted him to know that she understood that. The kiss was calculated to end their new-found dialogue on another kind of love, one that had come to them through their years of sexual bliss together.

Passion spent once more, they hurriedly dressed, knowing how angry Christos would be for the hours they had kept him waiting. They laughed, and teased each other about their enormous appetite for all that was sexual. Rashid left Humayun to finish dressing. She was to join him and Christos at a cafe a few doors away from the house. His leaving alone provoked memories of the last time they had left this house . . . they had not been together then either.

Memory took over. She had taken a swim. A gay and happy Humayun had entered the house. She had been surprised to see that Rashid had a friend who had come to stay. A handsome, tall, slim Frenchman with the kindest, most smiling sexy eyes she had ever seen. A warmth, a lovingness had come off him which had overwhelmed her. Unnerved by it and the intrusion of a stranger in the house, she had behaved outrageously with Rashid in front of Pierre.

That night the three of them had lain on thick goatskin carpets before a roaring fire. They drank Calvados, cracked walnuts and ate the sweet meat of them and plucked huge hothouse strawberries from a large bowl in front of them – delicacies brought over by Pierre from Paris for the New Year.

Rashid and his friend talked a great deal about Khania and the foreigners who lived there. Then, to her surprise, he had told Pierre about Humayun.

It all appeared so vivid to her now, their words and what happened ringing clear in her memory.

'Ah, my Humayun. Do you find her beautiful, Pierre?'

'I could hardly deny it.'

'Would you believe that she is my sexual slave?'

'Could a man expect such good fortune?'

Rashid snapped his fingers and she rolled over against him. Putting his arms around her, he said, 'Shall we prove to Pierre how lucky I am?'

With a neat movement he stripped off her sweater, baring the upper part of her body to Pierre's raw gaze.

'Your slave,' she asserted proudly.

Fondling her breasts with gestures that were frank

invitations to Pierre, he continued, 'And do you enjoy being in bondage to me?'

'How could it be otherwise?'

'Wonderful, eh, Pierre?'

'You are to be envied, Rashid.'

'True. And I like to watch other men's envy grow. Humayun, strip off your skirt and your panties, slowly, for me.'

She obeyed and could see the excitement her obedience stirred in him. Roughly he pulled and twisted on her hard, pointed nipples. There was a menace and danger in his eyes which she was helpless to resist. Entranced by it, she craved more instructions. She lay there in his arms with the firelight gleaming over her body. The three were silent for a few minutes, leisurely drinking and picking at the delicacies. Rashid broke the silence.

'Humayun, I want Pierre to see what a beautiful cunt you have. Spread your legs open.'

She had no idea what made her hesitate. She had no qualms about exhibiting herself to men; in fact she quite enjoyed it. It excited her to seduce, and the years with Rashid's father had taught her there was power and praise to be gained by doing it well. There was even a greater reward. It pleased Rashid's father to show her off and lend her to other men: to obey and please him became her gratification. Instinctively now she knew that it was Rashid who made her hesitate. Never had she been with such a young and exciting man, or one so complex, one who matched her own sexual appetites, and made it clear to her that he would keep her and enrich her life. In that moment of hesitation she forgot herself and her place. He reminded her sharply.

Though her hesitation was only for a moment,

Rashid registered it. He slapped her hard across her breasts. His excitement was palpable.

'Remember, you are my slave. Obey.'

She promised herself then and there never to need reminding in future. She would earn a place in his life that would make her indispensable to him.

Her arms extended upwards as her legs spread wide. He reached down with caressing hands and parted her pink and silky soft labia as wide as he could. With delicate fingers he toyed with the slit between her legs in a way he knew would bring her pleasure. Delight shone already in her eyes. Huskily he announced, 'Humayun, tonight is to be special. Let's show Pierre what a divinely erotic woman you are. Let us offer him a superb sexual exhibition. Then I will put you on the block. Auction you off to my friend. If he bids high enough, I will sell you to him, for a week. No more, only a week. Just long enough to see how much I will miss you. It's time we moved on from Khania anyway. What do you say, Pierre?'

'You cannot be serious?'

'Oh, but I am. Entirely serious.'

'And what does Humayun have to say?'

'Yes, what do you have to say?' Rashid asked, gazing deeply into her eyes.

The lust Humayun saw in the look he was giving her left her no choice. The idea of displaying their mutual lust to Pierre aroused her to answer, 'I am your slave. I will show my bondage in any way that you desire.'

'Answered like a slave. So, Pierre, will you make a market for her?'

Was Rashid likely to follow through, Pierre wondered. It was too bizarre. 'Whose are the rival bids?' he asked.

'Why mine, of course. Since I have the advantage of having had the lady, and know what a rare jewel she is, I will allow you to whet your appetite for the sale. You shall have a preview. At my invitation.'

So Pierre was tantalised, as only a man can be who desires but cannot yet have, who sees another man make free with what may soon be his. Rashid flayed bare Humayun's sensual being in every act of sexual humiliation possible. Humayun opened herself to them, turning them into acts of supreme pleasure that spilled into convulsive orgasms.

When he was finished with her they lay in each other's arms in front of the fire. Pierre, sitting only a few feet away from them, was overwhelmed with lust. An enforced voyeur, he was half spent by restraint. He found Humayun the most sensuous, sexually hungry woman imaginable. Her extraordinary physical beauty made her a siren he could not resist.

'Well, Pierre?' Rashid said, after some time. 'Actually, I need not ask, I have only to look at you to know that you must have her after the sample, the taste of what you will bid for. Take her. Come and take her.'

Pierre made no move.

'Go to Pierre, Humayun,' he ordered.

She remained where she was. Coolly, Rashid reached for a narrow black snakeskin whip. She knew that whip. Before the leather landed on her flesh, she had rolled over into the arms of his friend.

Pierre had watched them all through their orgy and had said nothing. He said nothing now. He placed his empty glass on the hearth, raised himself from the goat-skin carpet, and, taking her in his arms, he lifted her and carried her upstairs to the bedroom. He kicked the door open and laid her on the bed. He

51

undressed and then carried her into the bathroom where he bathed her, then dried her off and carried her back to the large, old-fashioned, four-poster bed.

He climbed onto the bed and made love to her like a man satisfying a long hunger. It was easy to control his more erotic and violent sexual desires, because he knew there would be time for those acts later. Revolting as he found auctioning off a woman for sex, he knew that he would outbid Rashid to win her. He had been corrupted by desire to take her as Rashid had taken her, even if only for a week.

Pierre raised his head from between her legs to kiss her passionately on the lips and then left her to pull on his trousers. After wrapping her in a blanket, he walked her down the stairs.

Rashid was asleep in front of the embers. First Pierre built up the fire and then he poured them each a Calvados. They huddled before the newly blazing fire, and then he woke Rashid.

There was an odd moment when Rashid fixed his eyes on Humayun. Pierre was made aware that it was not just Rashid's game, as he had thought. The way they looked at each other he knew it was *their* game, and realised that he was probably the first of many who would play a role in their erotic games. He poured a tumbler of Calvados for Rashid and handed it to him, saying, 'Drink up your Calvados, Rashid, you have an auction to conduct.'

Rashid looked at his friend and then set his eyes back on his sexual slave. He smiled.

The scene of all those years ago began to fade for Humayun as she stood before the mirror winding a more simple version of her white turban around her head. But the memory lingered of how she had been made to stand on a table in front of the fire, naked except for a black leather dog collar and a long, metal link leash. Rashid had paced around the table naked, whip in hand, carrying off the entire auction in a manner worthy of a Jamaican slave seller.

Humayun had been sold to Pierre Benois, not inappropriately, for a first edition of the complete works of the Marquis de Sade, with the cost of lunch at the Kavouria on New Year's Day for all the foreign colony thrown in. The conditions of sale had been that Pierre take his purchase on the night plane to Athens, after the luncheon, and that they leave Greece within five days of the sale. The week up, she was to be escorted back to Istanbul to an address forwarded to Pierre in Paris.

Humayun adjusted her earrings and took a last long look at herself in the mirror. It was difficult for her to equate the woman she saw with the memory of the girl who had stood on a table and allowed herself to be auctioned off to a stranger. Only in very few circles was it known that she was Rashid Lala Mustapha's sexual slave. Or that she was the overseer of Oda Lala's, that house of erotica kept by Rashid and a few friends for their sexual pleasure, where they were safe to dabble in their fantasies on the wilder shores of ecstasy. To some she was known as an exotic lady of the night who sometimes accompanied Rashid. And to all she was known as a mysterious creature who wielded great power over men with her beauty, sensuality and intelligence.

She touched the fine lines appearing at the side of her eyes. Not yet, no, not yet were they a threat to her. What happened to ageing sexual slaves? Even those such as she, with power and servants, with money and jewels and houses, had to feel the force of this question. In these last few months meeting and falling in love with Moses had made her confront it.

As with so much in her life, Rashid had been instrumental in bringing about her fateful meeting with Moses. She had seen him several times before they met formally.

It all began when she travelled in secret with Rashid to Oceanside, the sumptuous turn-of-the-century hotel on the shores of the Atlantic ocean in Massachusetts. Rashid had taken it over for the wedding reception he was giving for Mirella Wingfield, his former mistress, and Adam Corey, his sometime friend, and constant rival in love for Mirella. Rival claimant, too, for the attention of all who sought out the wealthy, the handsome, the intriguing among the world's males.

Humayun had been placed in a large, secluded suite of rooms in the hotel, protected at all times from intrusion by two of Rashid's Turkish bodyguards. She was there at his command, for his pleasure. She knew the form well. Discreet, invisible, silent, never to be detected by his high-society friends, until Rashid desired it. And, clever lady that Humayun was, she knew exactly how to fulfil the role yet not become a mere prisoner in the hotel.

She sensed that Rashid, Adam, and Mirella were entering a new phase of their relationship, the *ménage à trois*, even though it had never been alluded to by Rashid. On several occasions she had been a party to the lovemaking of Mirella and Rashid. Instinctively she had understood Mirella could never give up Rashid – no more than she could herself.

The first time she had seen Moses? She had been playing ball on the deserted beach in front of the hotel with one of her maids. Dusk was gathering about them. The ball rolled into the flotsam of the waves. It was about to be sucked out to sea in the undertow. One minute there was no one there, and she was about to lose the ball. The next, he scooped it up and handed it to her. Their eyes met for a second and their hands touched. A warmth and feeling of well being coursed through her. No words. He was gone.

That night, she found exquisite ecstasy in Rashid's arms. Yet the tall, handsome black man teased her reveries between the plunging orgasms Rashid drew from her. In the days that followed, she saw him through the windows of her rooms. It took her a little time to find out that he was the man who ran Mirella Wingfield's house. As a boy he had been a family retainer to her uncle. But that was all she did find out about him, except that he was indispensable to Rashid in helping with the wedding reception.

On the wedding night, there had been a ball. Rashid had arranged with Humayun for a selected few to enjoy a refined orgy in her rooms. She sought in vain the beautiful, silent black, the memory of whose half-naked form tormented her dreams. She must erase him from her mind.

From Oceanside Rashid took Humayun and the rest of his entourage to New York. She had been put up in a suite of rooms above his at the Carlisle. He had her squired around New York by an old friend. At night, when he desired her, he took her. The last thing she expected to be told, a mere two weeks after she had dulled her fantasy of sex with Moses, was that she would be travelling back to Istanbul with Moses. Or that Rashid wanted her to seduce him. To make love to him and care for him. And perhaps show him

Istanbul and Turkey for two weeks. Rashid tended to spike his thank yous with such gifts. Moses had exercised his brand of magic at the Wingfield-Corey wedding. Humayun was to be the spell Rashid cast on him in return.

So they had met; so they had fallen in love. The sexual byways she beckoned the relatively inexperienced Moses into captivated them. They began to influence each other's lives and thoughts.

His goodness, his kindness, the code he lived by and wanted her to live by, nearly convinced her that she was, as he believed, a victim of circumstances and environment. He desperately wanted her to change her life, and for them to marry. Before their two weeks were up, Rashid took note that Moses had been smitten badly. For perhaps the first time in their sexual games with people, Rashid and Humayun were aware that they had made a mistake to burst in on Moses's life. They cared for the man, and Rashid ordered, 'Take as long as it takes, but let him down gently.' He was not to be hurt. Perhaps Rashid really didn't want that to happen, but certainly Mirella and Adam Corey were devoted to the man: they would not forgive the hurt.

So Rashid was distracted, and failed to observe that Humayun was considering making her break for freedom. Tempted by real love, a one-to-one relationship, she began to feel the allure of a home and a husband, even children.

Considering . . . but could it be more than that? Because Humayun had been playing her role as a sexual slave all of her adult life. People could think as they liked about sexual slavery. Her heart had its reasons for feeling as she did about it. These fifteen

56

hours with Rashid had confirmed them. Being Rashid Lala Mustapha's sexual slave was something always strangely gratifying to her from the first time she obeyed him, her first time being auctioned to Pierre Benois, and ever since. The pleasures she derived from her role as sexual slave to Rashid had taken hold of her psyche.

This she had never questioned until Moses became part of her life. Now, looking at herself in the mirror, at ease and flushed with happiness, she knew that Moses would have to face the truth about her and Rashid. She was his sexual slave, true, but together they were mischievous sexual playmates. But could she be sure how that would strike an American negro, who was born free, and who believed every man should exercise his freedom whether he liked to or not?

Moses. He was awaiting her in Istanbul. Her heart warmed to the thought of it. She had never known such a good man, such an honest man. But sexual slaves who love their master share similar erotic appetites and have the courage to feast and satisfy them. Those sexual slaves find in their bondage a freedom that puts their spirit beyond the tut-tutting of fashionable opinion, and they do not marry and settle down to be a major domo's wife. Moses would have to be made to understand that his beliefs were a danger to the love they shared, that they were creating a conflict for Humayun hitherto unknown to her that she neither understood, nor accepted. Something would have to give. But what?

Nothing for the moment. There was still love and passion for her in Rashid's eyes and heart, and a day in the mountains of this miraculous island, she told herself as she swung away from the mirror and walked for the last time from Rashid's house in Khania.

Humayun half expected to be relegated to the back seat of a car and kept in waiting while Christos and Rashid enjoyed themselves. But no. She had been right about Rashid. He was not ready to give up their special intimacy, and so he kept her by his side.

The three of them and two members of Christos's household piled into a Range Rover and drove through the old port. At the baker's, they loaded loaves of bread and pans of sticky cakes and pastries into the rich man's jeep. At the butcher's, they bought three freshly killed nanny goats and two dozen chickens. Then they went to the ice house, where they got ice to keep the meat fresh. They barely had enough room for themselves.

At last they were ready and sped out of Khania, heading for the mountains and some of the hill villages where Christos was being fêted for his generosity: an oven for one village, a church for a neighbouring one, and a school for the district. He had arranged for Rashid's helicopter to pick up Humayun and Rashid and whisk them away from the mountain and Crete. They were travelling in convoy: the old Buick and two of Rashid's bodyguards loaded down with Humayun's luggage followed, and behind that car a pair of Harley Davidsons and two more of his men.

The Range Rover had been loaded with provisions, because Christos knew the hospitality he and his guests would be shown on arrival at any of the villages where he was to be honoured would be overwhelmingly generous. And the villages could ill afford it. They would cook every morsel of food, drink every drop of wine and strip the village and every household bare, from their genuine desire to make them welcome. Christos could not allow that. He knew this was the only way to stop them.

The countryside was looking glorious under a sun blazing as if for gods. A buzz of excitement and well being settled on the three of them sitting together in the back of the Range Rover, Humayun between the men. She had never seen Christos in such an amusing mood. Nor had he ever treated her, as he did now, without that fearsome undercurrent of hostility she sensed he had for her. Although she still wore her all white ensemble, she dressed down her spectacular look by not wearing her diamonds which she had tossed into her handbag. The men teased her about trying to appear ordinary. And then Christos surprised them both when he asked her to put it all on, and to stay by his side through the luncheon. Normally she would have been sent off with the women to some village house, while the men dined alone without them. At first she didn't understand this odd request, but then realised that, of course, he wanted her by his side. His preference for boys, if guessed at all in the mountains by these villagers, would shock them. Humayun would serve him well for a few hours as the woman in his life.

His request relaxed the three even more into good humour. They left the main roads an hour out of Khania, and bumped along on curving gravel tracks up one mountain and down another for an hour and a half. They were now taking breathtaking hairpin turns on hard dirt tracks with the occasional boulder pounded in to keep them from sliding down the mountain when it rained. Those were eventually left behind and the Range Rover bounced in and out of holes, on earth tracks barely wide enough for its wheels. Danger. Much shouting between the driver and one of Christos's men who was walking in front of the Range Rover, whence he threw the odd rock that had fallen onto their path over the side of the mountain, directing the driver how to manoeuvre to keep all four wheels on the narrow road. It all gave an edge more of thrill to what the three of them were feeling for each other. It made Rashid more sexy. Humayun sensed it and felt randy herself. Christos even touched her. It excited them all, this randiness that was taking over the fun and the fear.

Suddenly the jeep would burst into a small village. They passed through two more, waving to the people, but not stopping. The convoy pushed on to their destination. Hot dust from the dry roads got everywhere. Another hairpin curve and suddenly, from nowhere, appeared two huge Cretans blocking the road. They swaggered towards the jeep, slung their rifles off their shoulders and fired them up into the air, shouting in broken English, 'Welcome, Kirios Mavrodakis! Welcome!'

'That's some welcome, Christos!' Rashid said as the driver slammed on the brakes and they all fell over each other.

These were two young men from the village they were bound for. They barely had room to edge themselves over to the car door where they shook hands with Christos and Rashid. Then they sat on the fenders of the Range Rover, hanging on with more bravado then sense. Three miles more of hairpin bends and sharp curves round the mountain. At times the Range Rover had to stop and the men had to walk in front, supervising every inch forward because the narrow road had simply fallen away down the mountain. And then suddenly they were right in the middle of the village square.

The smell of woodsmoke and roasting lamb filled the air. The convoy stopped in a cloud of dust. When it settled they saw a sight typical of hill villages. Two old men sat drinking ouzo and playing tric trac under the shade of the tree in front of the kafenanon – a combination of coffee shop, office and general store. The cicadas were in full symphony.

The driver leaned on the wheel, exhausted. Rashid looked at the peaceful, sleepy atmosphere. He turned to Humayun and Christos and said, 'That do for a drive?'

He took a white handkerchief from his pocket and wiped some dust from the bridge of Humayun's nose. She removed the turban she was wearing and her shining red-gold hair tumbled onto her shoulders. They barely had a moment before the young men with the rifles were pounding on the horn. Slowly people drifted into the square and surrounded the Range Rover.

It was a delightful reunion for all. The villagers were intrigued by their guests and plied them with questions even before they were out of the car. A 1938 Chevrolet, battered and crumpled with a motor that sounded like an aeroplane, burst into the square in convoy with a motorcycle pulling a flat cart and half a dozen donkeys from the opposite direction. They were piled high with people and baskets of cakes and bread and olives, bottles of oil and ouzo and wine from the next two villages. They were all there for the village lunch. The excitement had been building for days. It was all planned, the cooking had begun hours before and, as the guests dressed in their best spilled out of the vehicles, others were even now walking into the square.

There was much clucking and praise and some chastisement for Christos, as his men unloaded the back of the Range Rover, putting things out of the hot sun onto the verandah of the village shop.

It was a day full of vitality. There was endless ouzo, arak and retsina and Cretan delicacies from all three villages. Opinions and arguments were expressed loud and clear with so many gathered together, the collective mind and voice of the villages that comprised its essence.

The women, with the exception of Humayun, all looked more like men acting as women dressed in black, their heads covered and tied in black scarves. Some had been bold enough to put on beautiful old embroidered waistcoats, or some traditional silver Cretan jewellery. They wore no make-up. Weathered skin allowed the natural beauty of some to shine through.

As for the guests of honour, they loved it all. Loved this personal and intimate Crete they were privileged to be a part of. They saw it at its best up in the village that day. The villagers displayed the stubbornness the Cretans are famous for. The natural pride that they have: the supreme arrogance and elegance of people from truly poor villages. The guests were aware of savage passions stirring in these people, made explicit in stories which made them understand that hundreds of years of sieges, battles, poverty and famine had served to shape their unyielding, obdurate character. They heard stories of famous vendettas, heroism during the Second World War and the German Occupation.

There was so much spirit, so much life in such a barren, poor little village. The three kept up with the drinking and the eating. They were moved by the passion and beauty of the tough and rugged men dancing together.

It was a wonderful day. One where reality was fresh and went from impulse to impulse. Rashid, Christos and Humayun could see that the impulses were not always praiseworthy. There was some pique, there were flashes of jealousy. And, although they saw no outburst of it, since they knew well what lust was, they saw it in some of the men's eyes. There was a natural cunning in the Greeks: Rashid had known it from dealing with them in business, and he saw signs of it here. He saw these things as part of their character and accepted them as such.

The eating, drinking, singing and dancing went on until late afternoon. Then, with much protestation the villagers finally accepted all the provisions Christos had brought, and the guests of honour were allowed to say goodbye and leave.

They left as they had come, in convoy, and with the same two young men and their rifles insisting – in case of trouble on the road – they see them to their rendezvous with the helicopter a few miles away. They were correct to accompany the convoy. There was trouble on the track. Half way between the village and their meeting place a tyre on the Range Rover went flat and they had to change it.

Humayun and Rashid struggled up a steep, stony hill. Arid itself, from the top it sloped down to a beautiful valley and an olive grove. Both were drunk and very happy. They had agreed to return to the Range Rover in half an hour. Now they wandered among the rocks and boulders until they chose a spot, a large sheet of stone made smooth as satin by the wind and the rain, balanced precariously like a shelf from the side of the mountain. From here they could see over the valley and the mountains to a ribbon of blue in the distance, the sea.

A warm, caressing wind rippled their clothes, and the untamed, relentless nature of the place took possession of them. Rashid kissed her passionately. There was a primitive, feral sexuality about him at that moment. Humayun recognised its possible dangers. She said, 'I think we must go back, darling,' knowing in her heart that was the last thing she wanted to do.

'We have half an hour. Take your clothes off,' he ordered as he started to undress himself. Humayun did not protest, but asked, 'What if they come looking for us?'

'Hunters must have their prey. You will be their prize, and I shall win you from them again. I shall watch the pleasure in your eyes and hear in your cries the delight of new young male flesh vanquishing you. I will watch them quake in the arms of the divine.' He laughed at her and roughly pulled her into his arms. He kissed her on the lips and bit her on the side of her neck.

Humayun began undoing her dress. He felt wild and desperate to take her. They were both naked when he pulled her down on to the warm smooth rock and fucked her. He probed her roughly with his penis, but was tender and passionate with his lips and his mouth.

For Humayun it was sublime. To be fucked, naked in the sunlight, in this barren place, encircled by mountains, by her master, the man she loved beyond life itself. She kissed and bit him with a savage passion of her own. She dug her fingernails deep into the flesh on his back, and gasped as she came in streams of exquisite orgasms.

He took her again in an animal fashion with even greater need and ferocity. In his mind and will he tore her apart with passionate frenzy. When he withdrew, he spun her around in his arms to kiss her again. Tears of overpowering frustration spelled out his inexhaustible desire for her. But with her kisses she soothed his madness, till slowly he became tender again and brushed her cheeks and forehead with his lips as one kisses a child.

Christos found them that way. He stood over them.

'We heard you cry out. It echoes in these hills. I knew you were in no danger. I knew it was the cry that comes from within, the one that comes from passion. No wonder your sexuality tortures me, Humayun,' said Christos.

Humayun saw the change in Rashid's eyes. The outside world had arrived, and he needed to make light of their overwhelming sexual togetherness. She diffused the intensity by raising her arm and extending a hand of welcome to Christos. Such well-timed gestures were what kept Rashid always interested in her. Christos was quick to remove his clothes. Rashid held Humayun in his arms and played with her breasts, kissed her lips, and said to his cousin, 'Kiss her, make love to her, fuck her well, Christos. I want her to have all of Crete inside her today.'

Christos did what he was told and took her the way Rashid wanted him to. Afterwards he took Humayun out of Rashid's arms and had her again by kissing her

sweetly, lovingly, with admiration and affection. Christos was extraordinary. For the first time in their love-
making, the cruel side of his nature, the ambivalence he
felt about her as a woman, was not there. She sensed a
change in him she did not understand, but instinctively
knew she would never again have sex with him, and she
felt more relieved than she would have expected.

Before Christos rose from the rock he caressed
Rashid's hair, bent forward and kissed him lovingly on
the lips. The three began to dress. It was Humayun
who broke the silence.

'Thank you, Christos. I will never forget these last
twenty-four hours I have spent in your beloved Crete.
Not as long as I live.'

Christos wanted to tell Humayun and Rashid that it
had always been a secret desire of his to have, just
once, sex with Humayun without conflict. That it was
he who should thank them for today, and that he
would never forget the joy he was feeling. But he said
nothing. Words might have broken the spell of the
moment.

Arm in arm they walked back to the Range Rover.
The convoy pushed on to its rendezvous with the
helicopter. The three stood together in the clearing on
top of another peak, surrounded by their convoy of
odd vehicles while the men loaded the helicopter with
Humayun's luggage. She and Rashid said their good-
byes to everyone and watched as they withdrew down
the mountain before the copter switched on its blades.

Alone now, high above the island they looked out
across the rugged landscape. It seemed almost fragile
under the vast open sky, amid the surrounding sea, the
light of the lingering sun and the strange, soft, warm
wind.

Chapter 4

'Hello. Hope you don't mind, I've come for breakfast.'

Rashid went directly to Mirella and taking her hand in his kissed it, then her lips. Mirella was pregnant and even more beautiful than ever. Rashid had not seen her in many months and had been desperate for a glimpse of her since she had telephoned him with the news of the baby.

Mirella's heart had leapt at the sight of Rashid, as it always did whenever they had been parted, even for a day. She had given up trying to come to terms with her physical attraction to Rashid, and felt only relaxed and happy that it was still there. She smiled the kind of welcome you give the *other* man in your life.

He went from her to Adam Corey, who stood and shook hands with him.

'We're always pleased to feed the hungry, Rashid,' Adam said. 'Could be you're in luck. Moses is cooking the breakfast this morning.'

One of the diminutive Turkish house maids scuttled from the breakfast room. A large round table of icy grey marble on its pedestal of entwined carved lions stood in a square bay window. The window was two storeys high, covered by antique Turkish wooden fretwork, the sort the women of the harem hid behind to watch processions from the palace of Topkapi. Encircling the table were half a dozen round-back chairs, cut and honed from single blocks of terracotta-coloured Veronese marble, made to look light and elegant by the superb carved lion arms and legs. Centre table, there was a huge bowl containing dozens of white moth orchids. There were tropical trees and caged birds around the room that was dappled with the morning sunlight filtering through the wooden screen of the window. It was an enchanting breakfast room.

The maid returned, ready to lay a place at the table for Rashid, and with her came Moses. The two men greeted each other.

'Some breakfast, sir?' Moses asked.

'How are you going to persuade me?'

'Mango juice, calves' sweetbreads marinated in a light olive oil, white wine, fresh parsley and basil and garlic. I barbecue them slowly so that they are firm and golden brown. Then there's kidney. They're served together with Ogen melon and a saffron sauce, and my special *Oeuf en surprise*. That's a *brioche* scooped out and filled with eggs, a dash of salt, pepper and a *soupçon* of nutmeg. And who else would go to the length of whisking them in butter to a creamy scramble, something like a mousse? Nor have I stinted with the chopped truffles braised in butter and folded in with the eggs. Back on go the tops of the brioches. And there you have your egg surprise. Lots of hot black coffee, to bring you back to earth again.'

'Stop, stop. Enough production secrets. Just bring it on, Moses. I certainly came to the right house for my breakfast this morning.'

Rashid heard Adam say, 'What's on your mind, Rashid? You didn't have to avoid a fast day or a kitchen strike at your place, did you? Something more than food has brought you out here so early in the morning.'

But at the same time he was thinking 'Moses. Humayun.' Reassurance came as he recalled the last order he had given Humayun, when they had parted upon arrival in Istanbul the night before. 'Humayun, kill that relationship.' But he had not come simply to banter about breakfast with Moses either.

From the moment he and Humayun flew off that mountain peak in Crete and waved goodbye to Christos and his convoy of vehicles winding its bumpy way down to the valley, the dark purple kidskin box on his lap had been his focus. Its contents, the fulfilment of a life's ambition, and the effect it was about to have on his life and, in no small way, on his country and his future, wonderfully concentrated his mind, no less then than when his team of solicitors and advisers met him at the Istanbul airport had Rashid's delayed reaction of supreme delight at having won his victory over the Oujies at last taken hold. It had been his intention to invite Mirella to lunch and explain why he had pulled off the business coup that he had. Then to make love to her and claim that business was one thing, their love another, and demand that she handle what had happened with sympathetic understanding for his position. When he woke in the early hours of the morning, however, he changed his mind. He thought it best to tell both Mirella and Adam at the same time. It was too big a coup to exclude Adam. And he did not want to depend on sex games with Mirella to take the edge off his actions. The fact was that Adam Corey could be a greater danger to Rashid for Rashid's duplicity than Mirella might be, even

69

though it was none of his business. Rashid had absolutely no qualms about announcing what he had to say. His victory was too sweet and far-reaching to touch any personal conscience.

He drank the freshly squeezed mango juice from the large crystal goblet on the Charles II silver plate in front of him. 'One thing about your husband, Mirella. He knows a trick when he sees one. Even at breakfast time. You are not going to like what I have to tell you.'

Before he could say another word, Mirella surprised him with an outburst.

'You're not coming? You're not flying out to Paris with us this evening for the reception? Adam's own daughter and Zhara and Ahmed being fêted and you won't be there? That's really mean of you, Rashid. Mean. You know how much I wanted all of us to be there together. Brindley and Deena are already waiting for our arrival. I don't see why, if my very busy English solicitor and my best friend can make it, you can't. All Adam's children and their mothers are at the Ritz and have been for two days. My mother and father and brother are at this moment flying from Massachusetts to represent the Wingfields. Even Marlo has turned up at the Hotel Crillon and is waiting for us. Adam's sister is flying in from London. Everyone has made such an effort to help me, and give family support to Zhara's first official public appearance since her marriage. Except you, my . . .' Mirella hesitated for a moment. There was a faint flush, but she quickly recovered herself.

'Ahmed is arriving with an entourage of a hundred,' she continued. 'And the French are making the most out of his visit and the private family and world of his new queen. You need the continued goodwill of the

French, don't you? And the jet-set media. You could make it easier for everyone by being there with us. How could you let me down like this? Let us all down like this? It's unforgivable.'

Mirella, tears sparkling in her eyes, jumped up from the table and fled from the room, her white chiffon and lace dressing-gown billowing out like some exotic cloud round her. She passed by Moses, who gave her a concerned look. He went directly to Rashid to serve him and Adam. The men remained silent until the major domo stepped away and waited off to one side near the Persian wooden coffer inlaid with gold, silver, and bronze birds, flowers and animals, which served as a console.

Rashid did not fail to register how excitingly beautiful and sexy Mirella looked as she fled from him. His appetite for her was never satisfied and, if it were possible now, he meant to have her much more than during these last few months. He liked having sex with her while she carried her child. He reacted to the swell of her belly under the clinging white satin and lace of her nightgown as the chiffon of her negligee had opened just enough to excite and tantalise him with her condition. She was not so large as to make their powerful sexual encounters awkward or uncomfortable. He made up his mind to have her in the next few hours for he feared he might not be able to get on with his day otherwise.

He cut into a sweetbread and, looking across at Adam, calmly asked, 'She's very tense about the Paris business. But I wasn't about to duck out of an appearance there for her. What was all that about?'

'Anxiety, anguish, needing your support. Affirmation that this pregnancy and having a child are not going to change her life. There have been so many changes in Mirella's life in such a short span of time. She has risen to them and projected another part of her hidden self to the foreground of her life. And she likes who and what she is, the life she's leading. Maybe she's not quite ready for another change. Or maybe she senses she is about to lose part of the life she has. Perhaps it's not for me to guess the motive, because it was directed at you, not me. I suggest you go to her after you have had your breakfast and find out. But do keep in mind, Rashid, I don't want her unduly upset by you or anyone else. I wouldn't thank you for that, especially now with only a few weeks to go before the baby is born.'

There was something, a look in Adam's eyes, a menace as yet not triggered against him. Mirella's husband and her lover were having their first intense exchange about the woman they loved. Discreet and civilised as they were, Rashid for the first time did not like the position he was in. The two aspects of his relationship with Mirella were uncomfortably close to clashing. But what was happening? he wondered. Had she found out about his business coup over her? If so, how? Or had her pregnancy induced a whimsical rage at one of his many, quite open sexual conquests? He would soon find out. The problem would pass.

The two men finished their breakfast in general conversation about their immediate plans. From Paris the Coreys were flying to New York, because Mirella wanted her baby to be born there in their Easthampton, Long Island, house on the ocean. Rashid would be in residence in his Southampton compound with a rota of house guests. The Coreys and Rashid would be back in Istanbul at about the same time, as soon as the baby was able to travel. The more they spoke about their movements, the more awkward Rashid was feeling. On the second cup of coffee he asked if Adam minded if he went up to have a word with Mirella, to reassure her he would be going with them that evening.

'Frankly, my friend, I think you are going to have to do better than that. I don't know what you have done, but I know my wife. That outburst was not for nothing.'

'Would you mind if I whisked her away for a few hours? Maybe I could take her and the Princess Eirene to lunch.'

It was now a kind of game. Neither of them was enjoying it. It was in fact making them tetchy. Both knew in their own way they would have words with Mirella about the little scene she had pulled, which had embarrassed them all. Implicit in their *ménage à trois* was the demand that none of them ever be placed in an embarrassing situation *vis-à-vis* their relationship. Mirella had let them down.

Adam did not answer Rashid's question. Instead he rose from the table. 'I must be off. Tell Mirella for me that I will meet her at the plane as we had planned. Rashid, we take off at four. No delays. We'll be cutting it fine enough as it is.' He went around to Rashid's chair and shook his hand. 'I'm pleased to have you with us this evening, Rashid. People see you as part of our extended family, and your absence might have caused some gossip we will be delighted not to have laid on us. By the way, what is the announcement that we were going to be upset about?'

'It can wait. See you at the airport later today.'

Rashid walked into Mirella and Adam's bedroom

without knocking. She was standing next to the window looking at the morning river traffic plying the Bosporus. She knew without even turning around that it was Rashid. Her heart began to pound. She placed her hands around herself in a hug, feeling a need to be held, and closed her eyes. He walked up behind her, with not a word said between them. He placed his arms around her waist and pulled her hard against him. With his hands he caressed the hard, round swelling of her belly in comforting circles, and he kissed her passionately on her earlobe and the side of her neck. Slowly he turned her around in his arms and slid the sensuous white dressing gown off her shoulders and let it drop to the floor. All words, all thoughts vanished. He had never seen her more passionately in need of him. Her sensuous and now very pregnant beauty dazzled him. She was bathed in an earth mother beauty that powered its own lust, and in it lay another sort of beauty . . . and yet another. Hers was the perfect beauty that the artist strives to capture in paint, the photographer tries to trap in his lens. It had to do with the light on her skin, the texture of it. She was the epitome of the scent and life of woman, birth, life, death, and rebirth. She was sensual and sexual eternity for him, and he proved that to her without a word.

He drew her by the hand from the window, all the while kissing and touching her. She was helpless to resist him for the sexual attraction was, as it always had been, mutual. The plunging neckline of the haltered, white lace top half of her nightgown was stretched taut by her full, rounded breasts, the long, tantalising nipples and their pretty pink nimbus. He was dazzled by the glamour of his pregnant mistress.

He sat down on the silk-covered bench in front of her dressing table after freeing his throbbing penis. Standing her in front of him he raised the white satin, bias cut skirt of her gown to above her belly. Then he lifted her very carefully and impaled her upon himself, while kissing the roundness of her belly and licking and sucking her flesh. With great delicacy he had her ride his penis, by raising and lowering her again and again, until her orgasms broke within her, delivering her into their special world of ecstasy.

He came once, and then very quickly again, yet was still erect when he laid her across the bed and went to her dressing room to choose a dress and shoes for her. The only words in that room were his.

'Here, put these on, let's get out of here. This is no place for us. I'll take you to our love pavilion. Of course I am coming to Paris with you.'

The party deliberately arrived late at the opera house to be sure the other guests were seated. A violin concerto was in progress, a rich hors d'oeuvre to the opera. Beneath the relaxed surface of the music was the tension induced by evident security measures.

'The Loves of the Indies' by Rameau, was to be given a gala performance in honour of the official visit of the Arabian king and his new queen. Their hosts: France and her President.

The lights were down when they slipped silently into their seats in the official box. Only the crystalline white spotlight on the latest Asian prodigy of the violin lit the opera house.

At the end of the last movement the music brightened with energy, then faded, as did the spotlight on the tiny oriental figure at its centre. Simultaneously, another light was trained on the President's box: it slowly grew bright and larger.

In their frame of garlands of red, white and blue flowers, the women in the opera box glittered in jewels of breathtaking opulence. The audience fêted the young musician before slowly turning their gaze to the new spotlight and the official guests rising from their seats to applaud the violinist. That brought up the house lights of the Paris Opera. The soloist bowed quickly, impersonally, and made his exit.

Applause from an audience of exquisite and bejewelled Parisians enveloped the honoured guests. Wagging tongues made a hum of gossip about a beautiful young Arabian queen and her distinguished companions.

The lights dimmed and the audience grew silent as the curtain went up on 'The Loves of the Indies'. The machinery of the media whirred approval of opera and audience alike, seeking substance for tomorrow's headline on how the young queen had won their hearts with her youth, elegance, simplicity and beauty.

The young queen of Arabia was Adam Corey's daughter, Zhara. The cameras lingered on her dress of pure white crêpe de chine, her tiara, and the necklace of diamonds and spectacular huge emeralds. Each of the deep green gems was the size of a gull's egg and had been sculpted and cut in the shape of different birds. They were suspended by tiny diamond chains in open circles of larger diamonds. Every time she spoke, moved her head or made a gesture, the birds moved and played in the light of their imaginary diamond cages. At the centre of a sunburst of diamonds in a brooch pinned to a royal blue silk sash of honour lying diagonally across the bodice of her dress was a single 40-carat diamond.

The President's wife was chic in ice grey taffeta by Balmain, her hair encircled by a slim diamond tiara, set off with an opal and diamond necklace and matching earrings.

The guests in the box were seated in a semi circle. At either end were the Guy de Rothschilds and the Adam Coreys. The Rothschild jewels were extravagant and beautiful but no more so than Mirella Wingfield Corey's.

As one of the French newspapers wrote the next day, ' "The Loves of the Indies" by Rameau was performed last night to an exquisite perfection, in honour of the official state visit of their Arabian majesties. The gala evening matched the on-stage spectacle of Rameau's opera. The audience, supremely elegant in themselves, were dazzled by the guests in the President's box. The real eye catcher of the evening was the beautiful new monarch with her parents – internationally famous, recluses more often than not, the fascinating Adam Corey and his wife.'

The article detailed the family background on both Mirella and Adam's side. Then it continued, 'Rarely has the public had a chance to view such an array of beauty in women and jewels as it did last night. The young queen's tiara is said to have been in her step-mother's Turkish family for the last four hundred years. Madame Corey, a woman of great beauty, was no less spectacular than her jewels. Her raven-black silken hair was crowned by a tiara of cushion-cut diamonds set in graduated oval shapes, the centre of which contained rare cabochon pigeon-blood rubies, the largest the size of a small hen's egg; the smallest, like a robin's egg.

'Her dress of flame red crêpe-de-chine was designed especially for the evening by St Laurent, and set off her necklaces and her choker of diamonds. The crimson dress – cut on the bias, and designed somewhat in the Empire fashion, that is to say, with the narrow waistband set under the breasts and flowing from there – hung to the ankle at the front and draped into a short train at the back. It was simplicity itself, cut by a master for a great beauty and a unique occasion.'

The article enumerated the other guests in the box, who included 'the handsome, dashing, jet-set bachelor Rashid Lala Mustapha, who, it appears, is as a close friend of the Coreys included in the unusual extended family they surround themselves with.'

The journalist made much of the supper served at the Elysée Palace, and how Parisian society was captivated by the young king and his queen that night. He gave Mirella high marks not only for her beauty and her jewels, but also for her accomplishments at the UN and what she was doing with her Cinderella inheritance in Turkey. He noted she was at the same time adjusting to her latest role as wife to the mega rich international businessman and adventurer, Adam Corey. He emphasised that she was a woman of tact and discretion, remarking how the dazzling beauty had taken a position, always behind not just her stepdaughter, but the President's wife and Madame de Rothschild as well.

None of that was very difficult for Mirella. Being in the spotlight had no appeal for her. But neither would she ostentatiously shun attention shown her. Mirella had always simply gone along with the flow of her life.

If she found herself now upon a wave, she rode the wave. There was an appealing feature for her in this particular article. Typical of the French and their love of intellectual chic, it celebrated at length her father, Maxim Wingfield, elevating him to the ranks of the greatest American philosophers of the twentieth century.

In fact Mirella herself felt the excitement of the gala that night in honour of Adam's eldest daughter and the king. She was so proud to have Zhara for a stepdaughter. Her sweetness, beauty, natural charm and her quiet intelligence for one so young, had made it easy for Mirella to love her as if she were her own child. The way Zhara was handling her love for the king and her position as ruler did credit to Adam and the way he had brought her up – and to Mirella, who had advised her through her romance with the young monarch. Mirella looked on as her stepdaughter enchanted Paris, no easy feat. She remembered how Zhara had made a statement to the world press at the time of her wedding; no, she was not afraid of the responsibilities of her new position – after all, with her father and her stepmother as an example to her of how to respond to life, what had she to feel insecure about? Mirella had never imagined a child's admiration and respect could stir such emotion in her.

At three in the morning Mirella and Adam sought out Zhara, who was dancing with her brother, Joshua. They kissed Adam's children on the cheek. 'Darlings, we are going to slip away now. Zhara, you are the most beautiful woman in France tonight, and the loveliest queen in the world. And I am very proud of you.' Adam's fatherly smile made Zhara feel that his last phrase contained the real compliment to her.

Mirella listened to Adam's words and yet again she was overwhelmed with love and admiration for her husband. How did he do it? Manage to love on so many different levels, in so many different ways, and to generate so much love for himself from others. Never asking, never taking, never demanding, but possessing them all, his common law wives: Marlo Channing, and their child Alice. Giuliana and their daughter Alamya. Aysha and their son Memett. Joshua, the oldest, and Zhara his sister, whose mother had died long ago. And now Mirella, his legal wife, and the child she carried, were part of Adam's clan that the world's press presented as an unorthodox family on the brink of becoming one of America's more interesting dynasties.

When Zhara put her arm around Mirella and said, 'Oh, Mummy, I am so happy and so pleased you came into our lives. Thank you for being so special and wonderful,' it was the cue for Mirella to weep. But the world and the President of France were watching her. They kissed each other and parted.

The Coreys said goodbye to their host and hostess and insisted they should not leave the ball to see the Coreys to their car. Then Adam waltzed his wife towards the exit and whispered in her ear, 'This night has given me some of the proudest moments in my life. You were dazzling. You conquered the Paris Opera like a true prima donna. Every male present wanted to be your leading man. You are the most ravishing woman in the world. And the only woman I want.'

They stopped dancing and slipped out of the room as unobtrusively as possible. Turhan, Adam's faithful manservant, had been waiting for them at the foot of the staircase that swept down to the main entrance of

80

the Elysée Palace. He helped Mirella on with the red silk chiffon cape, trimmed in a double row of Russian white fox pelts, dyed to the colour of the dress. Adam took her hand in his and kissed it. Together they hurried from the Palace, followed by Turhan down the stairs and into the courtyard to their waiting Rolls.

From the shadows of the balcony above the entrance, Rashid watched them leave. She had been magnificent. Their day together had been even more than that. Rashid could not remember a time when he had loved her more, when their mutual lust for each other soared unabated as it had, every minute of the day. He hadn't told her. He had tried several times, but such loving had left him no space to confess his crime. It was almost as if she knew and didn't want to talk about it.

He saw the summer breeze ripple through the red chiffon and furs swathing her as she turned to take one last look at the Elysée. She was the picture of elegance standing by the Rolls in the empty courtyard, lit by footmen with flaming torches, backed by security guards dressed in full regalia, silver helmets and breastplates included. And then she was gone.

He reached into the inside pocket of his dinner jacket and pulled out a small piece of white chocolate wrapped in silver paper. While contemplating the empty space Mirella's exit left in the courtyard, he unwrapped and ate it. A moment of instant pleasure, familiar and reassuring to him.

There had been something different, some subtle change in her behaviour, the uncharacteristic outburst which was not mentioned by either of them. It wasn't that anything was visibly wrong. Different, maybe. But what had triggered it? Did she, after all, know about his victory over her? Well, if she didn't, she was going to find out the hard way, with no cushioning explanation from him, because he had every intention of making capital out of her losses.

The dark blue Rolls sped through the checkered light of early morning Paris. It glided past the magnificent buildings, circled the Place Vendôme, cut back through empty narrow streets and came out on the Rue de Rivoli. The arches seemed to spread themselves for the sleek automobile as it angled towards them and out into the breathtaking space of the Place de la Concorde.

Mirella snuggled up close to Adam and, dropping her head onto his shoulder, said, 'What a night: I feel like I have all of Paris and France coursing through my blood. Paris, the whipped cream on the cupcake? That deflates it nicely. It's been too much: It's the *crème fraiche* on the *fraise du bois*. The tiara of cities. Oh, Lord, I could coin banalities for ever about this night, and still it would overwhelm me.' She laughed at herself, and the sound was full of charm.

They drove to the Tuileries and then on to the Jeu de Paume. The car stopped, and Adam turned and asked, 'I hope you are not too tired for this?'

'Tired? Punch drunk on glitz more like. But half of one eye is still open. Now what have you got to show me?'

The chauffeur opened the rear door. Adam hopped out, turned and, taking her by the hand, helped Mirella out of the car. They stood at a side entrance, the kind of door that is noticed by no one and rarely opened. Turhan knocked on the door. It was immediately opened by one of the board of directors of the Museum. With him was the curator of the Jeu de

Paume. The two men were dressed in tails. They too had been to the gala at the Opera House. Mirella and Adam stepped into the building. The door closed quickly behind them. The curator kissed Mirella's hand and exclaimed, 'What a joy to do this for you, Madame.'

The director also kissed her hand and said, 'Madame, you were the finest jewel at the gala.'

Adam appeared to be bemused and Mirella actually was. They chatted in French as the four walked down a long, narrow, dingy back corridor of the building. The stale air, musty smell and weak light filtering through naked bulbs on the end of black electric cable prompted Mirella to draw her furs close around her. A hundred yards along they came to a door. The curator opened it and they stepped into the grand, open space of the main gallery. Several guards were roused into removing their hats to greet the select party, then dispersed themselves through the gallery. Lights snapped on. The Jeu de Paume sprang to life out of the darkness.

In the early hours of the morning, with delivery vans rumbling over the cobblestones and through narrow streets to their destinations all over Paris, the Coreys were strolling through the peace and quiet of the deserted museum looking at some of the finest paintings in the world. They were among the last ever to see this famous collection in the Jeu de Paume, because the museum had officially closed the day before. The entire collection that had stirred so many hearts and minds was leaving its small and intimate home for the Louvre that very day. News of the closure had saddened Mirella. She had expressed to Adam that she would have liked just once to have shared the experience of the Jeu de Paume with him, never dreaming that it was possible. Adam made it possible. The Monets were Mirella's passion. She adored being surrounded by them. Just Mirella and Adam and the water lilies.

He was swept up into the power and beauty of the collection, enhanced tenfold by their seeing it under these perfect circumstances, in the exquisite silence and emptiness of the gallery and sharing it only with the woman he loved. He felt a new kind of passion rising in him for the sheer love of this richly various woman. He could feel his heart beat just a little faster, and a smile broke slowly across his handsome face. He walked up to her; taking her hands in his, he lifted them to his lips and kissed them tenderly.

'Oh, Adam, this is such an extraordinary end to an altogether extraordinary day!' Together then they absorbed the paintings, and for some time before Adam announced they had to leave, they lost themselves in the mind and imagination of those great men who had left their imprint in paint for others to search and find something that might add to their lives. The paintings were not lost on the Coreys. Their minds and their hearts, their very souls took flight, and they were humbled by their passage into worlds other than their own.

They thanked the men for arranging this artistic aubade, their farewell to the paintings in their favoured setting. Then they left the Jeu de Paume as they had come, through the side door where their car waited. The dazzle of Monet colour, the shifting floral shapes, still captivated their memories. A visual high. Words were banished by the intensity of their impressions. Mirella leaned against Adam's shoulder as the

Rolls picked up speed, leaving her beloved Paris behind, and headed for the airport.

The sun was just rising in the sky when they boarded Mirella's jet, the latest Grummond Gulf Stream. No sooner aboard than the steps disappeared, the doors closed, the motors revved, and the plane started rolling down the runway.

Once the pilot announced they were airborne, they freed themselves from their seat belts, rose from their comfortable, raw silk, club chairs, still dressed in their gala finery, and went through the main cabin to the master bedroom. There Mirella sat down at the dressing table to remove her tiara and jewels. A little overdressed for flying, she ruminated.

Adam stood near the large double bed, also shedding his clothes. He watched Mirella in the mirror and was enchanted by the scene. He slipped his arms through the sleeves of his black silk robe and walked up behind her to place his hands on her naked shoulders. He kissed the top of her head, not taking his eyes off her face reflected in the mirror. Slowly and lovingly he removed the long pins from her hair. It fell down in waves around her shoulders. He gathered some of it in his hands, buried his face in it and then kissed it. Bending forward, he touched his cheek to hers. Two lovers reflected in a mirror.

She reached up and touched his bare chest, turned around where she sat and gently pulled him down and kissed him tenderly on the lips, then turned back to look again in the mirror.

Adam slowly eased the straps of her crimson gown off her shoulders and down over her arms, lifting first one, then the other so that her dress hung free. He watched as the weight of the crêpe-de-chine pulled the top of her dress down to the tip of her breasts. Standing squarely behind her, he enfolded her in his arms, and with his hands gently pulled her dress down, exposing her breasts and already erect nipples.

He fondled them and watched himself doing it, saw Mirella's eyes close in ecstasy and delight at his touch. Slowly he straightened, picked up the heavy silver brush from her dressing table and began brushing her hair.

Mirella trembled, thrilling to Adam's sensuous sweeping of her tresses. She could feel the rampant hardness inside his trousers against her back. He bent down again and kissed her on the shoulder, whispering. 'Do change, quickly. I'm famished, and I am sure you are too. A shame to let what's waiting in the dining room go cold on us.'

She squeezed his hand and rose from the table. Adam unzipped her Yves St Laurent gown, bent down to kiss the small of her back, then turned away. She put on a black lace night-gown, over which she wore a champagne-coloured, silk-satin dressing gown. It closed high at the neck with a ruff of black ostrich feathers that extended to one side past the opening and right down to encircle the hem. She worked quickly at snapping the dressing gown closed, while she watched him standing in front of the mirror combing his hair, tying his robe. Then she accompanied him to breakfast.

They spoke few words in those last minutes in the bedroom, but their thoughts were busy – his fancifully upon the naughtiness of the sexy, black lace nightdress she was wearing, and how later, after breakfast, she would be made to feel the joy and the passion it evoked in him; hers sweetly upon how much she loved him, and was overwhelmed by the love, not unmingled with the lust he felt for her, her yearning to lie in his arms and have him hone that love in sexual intimacy. How remote what they had together was from the erotic hours she had spent all day with Rashid.

Rashid. Sometime before they landed she would have to talk to Adam about Rashid and her behaviour towards him earlier that morning at breakfast in their house on the Bosporus. It was an unwelcome task to tell him that Rashid had duped her, stolen her property from under her very nose. She had not picked up the warning signs and the bad news had been confirmed only minutes before she had joined Adam at breakfast. Rashid's arrival had taken her off guard, depriving her of the chance to plan her reaction. She had camouflaged her true emotions with the scene she had created. Since then she had made up her mind how she wanted to handle it. For that she would need the cooperation of Adam and Joshua. Adam was going to be very angry. Yes, before they landed in New York, she must come clean with him.

The dining room was small and circular and, for an aeroplane, utterly charming. Two stewards were in attendance. Mirella and Adam sat opposite each other at the round table. The room was panelled in French sixteenth-century *boiserie*, the colour of the palest honey. The light from the early morning sun reflected off the clouds filtered into the cabin through the portholes. Heavenly bright light, with huge white clouds below them and nothing but bright blue skies above.

Mirella looked at her husband across the low silver bowl filled with fresh white freesias. 'You do think of everything. What, of course, does one crave after a night like that?' They smiled as each said, 'A bowl of French onion soup!'

They laughed as they shook out their napkins and laid them across their laps. 'I can smell it. Mouthwatering. No other smell like it in the world. Delicious onion soup, so hot it burns the tongue. But the melted cheese soothes that. Then you bite into the fried bread on top of the golden liquid. Masochistic delight, for the average gourmet peasant in France! How I miss the old *Les Halles* – all that market bustle getting ready to feed Paris. I used to go there with friends at two, three, in the morning to share a bowl of it with the fruit and vegetable marketeers hawking their produce, to kill the hangover, tease the palate, and feed the soul. That's French onion soup for me.' She selected a piece of the hard, crusty bread covered with sweet butter, the traditional side dish eaten with the soup, and began munching on it.

The aircraft's two stewards placed the steaming soup in front of them, the earthenware dishes burnt brown around the edges, the cheese still bubbling from the heat of the oven. The aroma revived memories of so many wonderful mornings with Adam after the nights before.

Ice-cold champagne, vintage Krug, was poured into bulbous, shallow glasses with stems so thin that the glasses seemed to be afloat on air.

The red Ferrari homed in like a well-directed missile through the narrow, deserted streets where dawn was just eclipsing the street lamps. It pulled up short in front of the shabby façade of a restaurant that glowed with a warm yellow light and the chatter and bustle of patrons. Rashid snatched two bottles of champagne off the seat next to him and stepped out of the car.

That was the lady's first glimpse of him. He was the handsomest man she had ever seen. No, not handsome, beautiful. And the sexiest. Everything about him crackled sex: the way he moved, the way he breathed. She was mesmerised by every little thing about him. His impeccable dress clothes, the shine on his shoes, the silken shimmer of his white scarf and the way it swung with the rhythm of his stride.

The bell above the door tinkled when he opened it to enter the noisy, smoke-filled room where the aroma of onion soup and *escargots* clung like a mist to everything and everyone. All the tables were filled. Several people put out a hand to greet him as he passed by them. He stood in the middle of the room and called out 'Carmine' to the frizzy-haired blonde tart serving behind the bar. She looked up. A smile broke across her face as she caught one of the bottles of champagne in mid air. He shouted his order above the din: two dozen snails baked in their shells with butter and garlic. Then he managed to find an empty chair at a table where two workmen were tucking into steaming bowls as if onion soup was an elixir. He snatched three clean glasses off the tray a waiter was carrying and poured from the bottle for himself and the two strangers he had imposed himself on.

He tilted his chair on its back legs and leaned it against the grimy, pale green wall, relaxed and happy to be in the workmen's restaurant. Its fame rested on just two things: the snails and the soup. He had been a steady customer there in the dawn hours for years. It was one of the few places in the world where he enjoyed anonymity. Anonymity was the *plat du jour* as far as Rashid was concerned. The gala and reverential treatment given to the King and Queen and their respective families had included Rashid. Flattering and great fun. But he had had enough.

Sometime during the evening he had made up his mind the moment had come for him to concentrate on his own dynasty. All the chess pieces were in the right place now for Rashid Lala Mustapha to checkmate any challenger who tried to block his ambitions.

The aroma of fresh butter and garlic banished such thoughts as the waiter slapped down in front of him the stainless steel *escargot* plate, forceps, small double pronged fork, and half a baguette of warm bread. He ate the first huge, succulent snail, broke off a piece of bread and dipped it into the small hollow filled with sizzling garlic butter where the snail had lain in its shell, popped it in his mouth and washed it down with vintage Bollinger. He gave his mouth a satisfied wipe with the back of his hand.

He was starting on his second dozen when she made her move to his table. He looked up and she was there. He was quite startled by her sudden appearance, actually caught off guard. She was a beauty of great distinction who instantly captivated him with her looks, her height, her slender femininity. She had a symmetrical, exquisite facial structure and seductive black eyes, ebony satin skin, hair smoothed back and wound in a crown on top of her head and a regal bearing – it was as if all Africa was standing in front of him. Her feral sexuality actually overpowered him. Imperiously, equality discarded, he gestured the other two men at the table away. Mesmerised by her, he hardly snapped out of the spell she cast, even when the two strangers clumsily thanked him for the wine, shook his hand and bid him goodnight. But their intervention did rouse him enough to prompt him to rise from his chair and confront her.

Speech came first to her. 'May I sit down?'

He found her voice no less sensational than her appearance. The French accent was faultless to his ear. He held the chair for her. She slid into it like flowing black gold. She was dressed in a loose shift of indigo blue cotton as fine as silk. Around her throat she wore a narrow band of pure pink gold with a hand cut and polished diamond, large as a walnut, set in the centre.

He sat down, unable to utter a word, nor turn his eyes away from her. She reached out and picked up the forceps, caught a snail shell in them, then plucked a snail, and sensually put it into her mouth. He could see in her eyes she was delighted by the taste. She sighed and, replacing the utensils on his plate, she declared, 'For masculine beauty you score high, you know. "How many hearts has he broken?" I was asking myself over on the other side of the room. "How many women has he tantalised with lust?" I want you, for one day, this day. Is that possible?'

'Possible,' he answered.

'Ah, then let us not mince words. What would be the going rate for a man like you in Paris today?'

Such effrontery, Rashid thought, but felt himself restored to the controls of this encounter. He was amused that she thought he was a toy boy.

'At the end. You pay when the party is over, and my charges are determined by me, at that point. Are you sure you can afford me?'

'I don't believe that's the way to express it. Let me ask you instead whether you can afford me the pleasure my lust demands, whether you know how to obey a woman. No, no, we do the accounting here and now.'

She opened her small handbag and placed a thousand dollars in one-hundred dollar bills under the side of his plate. Rashid raised a single eyebrow. 'Ah, you see me as a cheap gigolo then. A sensitive man would feel insulted.'

'And I can see you pride yourself on your sensitivity. Maybe it will inspire you to please.'

'It just might,' he answered, amused still at the idea of her using him as a sex object. Who was she? What was she doing in this place? Why would a woman such as she need to hire a man? Those questions tripped through his mind, but he asked nothing. His body required to know her more than his mind did.

She stood up and smiled at him. She reached out and took his hand in her own longer, slender one. He rose slowly from his chair, lowered his head to place his lips upon her hand in a kiss calculated to send shivers of delight through her. He could feel her passion rising. A current of excitement was flowing between them at this first physical contact. Power and passion overrode the acute intelligence and royal bearing that emanated from this most unusual beauty standing before him. All the bones in the hand he caressed, and the feel and scent of her dark silky skin stirred him in a strange way. He looked into her eyes, and, not for the first time in his life, Rashid Lala Mustapha thought he might be in love.

'My place, or yours?' she asked, with a hint of defensive mockery.

'Mine,' he answered. Then slid the small bundle of hundred dollar notes from under the plate and into his pocket. A multimillionaire could not afford to be short of change.

'Your name?' he asked, wanting to savour her powers of invention.

'No names, and no tomorrows for us,' answered Tana Dabra Ras Magdala Makoum, with the calm of one who knew her name was neither credible nor communicable just now. He took her firmly by the elbow and propelled her through the room.

'Very well. It's your money, you call the shots.' But to himself he said silently, 'You just go on thinking that, you ethereal Ethiopian goddess.'

Chapter 5

Southampton, Long Island. The Palm Beach of the north. The summer session for the rich – old, nouveau, real and make-believe rich.

Rashid had been in residence for weeks. The summer people were in full flower, their social calendars filled. The country club with all its chic and exclusivity was brimming with competitive members.

Rashid was not considered 'old guard' or exclusive. People never quite knew where to place him. His intimate friends were in the same league as the Rockefellers and the Fords and the Guy de Rothschilds, others who resided in compounds and mansions on the same footing as Camp David and the Kennedy compound in Hyannis Port. His vast wealth and his family's royal connections, spread throughout the royal houses of Europe and the middle East via his family's palace in the Ottoman Empire, made it difficult to label him at all. He was therefore simply considered *almost exclusive* by the Southampton social pundits. However, Rashid's compound was considered something else, more difficult to penetrate than any of his high society friends' homes. An invitation to be entertained there was the most sought-after prize in Southampton.

Sousa, Sabrina, Amanda, Cynthia. Four beauties. All but Cynthia were jet set, society columnists' fodder. Beauties with ever so slightly tarnished reputations.

The four, with figures that made them super saleswomen for the right foods and hours of trendy exercise classes, were dressed from Rodeo Drive, Upper Fifth Avenue, Bond Street and Rue Faubourg St Honoré. Their beautiful faces and expressive eyes revealed sensuality, selfishness, vanity and desire. They were young ambassadors of the 'in life'.

Their conversation during dinner exposed what they wanted and what they were. Their long, well-manicured, plum-coloured finger nails and the correct amount of hand gestures expressed their charm, wit, and a measure of intelligence. And more than a measure of cunning. The kind that enchanted men into bed and, they hoped, to the altar.

Cynthia Cohen, with her dark brunette hair and amazingly voluptuous figure, was sheathed in an antique Fortuny pleated silk dress the colour of bronze. Cut in a high crescent from shoulder to shoulder at the neck, it clung to her body like a second skin until it fell from below the hip and the under part of her buttocks to the ground. She was dynamic looking and wore nothing underneath the dress. Her heavy breasts were still high for all their weight and the nipples showed through the pleats, which shimmered with every arm movement, every step she took. The tiny waist and voluptuous hips were tantalising to the men in the room.

Clever Cynthia wore no jewellery, not a ring on her finger, not a bauble in her ear, no bracelet hung on her wrist, no brooch pinned to her dress. She wore her tits like diamonds.

Sousa was more exotic looking, animal like, with flared nostrils set in a pretty, narrow nose, wide full lips and a touch of meanness in the eye. She wore thin, silk-satin evening pyjamas that fitted snugly on the hips and tight on the bum, in a delicate peach colour. They made her dark, mocha-coloured skin suggest she was a mulatto instead of the Arab she was. It was obvious that she wore nothing underneath the sensuous silk. The faint shadow of black nipples, pubic hair and the crevice dividing the cheeks of her bottom showed through the silk. They tantalised, and advertised coming events with every step.

The top of her pyjamas was cut and tailored perfectly. It had long, puffed sleeves that contrasted with the material clinging tight to her tiny, almost flat breasts. Around her neck she wore a strand of solid gold beads. Her curly hair, shiny and pitch black, fell to her shoulders, and nestling in it were small, life-like gold filigree swifts and swallows. Each finger of her hands had several thin gold rings on it.

She gave off the image of sex, sensuality and animal cunning. The scent of a classy hooker. The international jet set, mini intellect, in society from the wrong side of the blanket, and successful under it because of her dash and daring.

Lady Amanda was just plain gorgeous. A beauty in every sense of the word. Tall, slim, pretty. The right kind of subtly sensuous breasts and body. A haughty face with the perfect white skin of the perfect English aristocrat. The elegant nose that turns up naturally. The spoiled and petulant lower lip and the lovely natural, long blonde hair. Casual but proud in her looks and her manner, she was dressed in a St Laurent black trouser suit with a white satin blouse whose ruffles around the neck and wrists only added to the fresh innocent looks of Lady Amanda.

She wore pinned to the bolero jacket a Georgian diamond brooch in the shape of a basket of flowers. On her hands she wore two rings, one of small diamonds and emeralds, the other three bands of different shades of gold entwined.

Just a bit aggressive, yet haughty, she wore her English reserve like a crown, while managing to join in with the partying, and to hold her own among the other women at the dining table. When the men talked of the hunt, the horses and hounds, she more than held her own. She almost silenced them with her knowledge of the sport, her exquisite indifference to world affairs and to making a mark for herself in life. There was something else about the young and beautiful Lady Amanda. She signalled that, underneath that cool, upper-class English façade, hidden fires did more than just smoulder: they burned bright.

Then there was Sabrina Colefield. A combination of the centrefold of *Playboy* magazine, a Bo Derek poster and any number of top models featured in *Vogue* magazine. She was six foot two, with hair the colour of amber in the sunlight, casually brushed away from her face and falling to her waist. Her face could only be characterised as California. Health, sunshine and the sea came to mind. Every feature was as if chiselled by a sculptor – or by the most expensive plastic surgeon in LA. Her smile was a dazzler. It broke her face into all the laughter in the world, and the teeth that filled her face when she smiled did credit to dentistry.

The designer crumpled, white silk, ankle-length sarong she wore tied to one side of her hip did little to hide the seductive shape of a willowy yet voluptuous naked body and legs that seemed to go on forever. Her wrap-around blouse of long sleeves crossed between her breasts revealed a cleavage to tantalise. The sun-tanned, bare midriff delighted the touch, and when she moved the swell of her breasts and the outline of the rosy nipples through the fine wet-look white silk seemed to cry out, 'Take me, suck me, love me'. In fact everything about her seemed to call that same tune. She looked like a goddess, a siren just risen from the sea.

The men at the party, who had been invited to Rashid's for the weekend, were all old friends, international jet-setting bachelors, with a dash of bounder, or cad in each of them. Yet they were terrific: successful, handsome, intelligent with varied interests in sport, big business, the arts and ladies. Each in his own way was as ruthless a lady killer as their host, but with less imagination, stamina and generosity.

Rashid watched the four women closely, while still performing his role as the perfect host. He was the supreme woman watcher, an addicted seducer of the female sex. He found all women fascinating, irresistible. They were his passion, and erotic love and sexual depravity his twin gods. He gloried in his Don Juan complex. It was in fact the driving force in his life. The gossip columnists around the world claimed the handsome, Turkish millionaire playboy Rashid Lala Mustapha had two vices, sexual prowess and chocolates, and that he indulged them both to excess. And they were right. Women were to Rashid the siren call of adventure.

He slowly swirled the aromatic golden liquid around in the large Lalique snifter, raised it to his lips and took a swallow of the superb, fifty-year-old cognac.

Then he placed the crystal snifter on the marble-topped console. He looked into the Queen Anne gilt mirror above it and raised his hands to run his fingers through his thick black hair.

He stood there for a few minutes studying his own image and the room reflected in the mirror. He liked what he saw. Beautiful sensual people gathered together in a stunningly beautiful room. Bright, amusing friends sated with fine food and wine, engaged in entertaining one another, and an undercurrent of erotic tension that appeared to build moment by moment.

The sunken living room, a large and grand room of boulder stone and massive glass walls overlooking the Atlantic Ocean, looked soft and comfortable in spite of the clean cut, severe line of the modern architecture. All the furniture was covered in hand-spun yarns of beige and sand colours hand woven into sumptuous cloth. The luscious, deep-piled carpets that lay on the stone floor were the colour of sand. There were rare Chinese celadon bowls of enormous size filled with white roses, and on an easel stood the only painting in the room, an eighteen million dollar landscape. A Poussin.

Rashid caught sight of Cynthia's reflection. She was standing at the centre of the gigantic glass wall that had been partially slid open, engaged in conversation with his old friend Henri. But her eyes were set on Rashid, whom she could see in the mirror. Their eyes met. And for an instant they were locked into each other through the mirror. It was enough. He watched an embarrassed blush caress her proud, beautiful face, and her hand unconsciously touch her cheek, then caress a magnificent weighty breast. He had her before he even touched her, he knew that. But her embarrassment, and the anger with which she tore her eyes away from his and abruptly dismissed herself from Henri to walk through the open glass wall out into the sand and scrubby pines where she was swallowed up by the blackness of the night, told him she would be a worthy adventure. The chase was on.

He worked the room and his guests like the old pro he was, while making his way across it to find Cynthia. The view from the living room was through the pines and straight out to his private beach and the huge Atlantic waves on one side and across the lawns, so green and well manicured, on the other. She had chosen to take a path to the top of a sand dune where she faced the ocean and its rhythmic sounds.

It was warm, and yet Cynthia could feel a chill rising from the ocean and the beach below her. It had been pitch black when she had stepped out from the house, but now the clouds had parted to reveal a moon white and cold, and a night sky perforated with stars. She rubbed her arms up and down several times as if to warm herself, bring herself back to life. She had been unnerved by the passion she felt when Rashid and she had shared that intense look in the mirror, but had regained control of herself now.

She sensed his approach before he made his presence known, dropped her hands to her side and became determined to remain in control of her emotions.

'Don't be frightened, it's only me. Rashid,' he said coming up behind her. Before she could turn around to face him she felt his hands caress her arms, and his lips and cheek brush aside her hair, his kiss on the side of her neck, his tongue lick the back of her ear.

'Oh, but I am,' she answered in a husky whisper, as

101

she felt herself melt under his caresses, weaken as he enveloped her in his arms, become dizzy from the scent of his skin and the erotic strength and power of his body pressed into the back of hers.

'Of me, or yourself?' he asked, then gently sucked the lobe of her ear and gave it a tender, sweet, loving nibble. He felt her body give way ever so slightly, and heard the tremor of passion in her sigh as she turned around in his arms to face him directly for the first time. As she turned he slipped his hands from her arms and placed them firmly on her waist, pulling her even closer to him, and felt her breasts naked under the silk rub up against him and excite an erotic tug on his senses. Without releasing her, he traced the outline of her lips with his finger, teased them open by running the tip of his tongue between them until helplessly they parted. Her breathing was uneasy and she wet her lips with her tongue and waited for his passionate kiss. He laughed, and placed a gentle kiss upon her lips, the last sort of kiss she expected or wanted. They could both feel her heart beating wildly, 'Are you teasing me?' she wanted to ask. But the words stuck in her throat.

'Put your fears away, Cynthia, at least for tonight,' he whispered in her ear. 'I won't promise you'll be safe, or that your fears will not be well-founded, but I do promise you an erotic adventure. Was I wrong? Did I not sense the soul of a sexual adventuress call out to me when our eyes met?'

Somehow Cynthia managed to gain a vestige of control over her emotions. Not much, but enough to want not to be taken for granted or to play the game of seduction with him. That was her fatal mistake, and what he had banked on. The minute she said, 'Yes, I do believe you were wrong,' the clever, sexy beauty committed herself to the role of just another one of Rashid Lala Mustapha's sexual victims.

He gave a resounding laugh, and with his arm around her shoulders they walked together back towards the Louis Kahn house. A miracle of architecture glowing in the blackness of the night, set like a great jewel on a bed of sand dunes, scrubby pines and clipped green grass. The music of the ocean filled their ears.

'You're a liar,' he declared.

'Well, you'll have to prove that, won't you?' she said, feeling more sure of herself now that the game was on and she had decided to play.

'Will you give me one night, this night, to prove you wrong? All I will ask of you is to stay by my side, not leave me no matter what. Promise that, and to follow your natural sexual inclinations, and then we will know if our erotic souls did or did not call out to each other through that looking glass.'

She began to laugh, and he liked her spirit, the fight he sensed in her. How delicious it will be to break her, he thought. What fun it will be to tantalise her sexually, to spoil her.

She interrupted his thoughts. 'What a vain, pompous man you are, Rashid. Mighty sure of yourself, aren't you?'

'Oh yes, myself. And you?'

She began to laugh at him again. He slid his arm from around her shoulder to her waist, and they continued to walk side by side towards the house. He smiled in the dark.

'You don't know me, Rashid. Don't make the mistake of thinking I am just another New York Jewish princess looking to capture a prince. We Ann

Arbor, Michigan, Jewish princesses are a different species entirely. Of course, I will grant you the night, it's little to ask in return for your hospitality. The whole world knows that an invitation to Rashid Lala Mustapha's compound here on Long Island is a rare prize.

'I remember an article I once read in *Vogue* magazine about Southampton, you and your house. It said that the privacy of Rashid Lala Mustapha's compound was assured not only by the high wall of hedge running along Gin Lane and down the sides of the estate to the sea, but also by magnificent bronze gates, gate keepers and security men who patrolled the area twenty-four hours a day, every day of the year. The estate is elegant, serene and—'

'Oh, do shut up, Cynthia,' he interrupted and sealed her lips with a kiss.

She pulled away reluctantly, cleared her throat and carried on.

'As I was saying. It is claimed Southampton society considers the season officially open when Rashid Lala Mustapha arrives for the first time during the summer and is greeted at the front door of his house by his butler, Basil, who is backed up by the line of staff behind him in the spacious and elegant entrance hall. Basil, the elderly English butler, who was once an under butler in one of Rashid's father's residences, is the most sought-after major domo in the town. One of the world's most eligible bachelors, with a number of extraordinary homes around the world, Mr Lala Mustapha when in the United States prefers to receive house guests in Southampton rather than his suite at the Carlisle Hotel in Manhattan. The staff is well trained to cater just as easily for heads of state as for his small and very private parties, sometimes labelled notorious by the gutter press.'

'You rattled that off as if you had memorised the article, although I don't believe it was written as mockingly as you have interpreted it.'

'The style is not difficult to mimic as you go along,' Cynthia said.

'So why do you mock me and my life style, yet accept my hospitality? I would have thought that unworthy of you.'

They had reached the open glass wall to the living room and stood in the dark, bathed in the soft warm light from the room. Cynthia was flushed with embarrassment and at the same time tipped off balance by the sexual charisma of the man. The way he looked at her was like rape. The way he questioned her stripped her of her defences.

'You are quite right, that was unworthy of me.' Then, feeling compelled to answer his question, she continued in a low, throaty voice that enchanted him.

'I was mocking you without reason. It was a sort of defence mechanism. I instinctively feel I must protect myself from you. I don't want to fall for a notorious lover and end up another broken corpse on your well-known heap of ladies lost in love. I suppose like many before me I think I am worth more than that.'

Rashid liked her frankness. He placed his lips upon hers, kissed her lightly, licked her lips with his tongue and pressed his kiss deeper. Their lips parted and their tongues touched. They sucked a passion into their kisses, and Rashid slipped his hands through the sleeves of her dress and fondled her breasts. Her body gave in to him, and pathetic little sighs escaped from her. Rashid released Cynthia slowly and, caressing her hair he said, 'It doesn't have to be like that for you, if you are clever and don't fall in love with me. It can be like our kisses and much more. It can be sexual ecstasy for a night, maybe two, maybe even more, as long as you understand that I can love you, care for you in the throes of erotic love. But it can only last as long as it lasts because the true love, the lasting love women want from me is not the kind of love that excites my interest. You do well to protect yourself from me if that's what you're looking for. But, frankly, I don't believe it is. I believe what I saw in the mirror earlier: an erotic soul that wants to mate with mine. Think about that, and stay by me this evening, and let me know when you are ready for us to try for paradise, if only for a little while.'

With those words he took her sandals from her hand, and bending down on one knee lifted first one foot and then the other and brushed the sand from her feet and between her toes, then he slipped her shoe on. Raising her dress above her ankle he placed a kiss upon it with such tenderness Cynthia almost cried out, her pain of pleasure was so great. He adjusted the top of her dress for her and arranged her slightly dishevelled hair. With his handkerchief he wiped away a tiny smudge of lipstick. For several minutes they remained where they were, watching the other guests and listening to the sensuous sound of flamenco music from the Spanish guitar and singer who were there to entertain.

Unnoticed they quietly stepped back into the room and together found seats among their friends. The musicians delighted their audience and eased them into a sensuous romantic mood. As the evening wore on, the lights were replaced by dozens of white candles. By their light the party drank Roederer

Cristal champagne from priceless antique Venetian goblets filled with tiny white peaches. A free spirit descended like an angel upon them, and both the men and the women rose one at a time from their chairs, interpreting the music from their souls with every movement of their bodies. All who performed, in their own way, enchanted and seduced their friends. When Rashid danced he removed his dinner jacket, and his tie, and slowly he changed the entire atmosphere in the room. Even those who had seen him dance to flamenco music before succumbed yet again to his call to Eros. Suddenly sexual ecstasy was imminent.

He returned to sit next to Cynthia. She waited for him to touch her, whisk her away. He did neither. He gave her only a smile calculated to torture, because it was filled with promise and a sensuous silence that pounded in her ears.

Sabrina Colefield was the next to take the floor. She was magnificent. One could feel her reach down to the depths of her secret being and dance to it. An inner eroticism hidden by her California health-and-beauty look surfaced and smouldered before their eyes. The interplay between the musicians and Sabrina's provocative dancing only intensified the seductiveness of the music. Together they changed the atmosphere in the room to a sophisticated yet tantalising raunchiness that escaped no one.

Rashid was the first to join her and be led by the rhythm of her body. He gazed into her eyes and slowly untied the loose knot on her hip so that her sarong fell to the floor. He placed his hands on her naked hips and they continued. Paul Jarret took the floor. Standing behind Sabrina he too picked up the rhythm of her movements. He reached around her to untie the wrap-around blouse and slowly slid it from her shoulders and down off her arms. For some time the naked Sabrina danced sandwiched loosely between the two men.

Rashid returned to Cynthia's side and sat down next to her, never taking his eyes from Sabrina. He finished his glass of champagne in one swallow and then ate several dark, rich, chocolate-covered cherries. Turning to Cynthia, he gave her a lascivious, demanding look that inflamed her even further. He whispered softly, 'Open your mouth.'

She obeyed, and he fed her a chocolate-covered cherry. The chocolate cracked open in her mouth, and the buds on her tongue opened and tingled with the taste of bitter sweet chocolate and the succulent, natural, sugary yet sharp juices of the cherry. A confectioner's seduction of the tastebuds, bound for a split second to deliver ecstasy for a gourmet chocolate addict such as Rashid. It was not lost on Cynthia. Orgasm, that was all she could think about, the taste and delight of orgasm. Rashid and Cynthia stared into each other's eyes and, although Cynthia felt frightened, she demanded, 'Take me to bed, Rashid,' in an almost inaudible whisper.

He bent forward and whispered in her ear, 'Not yet,' then bit the lobe quite hard, enough to bring a tear to her eye, and a drop of blood to her finger when she touched it. He smiled and licked the blood from her finger, and turned his attention back to Sabrina.

She danced alone once again keeping her audience enthralled. At some point Rashid was able to read the need in her face. He knew what would come next. He had seen her dance like that several times. Before she had a chance to call out to him for a pair of large, life-like amethyst dildos, he rose to his feet and went to her. Again he allowed his body to move with hers and once they were in tune he caressed her shoulders and kissed her gently on the lips, first one shoulder and then the other. He signalled to the musicians, a movement of his head and a look, to cool down their sensual rhythms. They obeyed slowly and with a fine discretion. For some reason, this evening, he didn't want Sabrina's performance to turn into an orgy. That would have been inevitable had he not stepped in as he did.

Sabrina, dancing while moving the pair of amethyst phalluses in and out of herself, would have been an irresistible turn-on for the men in the room. They, he knew, would take her two at a time, as they had done on other occasions, while the women joined in on her with mouths and hands and tongues, at her demand. When Sabrina let go sexually, all she wanted was to be devoured, to die to her own orgasms. She was an outrageous nymphomaniac, whose secret was known only to very few.

Cynthia watched Rashid fondle Sabrina's breasts and slowly squat down, while kissing them and her belly, to bury his face for a brief moment in her mound of blonde pubic hair. She wanted to dash to him and rip him away from Sabrina, so painful was it for her to watch him with another woman.

He gathered the sarong up from the floor and, tying it around Sabrina's hips, kissed her on the cheek and whispered something in her ear. Her eyes shone with a wild passion, and she threw her arms around Rashid and said loudly, 'Oh, yes, yes, please,' and laughed. Several of the others joined them, giving hugs and kisses, and a great deal of admiration for Sabrina's dancing. Without a glance or a word to Cynthia,

Rashid and Sabrina left the room together.

A short time later, when Rashid returned to the living room, only Cynthia was there, disconsolately hearing romantic Spanish love songs. He thanked the guitarist and the singer and bade them goodnight. Then he went to Cynthia and, taking her hand in his he kissed it and pulled her up from the soft chair.

'I thought you were going to stay with me all through this night, never leave my side? Why didn't you follow us?'

Cynthia was incredibly happy to see him. He had come back for her. That was all that mattered. He wanted her and she wanted him. She didn't give two pins about pride or playing games with him. Passion was loose in her voice and her eyes when she said, 'I died a thousand deaths waiting for you to come back for me.'

'A thousand? Surely that qualifies you for at least one night of paradise.' He kissed her and felt her tremble to his touch. It was not a tremble of fear but one of excitement and expectation. He pulled her to him and kissed her again deeply, with great passion, and he felt her yield into him.

'You'll die many more deaths before morning, those small deaths that come from orgasms that take you out of this world. Are you sure that's what you want, to let me do as I wish with you to transport you there? I'll make you my sexual slave this night, and all I'll promise you is ecstasy, nothing more.'

She made no reply, but simply removed her dress and stood naked before him. She placed her arms around his neck and he picked her up in his. Bending his head to her breast, he sucked on the large, pointed nipple as he carried her across the room and behind the boulder-stone fireplace wall to his private wing.

It was an effective concept – to walk through the massive stone wall with a huge fire burning in it, and have it seal up behind you. It was achieved by having the last eight feet of each end of the forty-foot wall constructed as stone steps. Pressure on the third stair caused a portion of the stone wall to slide silently open to reveal the master bedroom.

The three solid walls of antique pine panelling took one's breath away. An enormous collection of original erotic black ink drawings by Picasso, signed and dedicated to Rashid, hung there. Two figures in several of the drawings were unmistakably Rashid and Humayun in their younger days. The fourth wall was made of glass and slid open onto a sand dune that rose above the beach and the ocean. Sunk into the dune was a private swimming pool. There were board walks of wood slats bleached by sun and wind lying on the sand around the pool. Great, thick, wooden railroad sleepers were pounded into the dune to form an elegantly rustic curved staircase to the beach below.

The bedroom was stunningly stark in its furnishings: an enormous bed in the middle of the room covered in soft beige suede that draped onto the floor; many large soft pillows covered in black and white unborn calf skins. The white marble floor had black panther skins and a rare white tiger skin scattered over it. On either side of the bed was a pair of transparent glass cubes, and on them stood Lalique vases with four dozen extremely long-stemmed, blood red roses in each, and a pair of Chinese pedestalled dishes from the Han dynasty offering a pyramid of white Belgian chocolates filled with fresh mocha cream. Against one wall a seventeenth-century ivory coffer of many small drawers, whose fronts were inlaid with occasional rose-cut diamonds, was set on its original stand. Placed on top of the coffer were a silver champagne cooler chilling two bottles of Krug, and a pair of Stuben champagne glasses on a silver tray. The bedroom looked dramatic, sensual and invitingly sexual. The scent of the roses mingled with the salt air drifting in through the open glass door to augment the lust enclosed in Picasso's lines that pricked the erotic senses with every glance.

Rarely had she known such ecstasy, nor a man who could tease her senses as Rashid did. With every act of erotic passion he heaped upon her she drifted off into oblivion, only to be wrenched back by him and by her desire for more. She never had a chance. He used her cunt as a vessel and drank champagne from it; he nibbled and ate at her genitalia until he could drink her orgasms as he had the vintage Krug he had filled her with. And all through the night and the dawn there were other erotic preludes to his fucking her. Cynthia was mesmerised by his beautiful penis. She felt his magnetism draw her flesh around him as he worked his way inside her, kissing her with his cock. To sense him moving in and out of her with tenderness and passion, and at times with unbridled wildness, drove her into a kind of sexual frenzy.

She had no idea at what point the erotic turned into a night of sexual depravity for her, because the last thing she could remember upon waking in the arms of her lover, Rashid, was standing with him in the dark of the bedroom looking through the glass wall at his private swimming pool, lit only by the moon and dozens of fat white church candles glowing under glass hurricane lamps. The scene she saw of Sabrina naked in the pool, her skin glowing like satin, being savaged by three huge men as they spun her round and round in the water, and the acts of lust by which the men had wrung fearsome screams of ecstasy from her, while Cynthia herself was being used mercilessly by Rashid from behind, seared in her mind. Only fragmented memories of what else had happened to her with Rashid kept slipping in and out of her mind, and she knew that she was blocking them out, fearful to be reminded how willingly she had acceded to his every demand.

She watched him as he slept and wondered how a man could be so beautiful, so sensual and seductive even in his sleep. He was the devil in the skin of a handsome prince, and she wished that she could find a wooden stake in her hand to drive it through his heart, destroy him forever, as that night with him had destroyed her for any other man. She would love him for the rest of her life, exactly what he had warned her against.

His eyes fluttered open. Their gazes met, and he smiled. She could have coped better with his wakening if the smile he presented was a morning-after smile, had it been a smarmy smirk, a sneaky know-it-all kind of smile, even an 'I told you so smile'. But it was none of those, it was more of a lover's smile, tender, generous and gentle. And that she found impossible to cope with.

'Good morning,' he said, stroking her hair and kissing her on the cheek.

'Hello,' she answered, wishing she could have said something more clever than that, something that would give her the courage to thank him and leave his bed with a degree of dignity. Not a word more could she muster.

'You were a delight last night, wonderful. Thank

you for being such a lovely and sexy lady.'

Then Rashid possessed her with before breakfast sex; but Cynthia made love. Afterwards they swam in the private pool and had breakfast together under the sun: rich, ripe strawberries dipped in fresh, pure Vermont maple-syrup, crisp bacon and shirred eggs, blueberry muffins straight from the oven, and many cups of hot black coffee.

They returned to the bedroom and lay together once more on the bed. Rashid opened the red Pretasi beach robe she wore and began to fondle her. She slid her hand under his robe and returned his caresses. As she felt him once again hard in her hand, he slipped out of his robe.

'Stay with me while I make my morning phone calls. I'm not ready to let you join the others. Let me be selfish and keep you to myself for just a little longer.'

All the right words a woman wants to hear after she has allowed a man to use and abuse her, devour and enslave her to him. But where was the passion in his voice to match hers? Where were the tenderness and loving and caring, the need that she felt for him in every pore of her body? They weren't there. Oh, the words were right, the charm and the suave manners, but where were the feelings?

Of course she stayed. Stayed and took him in her mouth and sucked and licked, and caressed with her hands, helpless to walk away from him and the stream of orgasms his fingers brought from his teasing of her clitoris and his probing deep inside her soft, moist vagina.

Lost yet again in her sexual madness for Rashid, she was unaware of how little what they were doing meant to him until she heard him. It was more the tone of his voice, the love instilled in every word he spoke that shocked her. She listened as if he were far away and his words had nothing to do with the joy of the sexual foreplay they were sharing. She wished she were deaf and could not hear what he was saying. But she wasn't deaf, nor was he far off, and she heard him clearly saying, 'Good morning, Mirella, my dearest heart. Are you alone?'

He paused and listened, 'Oh, good, then I can tell you how much I miss you. How exciting it was to make love to you and feel the baby inside you move at the same time. How can you ever know what a joy that is for a man?'

He listened while Mirella Wingfield Corey, his mistress, spoke. Then he answered her. 'Of course it doesn't matter to me that the child you carry is your husband's. Do you think I enjoyed it any the less, or that I love you any the less because it's not mine? Stop thinking this child is going to change our lives. Our love will never change, no matter what any of us do, you, Adam, or I.'

It finally got through to Cynthia what a humiliating position she was in. Suddenly she felt like a sex object, wallowing in loveless ecstasy. Whoever that woman on the telephone was, she had Rashid Lala Mustapha as Cynthia would never have him and it was too painful to hear it. She tried to pull herself away, but Rashid would have none of that, he was too close to coming. He held her tightly by the back of her neck and she almost gagged, so far down her throat was he. She heard nothing more of what was spoken. His voice suddenly sounded far off again, and the next moment she felt the hard thrust of a jade phallus fucking her, while she served Rashid with her mouth. He exploded with great force, calling Mirella's name over and over again, and followed through by pleasuring Cynthia with the jade dildo until she begged for mercy, so exhausted was she.

It was sunset when she woke up. She was alone. On the pillow next to her were a jeweller's box and a note. She read, 'Have gone with Amanda to a cocktail party at the country club. Meet us there. The chauffeur is at your disposal. Ring for the maid, she will bring your clothes and anything you need. The necklace is to say thank you for last night. Wear it this evening for me, and often for yourself, to remember how blissful paradise can be.

Rashid.'

Cynthia sat cross legged in the middle of the bed and began to cry. She was hopelessly infatuated with Rashid. She opened the Cartier leather box. There on the black velvet lay a twisted rope of several strands of angel skin coral beads entwined with strands of black and white seed pearls and a strand of small diamonds, clasped by an oval of black coral surrounded by diamonds.

The last thing Cynthia Cohen did before she left the room was to replace the note on the pillow.

'*Vogue* magazine, as it happens, was not flattering enough. But perhaps it was a different tour you gave them? The necklace is lovely. Shame the clasps don't hold.'

It sounded more cynical than she was able to feel. Bitterly she made her way from Southampton, fighting back her tears for paradise lost.

Chapter 6

The summer was coming to its natural end. Much too quickly, thought Mirella. And then, on the other hand, not quickly enough. Indecisive. That's the way she was feeling about everything these days. It had been the kind of summer that dreams are made of. Or so she was constantly being told by everyone in Easthampton. Not least the Corey clan: all Adam's children and their respective mothers kept drifting in and out of the house, until Adam sent them all packing back to Istanbul, with the exception of Joshua, whom Mirella and Adam spent a great deal of time with.

She sat on the sidelines of the tennis tournaments, days of golf, pitiful cricket matches, picturesque and amusing races up and down the beach on Corey thoroughbreds, in the dawn hours or at sunset. She described herself as a beached whale sending out dolphin signals. For days on end she lay on the beach in the sun or swam in the sea, unable to come to terms with her joy at carrying a child fathered by Adam, and the changes having a child was going to make in her life. Picnics and dinners were planned exclusively to induce an appetite for food, which in the last few weeks, after their return from the gala in Paris, she had not felt at all. Whether she was being social or reclusive, she felt fragmented. Little pieces of her seemed always to be somewhere other than where she was.

The whole clan, Rashid included, had sailed to Newport and lost in the races. They sailed to Martha's Vineyard and won the round-the-island race there. Mirella stayed at home and played pregnant. Together with Brindley Ribblesdale, her English solicitor, she plotted and planned how to fight Rashid and win back what he had stolen from her legacy. Rashid gave three grand parties. Only close friends – and an endless stream of pretty girls – were invited. They flew in from everywhere. Extra security had to be arranged when the President of France graced one of them. Mirella attended them all.

Several times during the summer, Mirella and Adam disappeared for a few days at a time. Twice they flew into the city and stayed in the Fifth Avenue house, where the doctors examined Mirella and made tests. They reassured her that all was well with her pregnancy and her baby, in spite of their earlier concern.

In Paris, as short a time ago as the night of the gala, she had still been so small hardly anyone would have guessed she was in the last months of pregnancy. Then suddenly she began to show, and rapidly grew heavy with child. That and the coming event of giving birth had alarmed her. What few maternal instincts she had suddenly offended her. Yet, when she stood naked in front of the mirror, she caressed the swell of her belly and found her body not unattractive. She often placed her hands between the underpart of her rotundness and the curve of her mound and enjoyed feeling the weight of her pregnancy.

And she enjoyed enormously the sex she had with

her husband and her lover. If possible, even more in these last few weeks than ever before. It had to do with men and their erotic adoration of her in her pregnant state, the caring and imaginative sexual intercourse they loved her with, especially Rashid. It seemed to keep her even more sexually excited than usual at a time when she had expected not to want sex. That embarrassed her. Hardly an hour went by in which she did not take in fantasy the phallus of Adam or Rashid, full and erect, to probe slowly, deeply inside her. Once she imagined having both their penises, side by side, fucking her. She would be filled with them, and baby, to bursting point. There would be pain, but there would be extraordinary physical and psychological pleasure as well when they all three came and bathed her and her child in their exquisite orgasms. Mirella felt woozy, overcome by lust and her erotic imagination. But she was not deluded; she understood well her anxieties about becoming a mother. They centred on losing her lust for love and an erotic life with her two men. On possibly transferring her feelings for them to her child. Maternity vied with her sexual power over these two remarkable men.

Her mother, Lily, had been of no help to Mirella during her pregnancy. Lily had been made to come to terms with her daughter being heiress to a fortune which she felt should have gone to herself if to anyone at all. Then Mirella married Adam. For a while, she had behaved better towards her daughter than she had since Mirella had been a child. Her new attitude towards Mirella had not come easily. In fact, it had been forced upon Lily by revelations made to her about herself and her own mother by the Princess Eirene, a close friend to Adam, Rashid and Mirella.

Rashid, too, had warned her to change her attitude towards Mirella or bear the consequences, which he assured Lily would ruin her life forever.

Lily recognised the evil streak in Rashid's nature and trembled before it. If she had had any doubts as to how far he would go to see that Lily behaved properly with Mirella, they were quelled when he consummated his psychological seduction of Lily with sex. It became the chain that bound her as it bound so many other women to Rashid. On Lily's chain there was an extra link: he blackmailed her with the threat to reveal their sexual dalliance, not only to Mirella but to the world. The gossip columnists would ruin all their lives.

The improved relationship between mother and daughter became strained once again when Mirella announced she was going to have a baby. The news threw Lily into a fit of anguish. She was obsessed with Rashid. She feared the baby might be his. That she could not endure. Her jealousy burned. She said nothing of her fears to Mirella. How could she, having no proof that Mirella and Rashid were having a sexual life together? Rumours were not enough. So she tried another tack. She simply suggested that Mirella abort her pregnancy, playing on Mirella's being too old, or unmaternal, incapable of handling motherhood. Wasn't she a career woman with no feeling for wifehood or motherhood? Mightn't she lose the adoration of her husband and Rashid? What of the sheer indignity of giving birth, the pain, the mess? Motherhood and mother love – they were traps. She created a whole line of monstrous mothers in the family. Genetically the project was just not on. Mirella responded finally by allowing Lily close contact with her only when either Adam or Rashid was with her. At those times Lily was an angel in a world of positive thoughts for Mirella.

During these last few months of her pregnancy, more and more, Mirella's thoughts kept drifting back to her maternal great-grandmother, Roxelana Oujie, her benefactress. This notorious beauty, at one time the most powerful woman in the Ottoman court, had ruled the Sultan with her magnificent looks and clever mind, and her sexual prowess. His children she loved and cared for in a ruthless way, so that they always added to her life, her power and her wealth. And her maternal grandmother, Inje, one of the last women to be born and live, as her childhood friend the Princess Eirene had, in the harem of the Palace of Topkapi. It took pregnancy to make Mirella finally accept how unlike her own mother she was, and how like Inje and Roxelana she had become. The solicitor, Brindley Ribblesdale, through years of sleuthing, had established her as the heiress to the Oujie legacy. Because of him she had discovered her remarkable ancestors, been seduced by Rashid, and married Adam. It had been hard to come to terms with the erotic and free-spirited side of her nature, the wealthy, opulent and exotic life she was living. After all, she had been brought up in New England under the influence of her father's family, the Wingfields, and her maternal grandfather's family, puritanical, high society, New England WASPs.

Adam understood everything she was going through. She knew that instinctively, and appreciated that he did not force her to speak about her anxieties, but waited for her to work them out, and approach him with actions rather than words. In this way he let her confirm her ability to rise admirably to the changes in her life and her work. Miraculously her moves always enriched their love for each other. He had been less understanding when, on her return from Paris after the gala, while approaching touchdown at Kennedy Airport, she had announced that Rashid had robbed her. She had explained how, and when, and why he did it. Adam acquiesced in her wishes that he stay out of the affair, and behave as if the crime did not exist, that he treat Rashid exactly as he always had until she had determined her response to his latest treachery. He knew from past experience that what Mirella finally decided would be the right thing for all of them. Adam had no illusions about their *ménage à trois* and how important it was to his wife and to their happiness.

It had not been easy for Adam to keep quiet and take no action against Rashid. But he had done as she asked. Then there had been Joshua to convince to do the same. Her stepson adored her, was in love with her, wanted her for his own. Having come to terms with his intimate feelings for her, and his love for his father, he won his painful battle with lust for Mirella. He had accepted that he could never have her except as a loving friend, his father's wife, family. Joshua took the position that, if he could not have Mirella as a lover, no man but his father would. Josh therefore resented Rashid's involvement in Adam's and Mirella's lives. Rashid's attention and devotion to Mirella irritated him. Obsessively. If he could discredit Rashid in Mirella's eyes, he did it. In fact, Joshua was the only real threat to happiness in this *ménage à trois*. By trying to remove Rashid from his parents' lives he disturbed the poise of love and respect on which the threesome balanced its survival.

Maybe she could just say nothing about her losses to Joshua? But she knew that would be a mistake. He was certain to hear about it. As usual Adam had come to her rescue. Together they told Joshua the news and convinced him that it was Mirella's business and he must obey her in this. He reluctantly agreed, but declared that he wanted Rashid banned from their lives forever. His father's response shocked him, 'Okay, Joshua, Rashid has a streak of bad in him. It's pathological. He has to make everything and everyone conform to his will. That's his way of life, the dark side of him. Mirella and I know that. We don't need you to be forever targeting his defects for us. But, in his own way, he loves us. As much as he can love anyone. And he has become a part of our lives, and I reckon it'll always be that way. So keep out. And I mean that. I never want to discuss this again, ever. Do I make myself clear?'

Adam had evidently achieved clarity because, from then on, it was as if the offence did not exist. When Rashid appeared, Joshua became elaborately civilised, downright charming with Rashid, as he had usually been before Mirella came into their lives. So much so that Mirella suspected Joshua now either accepted the situation or blanked it out of his mind. Joshua's change of attitude was a decided relief to them all. A constraint on the relationship had been removed.

Mirella and Adam were on their way back to Easthampton and their turn-of-the-century, weather-worn, grey-shingled summer mansion, after a session with the city doctors.

Adam sat with Mirella behind Sam, holding her hand. The helicopter veered off at a right angle from its pad on the edge of the East River near the 57th

Street bridge. They whirled their way towards the city's summer havens. Adam squeezed her hand.

'Are you all right?'

She nodded, and returned his squeeze.

'You don't look all right. You look very pale. Are you upset by what the doctor told you?'

'Not so much upset as annoyed with myself, because it's probably true what he said.'

'I think he was a bit harsh with you. I don't believe he quite picked up what you feel about having this baby.'

'I don't either, Adam.' She smiled at her husband and kissed him on the cheek, as if to reassure him. But she knew that the doctor had been absolutely right in what he said. She could still hear his words. 'Mirella, your baby is due next week, but are you going to carry on as you have been through this entire pregnancy? Delighted to be pregnant, yes, but so preoccupied with everyone, everything in your life, that you hardly have time to prepare yourself for the birth of your child. Go on that way and you will carry your baby for maybe two, even three weeks before you give birth. You're a strong-willed woman and your determination not to let this pregnancy interfere with your life has made you hold back. An attitude like yours could be affecting your baby. It just might not want to be born either. It's time to let go, Mirella, feel rotten, bloated, nervous and tetchy, cry, be unhappy, miserable. Or marvellous, or whatever. But relax and give in, let your baby be born. Become a mother.'

Even as his words went through her mind, she was thinking of anything but the birth of her child. Rashid dominated her thoughts. She had no doubt that Rashid loved her in his way as much as Adam did. But he lived

124

so determinedly to the full on his own terms, that even the taste of Mirella's real love was absorbed into himself. He lived for his involvement with women. And she now knew his obsession to restore to himself the power and wealth the Lala Mustapha family once wielded. How was she ever likely to change all this? He was going to die as he lived – in the thrall of sexual oblivion with women, tempered by a touch of love.

Mirella was preoccupied with the idea that the day was coming soon when she would confront Rashid and together they would both uncover that flaw in him, the inherent streak of evil that had stopped Mirella from submitting totally to him. She and Rashid had faced that flow in him once before, learned to accept and live with the darkest side of his nature, and to love each other in spite of it. Their all-consuming sexual love evolved into a love that reached deeper than either of them ever expected or wanted. It was bound to happen again if she confronted him with his latest act of disloyalty. At that time it had caused tension within the dangerous emotional triangle between Mirella, Adam and Rashid. For the moment Mirella felt that she could not afford either the tension or the possible consequences of such a confrontation. At least, not until the baby was safely born.

She distracted herself from thoughts of Rashid by switching to the most immediate problem she had, the plan she was creating with Brindley to retrieve every lost asset of the original Oujie legacy, including those which she had a year before sold off to Rashid of her own volition. Brindley had assured her that it would probably take the remainder of her life to do it, and she would have to take a much more active and public position if she was to achieve her goal. So far it had been mere planning and plotting – all talk. Was she actually capable of hardening herself into a more ruthless Mirella Oujie Wingfield Corey, able to keep her lover and deceive him in order to save the Oujie heritage for generations to come?

The helicopter dropped low over Fire Island and followed the magnificent long, sandy beach. Too late in the day, and too cool for sunbathers and swimmers, the beach was almost entirely deserted. Mirella watched the waves crashing up against the shore line – a sight she always found thrilling. They passed over the fashionable little houses and minute gardens clumped together that made up the famous or infamous communities along the narrow strip of land facing the Atlantic Ocean on the one side and the bay where the ferries crossed from the mainland to deposit the summer people. Mirella watched one community drift into the next as they flew the length of the island. She noted, too, sections of scrubby pine, a few uninhabited places left to the wind and the rain.

Seen from the air the island lay like a thin thread of sandbar waiting to be washed by the Atlantic Ocean into the numerous bays. It narrowed itself down and shifted inward towards the mainland. Where Fire Island ended, up popped the long sandbar that turned into Westhampton Beach.

Pulling the helicopter higher, Sam piloted it just above Dune Road. It flew parallel to the Ocean and Shinnacock Bay. Eventually the thin strip of land melted into the coastline and Southampton Beach, then the Southampton Beach Club. They whirled over it and on up the ocean's shoreline, then flew over Rashid's compound. His estate ran between the exclusive Gin Lane and the Ocean for a distance of a mile, and along the beach front for three quarters of a mile.

They swooped low over the beach and at the end of it swept the helicopter up over the sand dunes towards the main house. They flew over the magnificent blanket of bright green lawn between the neatly clipped, twelve-foot high boxwood hedge that served as a wall along Gin Lane, and the huge glass and stone house set in a forest of Japanese pines. With its formal lawns and hedges on one side, and sand dunes and long, windswept, wild dune grass undulating down to the cold, rough, glorious Atlantic on the other, the setting was undeniably impressive. Other modern architectural perfections, small pavilions for guests, tennis courts, pools, working studios, a pavilion for his jade collection, where several antique opium beds of infinite charm were arranged so that one could lie there and listen to music, were left behind as they turned into the wind and headed for their own compound, further down Long Island at Easthampton.

Mirella turned and looked over her shoulder as the compound receded behind them. There was Rashid's white Porsche convertible passing through the gates and pulling up to the main house. As she turned back Mirella's gaze caught Adam's, and suddenly she was absorbed by memories of the first night they met, when Brindley brought Adam to Mirella's house, as a friend, a Turkophile, the archaeologist who had discovered the Oujie journals.

He had been there when Brindley had announced how wealthy and vast the Oujie legacy was. He had been shocked at her indifference towards it, and her lack of interest in Turkey, where it originated and the country he loved. She could remember his words as if he were repeating them in front of her now.

'Mirella,' he said in a soft, hypnotic tone, 'I know part of your great-grandmother's estate. I have seen fields of poppies that go on for miles broken only by an ancient Greek temple or Hittite burial mounds. I have excavated Hittite cities that are on your land. I have walked up Mount Ararat in search of ancient objects, sailed along the Mediterranean coast of Turkey and watched the waves wash over the ruins of an ancient white marble amphitheatre – still on land that is yours. I have for years dealt with dubious men exploiting your land. There's bad management there that could destroy part of the history of civilisation. Right there on your land. I have canoed down the Euphrates: whole sections of it are yours. I have saved caravanserais, for the sheer architectural and historical value of them: some of them yours. I have slept in the conical churches of Cappadocia. There, too, are places of magic which belong to you. I have stood where Paul of Tarsus preached, on stones trodden by your ancestors. All this and a whole lot more is yours. You've got no time to go to Turkey? How can you liquidate your heritage? Why, Mirella? Is it because it brings you up against your own mortality, and you don't want to face that?'

She remembered vividly the look of disgust and disappointment that scorned her as not prepared even to learn with an open mind about her fabulous legacy, only wanting to liquidate it as soon as possible and get on with her life and her work at the United Nations.

Those lands he spoke of were some of the very ones Rashid now possessed. If Mirella had been angry these last weeks about Rashid's raid on her property – and she had – remembering Adam's words focused all that fury in an instant. She suddenly understood that she

128

had no choice but to turn anger into legal cunning. She placed her hands on her large, swollen belly and felt her baby. She took Adam's hand and placed it there. The infant soon obliged with a filial kick.

'Isn't it marvellous, that old miracle?' he said, a smile of delight on his face as he bent to kiss her tenderly on the lips. 'Don't be afraid, I'll help you, I'll be there with you and help you through this.'

'Like you do with everything in my life. What a good man you are.'

'No. What a good couple we are,' he generously corrected her.

She watched him change seats and take the controls of the helicopter. Adam: rock solid, morally just; a shrewd man whether in business or in love, as much an adventurer as a family man. A man in love with a woman he happily shared with Rashid because he knew and understood her. Knew that a *ménage à trois* need not be a threat to their love for each other or their relationship. If anything, it heightened what they shared.

Although Mirella never made sexual comparisons between her lover and her husband, never questioned or tried to analyse her erotic attachment to both men, she was often puzzled by the difference in their characters. Her pregnancy, for example. There was no question in her mind that she conceived with Adam during their first love-making in the new house on Fifth Avenue. They had been apart for several weeks when he had gone off to Africa, ostensibly on safari. He had returned to the west having effectively bound up the Marxist regime in Ethiopia in a business and financial coup that had launched Adam as a significant force in business in that part of the world. If Adam had any doubts that the child was his, he had never let on to her about them. Rashid, on the other hand, dared to hope that the baby was his. His constant insistence that she have a test to prove paternity had provoked Mirella into endlessly reassuring Adam that he was the father of their child. So Mirella had been perturbed to find that, although certain that was true, Adam would not be upset if he discovered it was Rashid's.

As the Easthampton house came into view over the horizon, she was wondering what sort of vanity it was that made her angry about that, actually jealous that her husband should accept the child if it were Rashid's? She remembered how that had shocked her into breaking the unspoken taboo about discussing the triangle with Adam. Adam's reaction was curt. 'Why are we talking about this, Mirella? Is it so difficult for you to understand that I love you? That I trust your love for me enough to want you to remain a free spirit. If that entails a love triangle such as we have, so be it. Rashid and I can live with the relationship because it enhances the lives of all three of us. And because we maintain a loyalty, respect and an immense consideration for each other and our positions. We don't ever challenge them. What have we to talk about vis-à-vis our unusual relationship? It just is, and will exist until one day it isn't.'

So she gained a single, brief glimpse of how he coped emotionally with the situation. The taboo of silence then reasserted itself. Their marriage and *ménage à trois* flourished and enriched their lives. She had sensed once more the broad emotional stability of the man she had married.

Rashid, in his own fashion, was no less remarkable about her pregnancy. His love for Mirella and the

130

unborn child she was carrying seemed to enchant him. Yet she was aware that it drove him further into sexual depravity with Humayun. He made no secret of it. Neither did he make a secret of Humayun's emotional control over him. So much so that, for a time, Mirella feared it was going to be a threat to the *ménage à trois*.

She had been wrong about that. The three were as close as ever, in spite of Rashid's thievery and Mirella's pregnancy. But all of that was about to change. Soon the baby would arrive and she would have her confrontation over her stolen property with Rashid. A confrontation all of them had obviously been avoiding. Rashid, true to himself as always, after his original attempt to tell Mirella himself, had been stopped by her outburst against him, never approached her about it again. Ruthless man that he was, and thrilled with his achievement, he had allowed the world's newspapers and *Time*, *Newsweek*, *Forbes*, *Paris Match* and *L'Express* to print the news. The fact that Mirella and Adam chose to ignore the subject of his property coup, and what it meant to him, seemed to affect him not at all.

The helicopter landed on the beach below the house, Mirella clumsily struggled from her seat, watched over by Adam, who laughingly picked her up in his arms and carried her down from the copter to stand her on the sand.

'You find my clumsy movements funny, do you?' she challenged.

'Yes, as a matter of fact I do. Funny and endearing.'

'Sometimes I think you enjoy this pregnancy more than I do.'

'I don't know about that, but I am enjoying it. As I have done with every woman who has carried my

131

child. I like pregnant women. Especially those I have impregnated. Marlo used to say it's the male chauvinist pig in me, pregnant with his own pride at having put her in the place where he thinks she belongs, tied down to motherhood. But I don't believe that's true. And I never thought for a moment she would succumb to motherhood, which, as you know, she has never done. Partial motherhood would be more like it.'

'I don't feel very maternal, Adam. Do you think that will matter to the baby?'

'Maybe it matters to some babies. But it won't to ours, because of our extended family. Remember, our baby will be brought up in the clan with all my other children and their mothers. There will be enough maternal love between you and Marlo, Giuliana, Aysha, and, though she is not a mother, Muhsine. The baby won't lack mother love. My other children surely must be an example to reassure you of that.'

That was true. She herself had experienced the maternal love the women of the *yalis* had shown her. And knew it to be rich and genuine. Her child, like all the others, would be enriched by life in this unusual household. Why, she had to ask herself, had it taken her so long to accept that? Was she in fact still suffering from her strait-laced Boston background? From middle-class American morality that demanded she be a *Reader's Digest* kind of mother? She was quite embarrassed for herself.

At dinner that evening, Mirella felt less fragmented than she had been for months. Brindley was there, Joshua and Adam. The Coreys usually made a point of dressing for dinner, and this evening Mirella had made a special effort to look beautiful for Adam and their guests. It was her response to her own wandering thoughts, to the doctor's harsh words, to her decision to get back what had been stolen and to leave a vast legacy to an Oujie-Wingfield-Corey dynasty. Most of all it had to do with at last being able to relax in her pregnancy.

She wore her hair up, pinned in place by tiny diamond birds set on combs, in a casual, very pretty manner. Her off-the-shoulder white cotton, batiste summer evening dress clung to her hugely full breasts and showed their luscious roundness and a hint of darker nimbus and nipple. The belly for once looked frighteningly large, as the thin material clung to it and outlined her flat pubis and seductive thighs with every step she took. Around her throat she wore a narrow ribbon, a bunch of fresh purple violets tied to it on one side. She entered the room. The men were stunned into silence by her rich, ripe beauty that appeared to be ready to open to them. When had she looked more voluptuous? For the first time she wore her pregnancy like a priceless jewel and dazzled them with it.

They looked in wonder and amusement at this new Mirella who ravenously ate through Moses's superb dinner of cracked crab mousse followed by fresh rainbow trout grilled with lemon, buttered and topped with slivers of toasted almonds served on a bed of fresh fried parsley, and surround by steamy rice dumplings. Then came a course of fresh white asparagus served cold in a vinaigrette dressing, a remarkably perfect Brie with water biscuits, and finally a Pavlova of mouth-watering meringue, crunchy on the outside and chewy on the inside, filled with fresh whipped cream, raspberries and redcurrants.

They were dining by dozens of candles under glass hurricane lamps, to a symphony of night sounds: the

133

ocean lapping the shore, the frogs croaking from their watery beds in the nearby ponds, and the crickets chirping on the wide verandah that circled the house. A heavy scent from the garden travelled on the night: end-of-summer flowers, roses and lilies, hydrangeas, scented creeping vines and mown grass. The moon and the stars came out in a grand display. Moses and two maids danced attendance on them with the splendid food and exquisite white wines, Montrachets of several vintages. Mirella kept trying to find a right moment to tell them, at last, what she was going to do about her losses. She did, finally, between the cheese and the dessert. She rose from her chair and proposed a toast. The men rose from their chairs and she held out her glass and said, 'Adam, my friends, I would like to make a toast to my unborn child, the next heir to the Oujie legacy. To him or to her I intend to leave, one day, the Oujie estate, having retrieved as much of its lost property as possible in my lifetime, and in the hope that its inventory records will then read as they once did at the time of the death of my benefactress, my great-grandmother, Roxelana Oujie.'

Then she drank from her glass. Smiles slowly broke across the faces of the men in the room as they realised what she was saying. They drained the wine from their glasses. They all began to speak at the same time, but she stopped them saying, 'Please, please, do sit down and let me say a few more words. This is not simply me seeking revenge on Rashid for his fraudulent acts upon my legacy. Nor do I want to create a new vendetta or perpetuate an old one between the Oujies and the Lala Mustaphas. Nor is it just avarice, or a desire for power or prestige. I have done it for myself. Adam's patience and character have given me the chance to appreciate my heritage, who I am, and what I am, to respect the past, and live bravely and honestly in the present. Because how I live and what I do, like everyone else, is the fragment of history that I alone have the making of. So that Adam may never again think, as he once might, that I am a pitiful descendant of a once remarkable family. I deserved that once, but I would rather not give him the chance to think it again.'

She began to laugh out of a sense of relief that the indecision had been lifted, and she added, 'Thank heavens that's all decided, and been said. Now I can get on with having this baby.'

Adam walked around to the foot of the table where she was sitting and kissed her, saying, 'You're some lady,' and turning to Moses, 'Get the corks moving on the champagne, Moses. We're launching a new dynasty.'

Joshua went to Mirella and raised her hand to kiss it. Then with an enormous twinkle in his eye, he asked, 'No holds barred? The works? You're going to go after Rashid, wheeling, dealing, through the law courts and all?'

'No, Josh, I am not. The Oujie estate is. And none of us will ever confront Rashid openly about it. I will do that, pick my time when I am ready, and let him know my intentions.'

Mirella felt exhausted, excused herself and went to bed. But she could not relax into sleep. She was to have lunch at the country club with Rashid the next day, just the two of them. She found that her decision in no way diminished the thrill she felt at the prospect of being with her charismatic lover.

Chapter 7

The car stopped on the Rue Quai Anatole France and
Adam stepped out and walked to the wall facing the
Seine. He looked over it to the Right Bank and the
Jardin des Tuileries, the Palais Royal and the Musée
du Louvre, then down to the cobblestone quay.

There she sat, those long, slender legs shod in high
heeled, black patent leather Maud Frizon sandals,
crossed and dangling over the side of the wooden
packing case, several smaller ones piled neatly next to
it. Her long black wiry hair shone in the sunlight. She
wore it down. It created a softly seductive, wavy halo
around her face. In a few days that face would adorn
every important newspaper and periodical in the
world. The face of female Africa.

Her dress was by Karl Lagerfeld, black silk, cut for
her, on her body, by him. Every *haute-couturier* Adam
had introduced her to wanted not only to dress her,
but capture her for the cat walk. To dress her was to
robe a dark and sensual queen who carried her clothes
royally. Wide, chunky, gold bangles on her wrists
twinkled against the blackness of her skin and dress.
Over one shoulder and arm, and draped on an angle
across her breasts and long and slender torso, and tied
under the other arm, was a black silk triangular shawl.

Adam registered her as the most stunning, sensual and interesting woman in Paris. Seeing her there excited him to remember when she had appeared so unexpectedly from behind a tree in Pythagoria on the island of Samos, brought there by Marlo Channing for a five-minute secret meeting with him. Their next meeting had been equally thrilling, in the highlands of Ethiopia when she had stepped out of the bush flanked by her two Amharic bodyguards. That night under the stars he had taught her how to make love, and become her first real lover. The last time he had seen her was in the Sudan, Khartoum, on a hellishly hot night in a hotel room on the Nile, when in the darkness she slithered naked from the foot of his bed up between his legs and proved to him that he had taught her well and she had practised much.

She was watching the barge that had off loaded the packing cases on to the quay pull away into the centre of the river. Adam spent a few more minutes looking at Tana Dabra Ras Magdala Makoum. She had been not only the white knight who had saved his company from a disastrous takeover, but also the saviour of her country from a more severe and heavily armed Marxist military regime, prepared in desperation for survival to become dependent on either Russia or the CIA.

Adam found her brilliant, cunning mind as dazzling as her adventurous sexuality. But there was in her a streak of daring he found dangerous. It combined with a lovelessness that had been carefully nurtured by the men who had exploited her extraordinary acumen for international economics and stunted her natural sexual inclinations. They had given her enormous power as the controller and investor of all her country's foreign currency, but they had made it conditional on her remaining a virgin. This cruel and damaging blight on her as a woman made Adam exceedingly concerned for her and her future.

Sex with her had been thrilling, more than thrilling. He was certain it could be dangerous for the man if she chose the wrong partner. Her ambivalent feelings about men might one day easily direct a knife between the same man's shoulder blades. Adam had no fear that they would be his. The knife might be reserved, though, for a man who tried to control her sexually, one who made demands on her, one who used her.

Tana Dabra carried the scars of mutilated labia, and, after years of masturbation, a well-developed, over-sensitive clitoris, all she had been allowed sexually by order of the regime, except for the occasional lesbian encounter. They were a constant reminder of the years of sexual humiliation and frustration men had imposed on her in the name of love of country. She had finally broken her bond with the men she had once believed were working for the people of her country, not just political power and a ruthless dictatorship backed by a vast military build up. As soon as she had accomplished that, she had cut the gold wires lacing closed the lips over her vagina. Those wires had kept her virginity intact, making her a people's vestal virgin since she was fifteen years old.

In part, Adam saw her as one of the walking wounded of this overly politicised world. She needed time to heal. Yet he knew this glorious beauty worked underground for the millions of poor peasants of Ethiopia, retrieving the hidden treasures of King Haile Selassie, the hiding places of which he had never divulged to the leaders of the coup that dethroned him. She smuggled them into the West, where she turned them into long-term investments for her people's future. Labelled a traitor by the military Marxist regime, and with a price on her head, she walked in the shadows in her country. At Adam's insistence, with one of the best public relations firms in the world, they were about to launch a plan for her to walk openly in the relative political sunlight of the West. A way which he hoped would stop the regime from killing her, or kidnapping her back to Ethiopia, where she would be punished and disposed of as they saw fit. She and Adam expected no less than that for her crime of diverting every last cent of Ethiopia's foreign currency earmarked for heavy duty armaments into agriculture and communications investments in the Corey Trust's companies. Through them her country reaped a percentage of the profits in commodities necessary for their survival. That was how she had bailed Adam out of an unwanted takeover and cut the regime's armaments ambitions.

Adam had made up his mind always to be there for her whenever she needed him. It was his way of paying his debt to her for what she did for him. Yet still he was aware that ultimately she had used him and the bail out of his company for her own ends. He saw himself as friend and protector, but had no idea how she regarded him. That was part of her charisma. Her elusive silence, her never giving anything emotional away. It was a tremendous turn-on, that sensual silence in which she was enfolded. That and the way she would appear from nowhere and draw him into her web, whether for business or sexual ecstasy.

'Tana Dabra,' he called, and waved as he walked towards the ramp that led down to the embankment and the water's edge. She smiled up at him and waved back. That was all it took, he was yet again seduced by her. She had stature but it was in her face, in the fierce passion and pride that shone through the black semitic features. The slow, seductive way she moved her long slender limbs was feral. Cunning and careful, like being stalked by a panther, leopard or lion, hers was a dangerous beauty, the kind that could kill, yet it made it impossible for the hunter, whether of big game or of women, not to try to capture.

With hand gestures – hands as if around the wheel of a car – and the wave of an arm, she told him he was meant to ensure that both his Rolls and the small black van she had instructed him to arrive with were driven for him down the steep ramp to where she sat.

'You came,' she said, looking quite happy to see him.

He took her hand in his and kissed it. Her scent was Coco, the delicious Chanel perfume he had given her in Khartoum. It did its work as all the advertising promised. He bent his head to hers and kissed her lightly on the lips. She was there and must be tasted.

'Don't I always arrive at your bidding? Had you doubts?'

'Only small ones. Obviously foolish ones.'

'You look marvellous.'

'I feel marvellous. I always do when I am in Paris. I have a passion for this city. I have always found what I needed here.'

'Tana Dabra, what are we doing meeting here? I am sure it must be against the law to use the quay as a landing dock for your packing cases. And I doubt that motor vehicles are allowed here either.'

'That's true Adam. And if you are on time, and have the four men I asked you to bring in the back of the van, then we have thirty minutes to load these wooden crates on board and no more. That's how long we have before the *gendarmes* will return to their patch.'

'If that's true, then what would you call those? Figments of my imagination?' indicating to her with his eyes, the hats, heads and shoulders of three *gendarmes* walking swiftly along the street up above them, partially hidden by the wall. Fortunately for Adam and Tana Dabra, they were too busy talking to each other to look down on the suspicious scene below.

'My God, you are quite mad. I can hardly believe you have done this and involved me in it.' With that he put his hands around her waist and swung her off the packing case. He walked slowly, as inconspicuously as he could, to the van and instructed the men to load up, quietly and swiftly, one eye on the hats above moving away from them. Within five minutes, the job was done.

'Involved you? How are you involved? As far as the world is concerned, you were riding along the Quai Anatole France and suddenly decided to get out and walk. Much to your amazement you saw a beautiful lady sitting on a packing case. A lady obviously abandoned and in distress. You recognised her as an Ethiopian, a stranger to Paris, and your curiosity got the better of you. Finding her not unattractive, you walked down from the street to see if you could be of assistance. You approached her, and while you were finding out she was waiting for a friend who seemed to be elsewhere engaged, a van drove down on to the *quai* and several men stepped out of it. They asked her politely to get off the packing case as they were there to collect the boxes for the *Sûreté*. A shipment of

142

bullet-proof vests is what their papers state. Hence the weight.'

Adam looked at the bright blue stencilled letters on all the cases. They read 'Deliver To Sûreté, Quai d'Orsay. Pick up from Quai Anatole France.' He was actually speechless for a minute. The moving men tipped their hats to the lady, and returned to the now loaded van, stepped in and pulled the doors closed behind them. The laden vehicle laboured across the cobblestones and slowly up the ramp leading to the main street. It disappeared into the traffic.

Adam began to laugh, shook his head in disbelief, and remarked, 'Not bad. Labelling them for the police headquarters. Inventing this barge drop-off station.'

'Quite so. Unbelievable but simple. How else would you smuggle 663 million dollars worth of gold, jewels and currency into France past customs and avoiding questioning by the Sûreté? It had to be out in the open and right under their noses.

'Let's walk,' she said, slipping an arm through his. Then recited, as if she had memorised something she read somewhere, 'We walked along the embankment together after the van left, followed by your car. You mentioned you had a great love for my country, and, softened by talk of Ethiopia, we exchanged names and were amazed to find that we had known each other by reputation for many years but had never met before this chance encounter. That's very important, Adam. We lunched together at Le Grand Vefour in the Palais Royal, where I informed you that it was my intention to make my home in the West and become a high fashion model in order to earn a living for myself. Not an easy decision, but one of necessity, since I have lost my position of standing with the regime, and feel too burned out in the world of high finance ever to put my head in that particular oven again. You were surprised but impressed when I told you that the politics of my country are beyond me and I no longer can cope with them, that I have served with my comrades as well as I could for a very long time as that other self that has been neglected, the female, preferably the self-indulgent, frivolous female. In my spare time I hope to use my business acumen to raise funds and invest them in solid shares and stocks and bonds. These, I hope, would multiply and be used wisely for the good of my people. And even that, at this point, seems an enormous burden that I am not sure I am capable of handling since I have been made *persona non grata* in Ethiopia. And you? You have taken it upon yourself to call the Minister of Foreign Affairs to inform him of all this, because you feel that it would be very bad form to block my good intentions and alienate the support of the western world. Have you got all that, Adam?'

The scream of police sirens pierced the steady hum of Left Bank morning traffic. The loud sound and warning raced closer. Hooting horns blared, and silenced Tana Dabra. The chaos of flashing lights and police cars cutting through the jam of cars on the road just above them transmitted fear and set the adrenalin racing. They watched three police cars flash by the top of the ramp and away from them, and their relief showed in their faces. They turned away from their fear and looked at each other. Tana Dabra smiled at Adam and placed her arm again through his. They resumed their walk.

'Meantime, Adam, in three days I will have converted the contents of those packing cases into dollars

– approximately 663 million of them – and will have had the bank drafts sent to your office, to invest in any Ethiopian owned and based companies you think need an injection of capital – any, that is, that the Corey Trust and my country share the profits of. Of course, as in the past, you will not convey any of those profits to those monsters in control of my country.

'This will have to be my last run from Ethiopia for a long while. It has become too dangerous for me. I was almost caught twice. The government must be made to think I have given up, copped out for a glamorous life in the decadent western world. Then in time, when they believe it for certain, when they've abandoned their pursuit of me, and I have made myself conspicuous and popular with the right people and the western press, I will sneak back in and begin my smuggling runs again.'

Adam took her firmly by the arm and together they stepped into the back of his Rolls, and he instructed his chauffeur to drive on. Then in a firm, almost angry voice, he spoke to Tana Dabra.

'I want you to listen very closely and understand what I have to say to you, Tana Dabra. You have had it all the way you wanted it, and have escaped with your life. What you have done for your country is phenomenal. And, as a result of that, what you have done for me is no less so. I have gone along with you because in the first instance you were clever enough to have left me no choice. I will never tolerate you doing that again, for many reasons – not the least of which is that I do not want you, ever again, to take chances you have taken in the past with your life. You have been lucky, but luck runs out. I and my company have worked very hard in the background to help create a new persona for you. We've set you up to take the world by storm with your brains and your beauty. Now I want you to promise me that you will try to put out of your mind the hardness and ruthlessness of the business world and power struggles. They have dominated your life and robbed you of first your youth, then your young adulthood and what should have been your glorious womanhood. Now learn to enjoy this new life of yours. I care for you, Tana Dabra. Enough to want you to take a few years off from the political ambitions you have for your country, and to find yourself as a woman and enjoy being one. Now, enough said, and on with this extravagant charade you have designed.'

Tana Dabra listened to Adam's every word. But that night with him, in the bush, in the highlands of Ethiopia, when he had taken her sexually for the first time, kept nudging her memory. He had been her first man. She felt he had taught her wonders and pleasures of the flesh she had never dreamed possible that had thrilled her beyond anything she could have imagined. He had opened for her a heterosexual world of sensual ecstasy where she practised other kinds of power over men than money, politics, and intelligence. Even as he spoke now, she wanted him as she had had him then and subsequently in Khartoum, Cairo, and Damascus.

Now she would have him in Paris. She took his wrist in her hand and looked at his watch, then into his eyes.

In a voice tinged with passion, she said, 'We have a few hours before lunchtime and the next act of my extravagant charade, and my launch into the big wide world as the other side of myself.' She leaned over Adam and pressed the button set into the armrest next to him. The glass window that divided the front from the back seat of the silver grey Rolls slid away.

'Avenue Montaigne. The Plaza Athenee,' she ordered. And as she reached to press the button, to raise the window once more, Adam took her hand in his, saying to the chauffeur, 'That will do just fine, Roberts.'

Adam pressed the button, and kissed her hand with lips she sensed were eager with anticipation. They gazed into each other's eyes and she recognised that look of lust that dominates, that blinds one to anything but the desire for copulation. Tana Dabra savoured that look she was able to draw from men's eyes.

Adam grabbed a handful of her hair and pulled her face towards his. He was intoxicated by her sensuality and pressed his cheek to hers, his lips to her forehead. The feel of her skin sparked a kind of wildness in his lust for this incredibly elegant, yet base and primitive female. He kissed the bridge, then the tip of her nose, each cheek, relishing the taste of her sweet, dark flesh. He placed his lips upon hers and nibbled and sucked on them until they parted and he found her tongue. Slowly he released her from the kiss and removed her hands which had sought his throbbing penis, and kissed the palm of one and then the other. Placing them together he held them firmly.

'Have there been many men? Do you have a great deal of sex?' he asked, looking away from her out of the window, in an attempt to distance himself from his desire for her until they reached their destination and some privacy. And yet not wanting to let go of the lust he was feeling for her.

'Yes, many.'

'What kind of men do you choose? What kind of sex do you have? Do you love any of them?'

Tana Dabra's heart was pounding. She felt a

moistness between her legs that Adam had drawn from her, and she too, felt the need to control her lust until they were alone. But it was difficult because she thrilled to those feelings. She looked away and out of the window as he did. They began to cross the Pont de La Concorde.

'I love Paris. I have always loved Paris. I am always dazzled by it. I was here for a short time this spring. The chestnut trees were in full bloom along the avenues. The luscious large green leaves and the clusters of blossoms looked like upside down, flowering ice cream cones, weighing down the boughs of the trees. They were lovely, floating up and down in the faint, warm breeze.

'There were flowers springing up everywhere in bloom along the city streets, heavy with scent, radiating renewal. Boxes of them in front of shop windows; urns bubbling over with them; vendors with baskets full of carnations, tulips, freesia and mimosa. Oh, how the French love mimosa! I saw them as delicious delicacies, and wanted to gobble them up like wonderful, Parisian chocolates, exquisite eclairs and sticky marrons glacés. I thought to myself, maybe that's love in the air.

'The French women seemed to bloom just like the flowers. Hundreds of French women walking about the streets like animated lilacs, roses on the march, daffodils chattering to narcissi. The Parisians seemed more elegant and pompous, full of themselves, just like the season. Ah, Paris touched by spring! There's just no other city like it in the world. Well, everyone feels that about it. But it's still true.

'I loved it. Just as I always had from the first time I had seen it many years before. Paris has always been good to me. I have grown up in so many ways here. But there was always something in me that wanted to attack the French, Paris, and spring time in Paris especially. I was always looking for clichés to knock it, to make it less than it is, but they never undid its indefinable spell.

'I was approaching the Café Lipp, where I was to have a drink with a young Greek painter I had met at a smart *vernissage* the night before. His paintings were interesting, but I was looking forward to him, the meeting and the drink. As I approached the tables under the canopy I smiled to myself, wondering. "What do the Parisians do with all the ugly people? Everyone is so beautiful in Paris today." The small, white marble tables were filled with beautiful people. I just wasn't seeing the ugly ones.

'I saw the young man sitting towards the back at a table close to the café's huge window. He stood up and waved. His name was Minos. I was with him only five minutes when I suddenly realised I didn't want him any more. It had been a mistake. There was something ominous about him. He had said nothing to offend me, but there was something in the manner in which he asked me questions about myself that displeased me. He was a malcontent, who kept trying to make me apologise for my looks, my sensuality, any successes I might have. I disliked him not so much for that but more because, in the few minutes I was with him he made me realise that Paris, the luscious, beautiful mistress of all cities, with all its beauty and grandeur, with all its chic and cosmopolitan atmosphere, was basically, under all its perfume and cosmetics, *petit bourgeois*, just like the dreadful Minos. How clever of the French to trick the world, I thought, and stupid of

Minos to give himself away so badly.

'I hurried through my drink, for I had promised to visit Minos's studio and look at his work. He was handsome, vain, arrogant and talented. He was young and cynical. He reminded me of the Greece I had known one summer, and the heat of that summer and all the Greek men I had not fucked with, and wished I had, of the passion to experience them which I had missed. If he had only not spoken, not opened his mouth! We walked in silence towards his studio, and I thought, "Maybe".

'Once in his studio, the maybe was engulfed by an unease that continued as I looked at his paintings and managed to find the right things to say to the man about his work. He looked at me with a certain disdain. Pompous, sure of himself and his art, he could not have cared less what I thought. He accused me of being condescending about his work. He trapped me in a corner and, with one hand leaning against the wall, he blocked me from moving. With the other he taunted me with a jab, a light slap across the face. He accused me of coming to the meeting with him for the same reason that he had sought it: a fuck. It was, of course, true. I picked up my purse and started to walk away from him and his terrible studio. His accusations of leading him on were ringing in my ears. It appeared that turning my back on him and walking out was not the most clever thing I could have done. He spun me around and slapped me hard on the face. I was a spoiled, rich, black African bitch. Then he started tearing my clothes off my back.

' "No, don't tear my clothes!" I shouted at him. But he had me pinned to the floor by his weight on top of me. He pulled off my shoes and tore my tights away.

150

He virtually raped me, was brutal and indecent with me. He fucked me without a degree of tenderness, love or affection. I fought him, and the harder I fought the more violent he became. Finally I understood that to fight him was to prolong the agony. I was more shattered than shocked, and, even more, I was disgusted – disgusted with him for forcing sex upon me against my will, a crime that deserves some punishment and disgusted with myself because I experienced a kind of sexual thrill in his savagery. It's what men want to think women get from it. I was sickened to find it in myself, however briefly. I could understand how the violence and loathing he must have had for me excited his sexual lust. I hated him and myself. With a knife in my hand I would have killed him. No hesitation.'

Adam still held her hands and now he raised and kissed them. The anger in her eyes changed her entire face. It made her more hardened in her beauty, in her sexual lustiness. She was thrilling to be next to and his desire for her sharpened. He began to speak, but she stopped him. Releasing her hands she placed her fingers lightly on his lips. 'Please, there's nothing for you to say or comment on. Let me continue. Hear out my little saga,' she said. Adam nodded.

'When he had quite finished with me,' Tana Dabra continued, 'I put on my shoes, leaving my torn tights behind. I straightened my dress the best I could, repaired my face, covering the tear streaks and running mascara. He lay naked, splashed with his own semen streaked with my blood, which he had smeared over himself so proudly. He smiled, full of himself, because he had conquered me against my will. He never rose from the floor or made any attempt to keep me from leaving the studio.

'I walked past a table with a large, heavy glass pitcher filled with water standing in the middle of it. I put my handbag down on the table and picked up the pitcher, walked over to the Greek, who had hauled himself into a club chair, one leg draped over the arm. He was concentrating on his flaccid penis, playing with it, oblivious to me. With both hands around the pitcher I threw the cold water in his face. Before he could recover I rushed towards him and smashed the pitcher over his head, scooped up my handbag and walked quickly through the door. My feet hardly touched the stairs as I fled down the four flights and into the street.

'Why do I tell you this tale? Because that incident was a turning point in my life. I had dropped my guard and allowed a man to choose me, and it was the first and last time I allowed that. I don't intend that to happen ever again. Fame, fortune, whatever we have designed for my new life and future, in my sex life I will be master, as I always have been since that night you taught me how to make love, and enjoy sex and outrageous lust.'

Tana Dabra reached out and caressed Adam's cheek. Then, putting her long slender hands on either side of his face, she held it as she parted her lips and kissed him. It was a kiss filled with urgency and need, with a passion that was not to be extinguished. The kiss sealed an unspoken bond of lust between them.

They entered the restaurant and were made a fuss of at once. While they were being shown to Adam's favourite table, Tana Dabra turned around and touched his arm. She looked into his eyes and smiled, then whispered, 'Thank you for an exquisite last interlude, Adam. And now we begin our charade. If I am lucky, it may turn into reality and a new life.'

Every eye was drawn to the couple. Where else in the room was there the equal to the beauty and suavity of the ebony-skinned woman ashimmer in black silk? So tall and slim, she moved more with the rhythm of a gazelle in a slow walk than of the fashion model she was about to become.

Seated, she remarked, 'I could eat much more than a model ought to.' But she cast a casual enough glance down the menu.

Adam carefully removed it from her hands and asked, 'What did you mean exactly by "an exquisite last interlude"?'

She gazed into his eyes. There was little to be read in hers now. Lust had faded from them, satisfied by the recent interval of sexual exploration and ecstasy. Only calm shone in them, an incredible stoic silence that gave nothing away, that was in its own special nothingness so magnetic and seductive.

'Just that, Adam. In Africa, you're mine. Nothing, no one stands between us. Those secret sexual trysts in the wild burn in me like a fire, as I know they do in you as well. And they always will. But, here in the West, you're not mine. You belong to your wife. I saw that in your eyes as you looked at her the night of the gala. There was the same lust that you feel for me, but there was more. Something that was never there in your eyes for me. Something I have never known. I think it was love. I would rather have you totally in Africa, than to have bits of you in the West. Now, please, can we order, and get on with this charade that both of us need to maintain?'

Adam wanted to say that it didn't have to be that way. But how could he when he knew it did? There were other things he wanted to say to Tana Dabra but could not. She had preempted him, found for both of them more *savoir faire* and honesty than he could have done. So, out of respect for what they had together, all he said was, 'Is there something special you would like us to have for lunch? Or would you allow me to order for both of us?'

They were gazing into each other's eyes. Rekindled flickers of lust in them warmed Adam and Tana Dabra and made them grateful that understanding was there, words superfluous. The eyes confirmed everything.

Tana Dabra gestured with a hand that the ordering of their meal was his prerogative. She watched Adam, studied his face, as he spoke with the maître d' about their meal. Kir Royals arrived, and he broke off the ordering of their food to raise his glass in a toast.

'To your corner of Africa, *your* summons, and *our* joys in the wild . . . under the whitest of moons.' They touched glasses and drank, the champagne and cassis a celebration of blends, his toast so genuine as to awaken something in her heart. They smiled, and he returned to the menu and continued selecting their feast.

Nothing could distract her from his face, the sound of his voice, not even the lordly elegance of their famous restaurant, Le Grand Vefour, which had flourished in the eighteenth century around the gardens of the Palais Royal. It had continued undiminished in grandeur during the revolution, despite the food shortages that had forced the ordinary people of Paris to go hungry. In those days long ago men and women had dined there on foie gras, woodcocks, gratinéed quail, sweetbreads, and truffle-stuffed hens. They had quaffed Sauternes and champagne the day Marie Antoinette's head had fallen from the guillotine. Tana Dabra couldn't be distracted by the present either. The restaurant was full now of chic men and women dressed in Parisian *haute couture* and bejewelled by Boucheron, Van Cleef and Arpels. It was not that she was oblivious to her surroundings, the hovering waiters and the sommelier, with his silver necklace worn as a symbol of his station. She simply wasn't distracted by them.

She had chosen well when she had selected Adam, this handsome adventurer, as her first male lover as well as a secret business associate. So magnificent a deflowering as to leave her with a lust for male lovers created a permanent debt. He had added a sexual dimension to her life. Thereafter, with every orgasm achieved with her various lovers, another part of Tana Dabra came alive: the female, the woman latent so long within her.

And there had been lovers enough. After her first encounter with Adam in the highlands of Ethiopia, she had been obliged to roam cautiously through her country, Somaliland, Sudan, Egypt, Kenya. She had chosen the most handsome and virile men for herself. Proud and noble black tribesmen and white hunters and governors found her irresistible and she tasted all kinds of sex, revelling in it. She teased her conquests with her sexual lust, and with her sudden appearances and vanishings. Few knew her name, where she had come from or where she was going. Her survival demanded anonymity. And then necessity turned to

155

habit, and that habit became her sexual pattern, until she met the Greek, Minos. After Minos she discovered gigolos, or toy boys as she heard one style himself. And that, since the spring of the year, had been her pattern for her sexual love life.

They were wonderful studs, obviously, or they would be out of business. And very good actors. But oh, the dullness of the humans within! Except one, maybe. The beautiful gigolo in expensively impeccable evening dress, driver of a red Ferrari, who she had found eating escargots in a workmen's cafe at four o'clock in the morning. She had paid a thousand dollars for him for the night: it had to have been worth every penny. She had been gone before he awoke, but had not neglected to extract from him a telephone number.

The menus were whisked away, the wine ordered, extra spoons, knives and forks added to the place settings before them, crisp white damask napkins draped across their laps. And then they were alone.

'I had no idea you were in Paris on the night of the gala. Were you at the ball?'

'No, I saw you at the opera house. I all but spied on you through a pair of opera glasses. That's when I spotted the look in your eye that you reserve for your wife.'

At that moment Tana Dabra remembered that she had seen a flicker of just such a look on one other occasion. The toy boy. The thousand dollar gigolo, before he fell asleep. And there had been words, words she could not remember because she had scarcely bothered to listen to them. She had put it down to toy boy sex patter.

They drank their Kir Royals in silence, awaiting

their first course, rich and voluptuous silence that spoke volumes for them. It was not so much that they had little to say to one another, rather the opposite. They were tuned in perfectly to the silence that allowed them slowly to drift apart and yet remain together in the distance it created between them. It allowed Adam and Tana Dabra to settle into the atmosphere of what was unquestionably one of the loveliest restaurants in the world.

'I love it here, Adam. It's exciting, and I am slightly mesmerised by these murals. They must be very old. I have seen few restaurants like this before.'

'Believe me, with all its history, and the world's famous and infamous who have dined here, it has seen few patrons like you either.' They both began to laugh, and Adam realised he had rarely seen or heard Tana Dabra laugh before. The lilt in her laughter gave him hope for her happiness.

'They were painted in the reign of Napoleon III. And we are sitting where Victor Hugo used to sit. You see, it is labelled with his name.' Tana Dabra turned around to read the metal tag. 'Over there is where Honoré de Balzac sat to dine. They say of him that he used to wolf down a hundred oysters, twelve lamb chops, a duckling with turnips, a brace of roast partridges, a whopping sole in cream sauce, an assortment of desserts, and twelve pears. At a single sitting, note.'

Tana Dabra was wide eyed. 'It's not possible,' she exclaimed, aghast, but then recalled statues she had seen of the man. Gargantuan.

'Oh, but I assure you it was, and he did. There are many stories about the Parisians and their appetites that appear to be impossible. There were fabulous restaurants. One of them, the Café Anglais, was the site of the spectacle of three Parisian gentleman spending the equivalent today of two thousand English pounds. On what? Well, a feast that consisted of a hundred pairs of frog's legs. It took fifty workers to break through the ice and catch the creatures.'

'And what are we going to dine on?' There were extravagances she did not aspire to.

The first course arrived just as she asked about their meal. Adam and Tana Dabra lapsed into silence again, savouring the elaborate service of their hors d'oeuvres. The sommelier poured the first of the wines they would drink with their lunch, a Chassagne-Montrachet '69, a great white burgundy: strong, perfumed, intense, dry yet luscious. Perfection with the pâté of crayfish Adam had ordered for Tana Dabra and the crayfish soup he chose for himself.

They raised their glasses and touched the rims together, searching each other's eyes. The flickers of lust were still there for her in his, and sexual feelings began to smoulder in her. But she saw not a trace of anything else. Even in the thousand dollar gigolo, she was now sure she had seen more. They smiled and drank a silent toast to one another, and she knew she would find that toy boy and have him again.

They barely exchanged words over their lunch together, except to comment on the exquisite food, the ambrosial wine. They savoured every morsel of the dishes that made the restaurant famous: salt cod with celery and bay, bass with mustard, garnished with deep fried fennel, fillet of lamb in a potato cake, veal kidney with sweetbreads and lemon, and every drop of the Richebourg '66, from the nineteen-acre Grand Cru vineyard in Vosne-Romanée.

More than once their eyes met and each of them

158

acknowledged behind the gaze that their sensual delight in each other earlier in the day, and now over a meal, would always be a part of the fullness of their lives. Unthinkable as it would have been to them, how could they know these would be their last moments alone together?

They were just finishing their desserts – a concentrated mousse of raspberries placed on leaves of dark chocolate, and a bitter chocolate mousse veined with crême fraiche, and drinking Fargues '70, a Sauterne, white, sweet, and fruity, extremely elegant and light – which sealed the occasion for them as if with a flutter of butterfly wings – when the maître d' arrived. He excused himself to Adam, and bent down and whispered something in Tana Dabra's ear. She said nothing to Adam, only raised her glass and he followed. She smiled at him and they drank.

Coffee was served and cigars were brought. He chose a vintage Davidoff. The tobacco steward prepared it for him, neatly, cleanly cutting off the tip and warming the end over a flame. Adam placed it between his lips and proceeded to light it, turning it slowly between his fingers over the flame held by the steward. He puffed the cigar, now lit evenly, enjoying the bite of tobacco on his tongue.

'I shall always remember how sexy you look as you light a cigar.'

Her remark caught his attention. It ranked among the more personal things she had said to him. He smiled at her. 'Only that?'

'Oh no, much more,' she said returning his smile.

Abruptly she changed the subject. 'Our charade. I hope you remember your lines. And the timing. It was your plan to make me safe from the regime, Adam. It was my choice to decide when and where. This morning was the when. On the quay was the where. And so far it has been not only successful but enjoyable. Now comes the hard part. We are about to go public, perform our next impressions. We must be good, because this time the world will be watching. There's a TV cameraman from the evening news programme here to photograph Paris's newest discovery: one black African goddess.'

She reached across the table. He took her hand in his, and was aware of a slight tremor in it. He lowered his lips to her long, slender fingers and kissed them. He repeated the kiss lightly on the back of her hand. When he looked up, he saw that she had closed her eyes. Slowly she withdrew her hand from his, and opened her large black-brown eyes, the more seductive for the tear of farewell he saw in them. She held up her hand to silence him before he could break the spell with words, gathered her handbag and slipped away from the table.

He sat for a while after she had gone, contemplating the erotic trysts he had had with this courageous and most extraordinarily clever, yet pagan creature. He knew that the adventurer, the hunter in him, would always respond to her call.

Before he followed her instructions and placed his calls to Addis Ababa, he made a detour to the Place Vendôme. He purchased a 59-carat, oval-shaped and cushion-cut, pigeon-blood ruby of extraordinary quality. Encircled in magnificent sapphires and mounted on a thick, black, silk braided cord with a clasp of sapphires, the necklace would be just large enough to collar her throat. On the card he wrote:

'Tender is the night.'

Chapter 8

'Well, here I am,' she announced, throwing her leather shoulder bag onto one of the beach chairs, a broad smile spreading across her face. She threw her arms out, stiffened her body, freezing it for a second in a presentation pose.

Deena stood, as if rooted in the sand, her high heeled black patent leather sandals dangling from one hand. Moses was behind, loaded down with all sorts and sizes of gift-wrapped boxes, their bright papers and sumptuous bows glinting in the sunshine that was trying to break the greyness of the day. Behind him stood her husband Brindley, tall, slender, handsome and distinguished, every inch the English gentleman, and, solicitor that he was, was impeccable in his Savile Row clothes except that he was bare footed, with trousers rolled up to his knees. In one arm he carried a collection of vintage, worn and weary-looking teddy bears. He trailed behind him a stuffed, life-size baby dromedary camel on wheels.

Mirella lumbered out of her chair, tears of joy filling her eyes. Deena broke her pose and the two women rushed into each other's arms. Moses and Brindley, Rashid and Adam, who had been sitting with Mirella, watched the reunion with smiles of delight. And there was relief that Deena, Mirella's oldest, closest friend, had arrived to be with her until after the birth of her child.

'Oh, what an entrance. You're just what I need. How did you know you're just the person I want with me now? I didn't let on over the telephone, did I? I thought I'd kept my anxiety nicely suppressed.'

'Well, you did, but this lot didn't, and thank the lord they didn't, because here I am, and thrilled to see you and be with you. Fresh from playing lady of the manor in Gloucestershire. Getting into breeding horses I am, my dear. As one of those horsey English beauties said, "Her first season at Ascot, the right hat, and she fancies she's in the business. Someone should advise her the bloodline is everything." You know, the great English put down. You should have seen her face when I popped up from behind the hedge, where I was sitting with one very amused Royal, who enjoys a grand-scale gaffe like that. "Oh Daphne, how good to know that I got it right first try. I'm only sorry it makes me odd woman out in a society that reveres a loser," I said.

'Thank God for our Vassar days, Mirella, and your classy family. First-class training ground for a Brooklyn Jewish princess who marries an English lord of the realm to learn to soak up that sort of kindergarten bitchiness.'

Mirella hugged her friend again, 'In your own small way you're wonderful,' she said.

'Just don't talk *wonderful* to me. Look at you. How can a woman about to pop out a baby at any minute look so ravishing, and have so many men dancing attendance on her? Not excluding my own husband. I wish I had your formula. How do you manage to keep

162

two of the most handsome, sexy and interesting men in the world? And my husband and Moses?'

She looked away from Mirella for a moment to Brindley, shrugged her shoulders and said, 'Sorry about that, darling, but you always say you want to deal in realities.' A quick smile at Moses. Then she turned back to Mirella, 'And turn them into a bunch of nervous wimps? Here were you and I having a gossip every other day over the ocean. But not a hint did I have that you wanted me to come. I can't remember how many times I asked if you wanted me with you for a few weeks, and got the impression that it was too personal, private a time, that you only wanted Adam with you.'

'Well, that was true, Deena, up to a point.'

Adam interrupted them, took Deena in his arms and gave her a great hug, whispering in her ear, 'Thank you, I'm so grateful,' and kissed her welcome. She rolled her eyes as if in ecstasy, and gave a great sigh. Then Adam turned to Moses and suggested he put the boxes down or take them off to the house. Then he went to admire the genuine Mongolian dromedary on wheels.

Rashid was next. He hugged and kissed Deena and whispered, 'I will be ever grateful to you for this, Deena. I'll call you later.' Then he went to join Brindley and Adam. Mirella sat back down again in her beach chair, shaking her head in wonder over her friend and her entrance.

'Shall we go back to the house, Deena?'

'I should say not! Moses,' she ordered 'put the parcels down. We'll open them here on the beach. Now that's what surprises and presents are all about, the fun of the moment.' Moses went to where she stood and, bending down, whispered as discreetly as he could, hoping Mirella would lose his words in the sound of the ocean and men's voices,

'Don't tell her I called you.'

Deena was fussing with the boxes, obviously looking for a certain one. She looked up and said, 'What are you on about, Moses? Not tell Mirella you called? Don't be ridiculous. In fact, you should have been the first to call. No matter how many years I know you and confide in you, and think of you as my own ear and eye in Mirella's house, you always manage to overdo the discretion. You were acting as an even worse wimp than the others about her. Matter of fact, you came last in the race to the telephone.'

The menfolk looked every which way but Mirella's. Suddenly there were things for them to see all around the beach. That broke both women up with laughter.

'Well, whaddya know?' chuckled Mirella. 'I had no notion.'

'That *was* the idea,' said Adam, awarding Deena a forgiving look.

'Oh, I am really going to enjoy hearing every bit of this,' teased Mirella, looking at the men.

Rashid for once, in a merely domestic matter, was short of excuses. He gave up and declared, 'This is your baby shower.' Ridiculous enough to make him throw up his hands and begin to laugh himself. Self-mockery rippled around the group.

'I'm going up to the house to change, and I think you should too, Deena. It's a bit damp and chilly down here. And you're not exactly dressed in beachwear.'

'True,' she said, going to Brindley while pulling the pin from her small but very chic, black lacquered straw hat. She handed it to him. Then unbuttoned the short, white peplum jacket, trimmed in black, and gave that to him as well. Mirella watched her friend standing in a pretty, black and white, large floral Italian silk dress with a stylish short skirt. Deena dug her bare toes in and out of the sand while she asked him to bring trousers, a top and a sweater down for her, so that she could stay and talk to Mirella.

Mirella looked up at the sky. She thought that the weather, so changeable all day, was going to hold. Just at the moment the sun was out, making the beach, sand dunes and ocean shine bright. And the air, even with its end of summer nip in it that made everything seem fresh and new, was still warm enough to suggest swimming.

But the day had been overcast, with a sky of milky grey broken by occasional rays of diffused sunlight. The very smell of the ocean, damp sand and intermittent swirls of mist that rolled in over the ocean, made Mirella feel closer to life. For some days now, it had been almost impossible to get her away from the ocean shore, or keep her from swimming in the rough, cold salt water. She craved swimming almost obsessively and she yearned for the long gusts of warm wind that came hurtling across the waves onto the beach, spraying a fine mist over the sand before soughing their way out to sea again. The sunshine and the grey calms were so theatrical in their contrasts that she liked to imagine a god of some sort was turning it on and off at some celestial control panel.

Deena picked up a stack of gift boxes and dropped them at Mirella's feet, then plopped into the chair next to Mirella's and reached out to take her hand.

'We can't open a thing until Brindley gets back. Wait until you see the things I have bought for you and

165

the baby, what a shopping spree I went on!'

Before she had a chance to catalogue her purchases, Rashid said, turning from the women to Adam, 'I think it's time we checked the rods.'

So the women watched the two men walk away from them, and Deena said, 'They are still both passionately in love with you, Mirella.'

'Yes, I know.'

'Then, what's wrong? They are very concerned, really anxious. Enough to call me – each of course, not wanting the other to know or you to know – that they felt you needed me.'

'Nothing is wrong, I promise you. I'm fine, the baby is fine. And any day now it's going to pop out, as you so aptly put it.'

'Well, if nothing is wrong with you, then something is wrong with them. And my husband, and Moses.'

'They called as well?'

'That's right.'

The two women remained silent for a minute, Deena closing her eyes and letting the rays of the sun warm her face. She sighed, 'I'm so happy they called and I'm here. I love England and our country seat, Lyttleton Park, but boy, do English trees ever stop dripping? Summer, winter, all the seasons, dripping trees. I miss the Hamptons. No matter how much it rains in the Hamptons, it's not a place of endlessly dripping trees.'

Mirella began to laugh. Deena said ordinary things in ways that induced gaiety. 'It's been a wonderful day. A funny beach day, but the kind you get here at this time of year. And just the sort I like.'

They sat in silence, in their wooden deck loungers – salvaged from the *Normandie* when it went down after a fire while docked in the Hudson River – stretched out along the water's edge, the men's fishing rods set up nearby for surf casting. Rashid's Scottish ghillie and Moses had been working at the sport along with the other men since early morning.

'What did they say?' asked Mirella.

Deena turned in her chair and lay on her side facing her girl friend. Mirella most clumsily did the same.

'Adam? That you were very well, happy. The nurseries in all the houses were ready. That you would have the baby here in Easthampton, in the house. A nurse, a nanny, were already in residence, a midwife and a doctor on standby. And that you want nothing to do with any of them until you go into labour. All you want is to swim in the ocean. Immersion all the time, with no clothes on. Swim, and linger on the beach. He says he goes along with you sometimes and it's very exciting and he can understand how you feel. It's a primitive kind of thing, a sort of watery nesting instinct. Maybe a desire to return to the sea, if that's really where we all came from. Anyway, some sort of natural thing like that. He has suggested that you have Dr Michel Odent, the French pioneer of natural childbirth, take over the birth of the baby. Maybe even deliver in a pool of water, as some of his other patients have. But you declined all that, claiming you are organised enough with the help at hand.

'I think he admires you for it. He sees it's right for you to want to have the baby with minimal fuss and organisation, since you believe that giving birth is an irrational, emotional, and sexual experience which is difficult enough already. He says that in these last weeks of your pregnancy, more than ever, you have wanted to go along with your feelings, not with what the doctors dictate. And that he goes right along with you. That you are not obliged to choose how to have the baby until you are ready. That you have left all your options open, and that he wants you to have the baby any way you want: in a darkened room, in a squatting position, or hanging from his neck – does Odent really recommend that? – or in a hospital, or lying in bed at home. You have both talked it out months ago, but now you skirt the issue. All you do talk about, and endlessly, is swimming, how you crave swimming. And the reason he wants me to be with you is that he thinks you might confide in me something you'd hesitate to confide in him.'

'Well, everything he told you is true. I give him full marks for sensitivity to feminine anxieties. When did he call you?'

'A few days ago. He called from Paris. Said he had flown Concorde over for an emergency meeting and was Concording right back to you. He was scared you might go into labour with him not there for you.'

Tears filled Mirella's eyes.

'Oh dear,' said Deena, taking her friend's hand.

'I want to tell you about it, Deena. He is, of course, right. You are the only one in the world I would be able to talk this out with.'

Brindley arrived with the beach togs for Deena. She ducked into the gaily striped canvas marquee the Coreys used for changing.

'Not bad when you need her, is she? I hope you're pleased to have her here. If you don't want Deena to stay, she will understand. Just seeing you for the day and going on her shopping spree for you and the baby will have compensated for the flight.'

'I'm thrilled she's here, Brindley. I didn't know how

much I wanted to see her until I saw her, if you know what I mean. But I am curious. Why did you ask her to come and stay with me?'

He covered his embarrassment very professionally and looked directly into her eyes.

'You gave up conventional life when I discovered you were the sole heir to the Oujie legacy and you inherited, then met Rashid, and chose to marry Adam. I have been close to you through it all. I feel I know you quite well. The new life you have created for yourself in the last two years seems to work. You have learned to navigate in the fast lane with Rashid and Adam because all three of you in your own ways run there alone. You have a keen sense of how to keep your identity, a part of your self, from them. You retain a kind of mystery. That always surprises and intrigues. It's part of your fatal charm. It's what makes you a femme fatale. I sensed that you were worried about losing that with the birth of the baby. Am I wrong? Is it just I who is concerned that you will lose it, your emotional life will come unstuck and tumble down around you? Oh, I didn't mean to say all that. I am being melodramatic, I suppose. Sorry. But you and Adam and Rashid are romantics. And there is nothing romantic about having a baby. Miraculous certainly. Enriching. But hardly romantic. Silly of me to feel this way, I suppose. So silly that I never explained my feelings about it, even to Deena. I simply told her I was worried about you, and that your mother Lily had been a bother. I knew that would get her here fast.'

He smiled, and she returned his smile. But Mirella was quite overwhelmed at how astute and caring Brindley was being. His steady, sincere gaze did not conceal his embarrassment from her. She felt she had to say something to him to lift his unease.

'Why does everyone but me have a clearer vision of who I am and what I am, my strengths and my weaknesses? Why am I so slow to understand and to act upon my feelings?'

'Because you are too modest about the power of your personality. You're not vain enough about your beauty, or greedy enough to want everything on your terms. Because being a wealthy, powerful woman, a wife and now almost a mother, is still new to you. You are still living in the first forty years of your skin, which we know nothing about and cannot possibly understand. But Deena can, having known you for so long.'

'Nice of you to put it that way, Brindley. No wonder I make no big decisions without my lawyer! I had no idea you offered a guidance-in-pregnancy service! Thanks for asking Deena to come.'

He smiled and inwardly gave a sigh of relief. She would do the right thing for all concerned, he was sure of that now. A gust of warm wind blew up, and he looked up at the sky. The weather was changing yet again.

Deena reappeared, dressed in white cotton duck trousers with turn ups, a halter top of white silk that barely covered her breasts and left a bare midriff, and over her shoulders a nubbly cotton knit cardigan. She gazed skyward with her husband and said, 'Would you believe, I've forgotten my bathing suit? All this shopping and I forget the one thing I need. Just typical. Well, I'll just have to wear one of yours, Mirr.'

Brindley went to her and took her in his arms and kissed her, saying 'Let's wait until lunch to open the presents. I'd like to get a little fishing in, and it won't be long. Look, Moses is lighting the bonfire.' Before she could object, he was on his way to join the other men. She sighed and nodded assent. As she sat down again in the wooden lounge chair and swung her legs up on the footrest, she said to Mirella, 'Isn't it a miracle that with all the schmucks that I dated and suffered in my life – the pseudos, the suaves, the Jewish doctors, dentists and lawyers, the *goy* boys and the *gonifs* – that I should end up with anyone as special as Brindley? I am not going to analyse it, but I sure would like to know what it was that I did right to deserve him and so much happiness.'

She watched her husband pick up a rod and cast it into the waves, then turned her gaze back to Mirella. 'It's different for you, Mirella. You and Brindley, Rashid and Adam for that matter, were all born into privileged lives. It's a lot different from working for a privileged life. You somehow never quite get rid of the callouses on the hands from climbing those rungs. I wonder if I will ever stop being grateful for being me, knowing you, and having married Brindley. It turns out that English bitch was right: "It's all in the bloodline".'

'Bloodline and luck,' added Mirella. 'Those two things are on my mind all the time these days. The luck of having Adam for a husband and Rashid for a lover, a devoted Moses, about whom, by the way, you and I must have a talk, and Brindley, the greatest piece of luck I have ever had. Without his diligence in finding the rightful heiress to the Oujie legacy, none of us would be together or where we are now.

'Deena, you are my oldest friend and know me better than anyone. Surely you must see the character change in me. It troubles me less and less with every shackle of middle-class morality I shed. The more I live in this *ménage à trois* with Rashid and Adam, and delve into the archives of my ancestors, the more I become rooted in an unconventional marriage and family clan, and take on the responsibilities of the Oujie legacy, the more I am aware of nurturing my own independence and individuality. And I feel the need for my own space and time, my freedom, as well.

'Right from the beginning I understood that need in both Rashid and Adam, but until now never really appreciated them. I am never hurt or feel abandoned when Adam goes off alone on a dig, or to his tent on the banks of the Euphrates, or on a safari. It never crosses my mind to be concerned if he has another woman, or what he does. Every day of my married life he has been in contact with me one way or another. So has Rashid. And I share with both of them whatever parts of their lives they choose to offer. Life without their love and devotion is unthinkable to me. Yet, something in me holds back from becoming dependent on them. I find myself becoming more like my great-grandmother. There's the bloodline in my case. Powerful, holding my lovers through sex and through some strange power inside me, some charisma I don't fully know about – and not only enjoying it but cultivating it with every breath I take.'

'And love,' added Deena.

'Yes, and, of course, love. Having a baby has not interrupted my erotic life with either my husband or my lover. If anything now, my appetite for sex is insatiable. My pleasure in any sort of sexual act has increased tenfold to being a kind of erotic madness. It worried me at first, this deriving so much bliss from such sensual instincts. It made me think of Humayun, whose entire life is controlled by sexual ecstasy. All sorts of questions preyed on my mind. Would I get to be enslaved by sex and my husband and lover, as she is by Rashid? Was I risking making one instinct in myself the whole human being? My unborn child: what effect might the love, and so much lust, have upon a living but unborn person? And Adam and Rashid? I am aware of what I am doing to them, binding them closer to me than ever before. My pregnancy not stifling my lust for them has acted like an aphrodisiac. I am closer to each of them than I ever dreamed it was possible to be with another human being. In spite of Rashid's treachery, and his erotic life away from me, the love spiced with lust that we share is stronger than ever.

'They were right to call you. I guess that's love taking care of its own. I have a great need to blurt all this out to someone, and it could only have been you. Never one of them. The basis of our *ménage à trois* is that I never discuss one of the men with the other. Or the fact that we are even living in such an arrangement. And I know the men never allude to it with each other either.

'How can I possibly tell Adam that it's better if he's not with me while I am giving birth to our baby, without explaining why? And how can I possibly explain? I know it was not Rashid's seed at the time I conceived. But Rashid's extraordinary sexual prowess with me all during my pregnancy has involved him intimately with my unborn infant. That child has become a part of Rashid's and my erotic life. Rashid has felt that child grow in me just as much as Adam has. He believes he has a certain right to share in the birth of this child. And, God forgive me, though I find it out of the question, so do I.'

Mirella was aware of the blush of embarrassment that had come into Deena's face. 'Oh God, does this shock you?' she asked, suddenly sensing a rawness in what she was saying.

'Sort of. But probably more by your courage and passion than anything else.'

'Courage and passion.' Mirella repeated the words and pondered them for a few moments. The women remained silent and watched the men standing in the wet sand, the waves rolling over their feet as they cast their lines into the surf.

Deena broke the silence. 'What are you going to do, Mirella?'

'Not what I want to do, but what I have to do. I will send them both away until after the birth of my baby. If I don't, I may wreck what I have with them. And I have no intention of doing that. I didn't see it before, but I see it clearly now. I find being pregnant a physically unpleasant experience. The act of giving birth is an ugly business. Not to mention painful. It'll be hard work and disgustingly embarrassing. The very idea of losing control of my bodily functions, the mess of the breaking of the water, the afterbirth, the puffing and the screaming, the sweating and pushing. That is not something I want to share with Adam or Rashid. How can that add to the beauty and erotic love we feel? I turned them on to how erotic it can be fucking and making love to a pregnant woman. I managed to use my desire for sex and the state of sexual ecstasy to block out all the negative feelings I have for my condition. That's it, Deena. There is no more for them, except to see the miracle of what love and erotic passion can produce. The miracle of birth is for me. The miracle of a baby is for them to see and touch and love, when I bring it to them. It's my privilege to have my baby the way I want to. And I intend to have it without exposing my agony to those I love.

'I almost fell for the propaganda of the wonders of childbirth. the miracle that the fathers should be able to share in. That may be good for some, but not for me. This is a job I will do the way I feel is right for all of us. It's my body and my baby and my choice. And I hope you will wait it out with me.'

The manifesto had jerked tears from her eyes as she struggled from the deck chair. Deena jumped up and helped her, and then took Mirella in her arms and hugged her, comforting her.

'Of course I will stay,' Deena said. 'That's what I've come for, what the men want, we all want. And, just for the record, I couldn't agree more with you about not wanting my man around through all the mess. They will understand. And tough if they don't! If they're so anxious to be involved with the birth they should have arranged to be women. And, let me tell you, if men could have babies instead of women, you would see how fast the world population explosion would fizzle out. Fizzle out? Christ, we would be lucky to see children on earth at all. It's bad enough when they cut a finger, catch a cold. Ah, those delicate creatures who like to make war in between bouts of hypochondria.'

In the distance, the men skipped backwards from the incoming chill of the water. Mirella was both laughing and crying at the same time, she was so relieved. Deena watched her and at first was concerned, but Mirella's laughter was infectious. She responded and began to laugh and shed a few tears in sympathy. understanding very well the emotional burden her friend had been carrying for too long: having a baby at the age of forty, living outside the confines of convention, trying to integrate lust with her life.

They linked arms and started walking towards the bonfire where Moses was preparing food. He had built it on the beach close to one of the higher sand dunes that gave a little shelter from the wind. The sun switched off once more. A chill wind with salt water spray riding on it blew in from the ocean and across the beach. The weather was overcast. But any beach buff like Mirella and Deena knew that it would not rain, and the day on the sand was far from ruined. It was just another of those Long Island late summer beach days, when you could still get a burn, even though it was a half-sun, half-wind burn, still take a swim and catch a beach cold.

Moses picked up a plaid blanket and a megaphone from one of the canvas and wood director chairs placed near the fire. He wrapped the blanket around Mirella, saying, 'Just till the wind dies down.' He handed Deena the old-fashioned megaphone.

'You just had to have been a cheerleader, Miss Deena. So how about cheering those Isaac Waltons over here for lunch, please?'

The two women looked at each other and wiped the tears from their eyes and burst into a grin. Moses couldn't help smiling as Deena leapt into the air, arms outstretched, waving the megaphone, which she could barely manage because of its size and weight, then landed on her bare feet in the sand. She struck another one of her poses and shouted through the mouthpiece.

'Right again. Mose. You have here Vassar's first Jewish princess cheerleader. Chicadee-boom-boom.

And there are not many colleges that can boast of having had one of them. Rah, rah, rah.' Then she dropped the megaphone and doubled over with laughter.

Moses watched the two women of whom he was so fond quickly changing from beautiful sophisticated ladies into silly, giddy preppies. And it felt OK. Deena picked up the megaphone again, and hand on hip, back arched, breasts stuck out and pointing to the heavens, head thrown back, she began her knee-high strut while she shouted to a sing-song beat through it. 'One, Two, Three, Four, Who are We Rooting For, America, America, rah, rah, rah. Remember the Rosenbergs, and don't forget Hiroshima, Senator McCarthy Was A Fascist Fag, A Vicious Fascist Fag, Vote for a free and honourable America. Vote Democratic. One, Two, Three, Four, Who are we—'

She fought against more laughter and lost. She lowered the megaphone and collapsed on her knees next to Mirella, who was leaning against Moses, both lost in hilarious surprise at Deena's performance. Struggling to stand, she settled for resting the megaphone on one bent knee and shouted through it, 'You also have here, Vassar's last Jewish princess cheerleader. Straight A's, valedictorian of my class, and I flunked cheerleader. That bastard McCarthy had a lot to answer for. Give me a V. Give me an A. Give me an S. And an S. Give me—' she fell back and sat down hard on her bottom in the sand.

When she looked up it was to the sound of Rashid, Adam, Brindley, Moses and Mirella clapping. She smiled, and after Brindley helped her up and took her lovingly in his arms, kissed her, they all praised her performance.

'If I was so wonderful,' Deena said, 'then why did the Rosenbergs die in the electric chair? And why did McCarthyism go on for so long and damage so many lives? And why are we stuck with schmucky Republican presidents? And why did one of the best women's colleges in the world bust my cheerleader dreams over a little slip of the tongue in a sports arena?'

These gripes, all muddled together, made them laugh again, and even she had to smile. Only Brindley responded to the undertone of self-disappointment in her voice. 'So you could grow up, marry me, and take on Lyttleton Park as lady of the manor, reorganise the village fêtes and put a colonial spark into the English social season. So you could take on London, Gloucestershire. England. And the world. And spruce them up a little with your charm, wit, intelligence and beauty.'

'Then you don't mind that I'm a failed cheerleader? Or an ineffectual liberal Democrat, whose success in that common *trade* – as you English term business – of public relations has turned me into a wealthy closet Republican who still votes Democrat?'

'We've decided business is not entirely "common" now. What quaint words you colonials use,' Brindley said. 'Mind. I all but say a little prayer of thanks. You might have married an American football player, or joined the Salvation Army and cheered for them.'

'Not possible. It's just as hard for a Jewish princess to crack the Salvation Army as it is to break into the ranks of the cheerleader brigade.'

The banter continued until they opened the thermoses of chilled dry martinis, malt whisky, hot beef broth, cold vichyssoise, coffee, tea. They uncorked bottles of chilled Chablis and several of a perfect claret

178

that were waiting for them on a low table near the fire. It groaned with the weight of covered silver dishes containing thick sirloin steaks, lamb cutlets and poussins, all of which had been prepared in several different marinades and were ready to throw onto the fire to be barbecued on request, for serving charred on the outside and bright pink on the inside. There was garlic bread made from long French sticks, wholemeal rolls, loaves of rye, soft white English cottage loaves, cakes and pastries. Baskets of *crudités* were beautifully arranged, with every raw vegetable that was in season scrubbed and cut to a perfect size for eating in the hand and on the run. Which was the way the entire buffet for that day was designed, so that the men could still tend to their rods set in holders stuck in the sand, as they dashed back and forth from the water's edge to grab a sandwich of sizzling steak, a handful of celery, a carrot, leaves of radicchio, cos and several other lettuces. Or, if time permitted, a plate of lamp chop, or a bowl of chilli, from the pot set in the embers and gently bubbling away.

The scent of the beach mingled with wood smoke and herbs: rosemary, thyme, dill, tarragon and sage, along with pungent spices: ginger, garlic, cumin and coriander, and sizzling gristle and roasting meat. In the afternoon the sun came out. A haze of heat settled over the beach and sapped the women of energy. They did little more than gossip and tease the men when they let go of their rods for long enough to rest and sit in the sand at the women's feet. After the gifts had been opened and admired, Mirella and Deena sat together and watched the men surf casting. For a long time they said nothing, just watched and listened to the roar of the ocean, and dozed in their chairs.

179

In the late afternoon it was still hot. The heat and humidity were beginning to take their toll on Mirella. She stood up and shed the attractive cotton kaftan she was wearing, and spoke to Deena, who was roused from her lethargy by Mirella's announcement.

'I must go for a swim. This is the moment of truth. A cliché maybe, but fairly apt.'

Deena tried to raise herself from the chair, but was so dozy she slipped back and fell into a deep sleep, barely hearing Mirella say, 'Don't bother, Deeny. Adam or Rashid will come with me.'

Deena had no idea how long she had been sleeping when she woke up with a start. Her first thoughts were of Mirella, and Mirella wasn't there. Suddenly Mirella's last words returned to her like a ringing in the ears. Deena jumped out of the chair and ran, panicked, across the hot sand and down to the water's edge. The ocean seemed if anything more rough. She raised her hand to her forehead to create a shade for her eyes the better to scan the waves for her friend. A large wave crashed and rolled on to the beach and over Deena's feet. She felt the undertow suck the smooth wet sand from her toes. And then she spotted them floating on the waves quite far out. Adam, Mirella and Rashid.

It had been five days since that day on the beach. Five glorious and happy days for Mirella and Deena, alone in the Easthampton house, except for the staff and Moses. He remained with the women at all times, or at least within shouting distance of them, by order of Adam, his only request before he had left for Istanbul. He had gone when Mirella asked that she be allowed to have her baby and bring the infant to him in

Istanbul. He had understood perfectly and had raised no anxiety in her by his reaction, merely going the following day.

Not so Rashid. He acquiesced to Mirella's wishes reluctantly and left her in Easthampton, but remained in his Southampton house, making her nervous by being so close. They had two erotic encounters in his house before the baby was born. With each visit she made to him, she was aware of Rashid's anger borne by being thwarted. She assumed one source of his anger was her decision not to have him present during and after the birth of the baby, or to allow him to see either of them until she returned to Istanbul. Her acknowledgement of his takeover of her holdings had certainly been another. But she knew him well. There was something more that had escaped him. Something else he wanted that he could not get, and of which she was sure he was still in hard pursuit. What was it? Or who? Those questions troubled her.

She had a kind of answer on the first day she arrived at his Southampton compound. Humayun had been sent for and was discreetly in residence. The swiftness with which Rashid replaced Mirella in his erotic life always smarted, and this particular time more so than ever. The manner in which he subtly taunted her with Humayun's presence always incited her to greater passion in their erotic games. She knew he had reintroduced Humayun to exhibit his power over her whether she called the shots or not. She wanted to say, 'Isn't every young, middle-aged or old beauty on Long Island enough for you?' But she couldn't because she knew they were not. So she said nothing. After their long and passionate afternoon of love-making, lying with her in bed, on his side – a small pedestal dish of

Leonidas white chocolates in one hand, from which he was creating a pattern on top of her domed belly – he surprised her by saying, 'Mirella, I want you to do something for me. I want you to speak to Moses on my behalf.'

'Moses?' Puzzled, she attempted to rise. He stopped her with gentle hands. And she let herself fall back among the pillows propped up behind her. The chocolates hardly moved.

He placed the empty pedestal dish on the night stand, and then turned back to her and said, 'You wouldn't want to upset my chocolates, would you?' He chose one and fed half of it to her before popping the other half in his own mouth. While she was still chewing he placed his mouth over hers and licked her lips with his tongue, casually caressing her nakedness with roving hands. He took another of the white chocolates and ate it, and the delight the chocolate gave him appeared in his eyes. His caresses grew more daring between her legs and, while exciting her with fingers spontaneously probing within her, he said, 'Moses is in love with Humayun. He wants to marry her.'

She reacted with such surprise that she found herself speechless. Rashid took advantage of the moment to bend his head to hers and kiss her again on the lips. He pressed his advantage.

'Let me tell you about it before you say anything. You knew ages ago about my giving Humayun to him as a gift for a couple of weeks. Well, what you didn't know is that the poor devil flowered erotically under her guidance. And, for what it's worth, she learned to have deep feelings for him. When she came to me and asked me to rescind the order I gave her to make

182

herself available to him, she told me the affair was getting out of hand. I instructed her to let him down gently. The last thing I wanted was to upset Moses. I like the man, and I could see a hell of a lot of sexual power in him trying to find a way to get out. As a gesture of thanks for all his kindnesses to me, I wanted to help him find sexual ecstasy, not hurt him.'

Rashid ate another chocolate. Then he snuggled closer to her and, placing an arm around her shoulder while he pressed even deeper with embedded fingers now covered with her come, he was delighted by the look of lust he was teasing from her.

'He is, I am informed, a very well-endowed and imaginative lover. Got a great deal of stamina.'

'I don't want to hear about that, Rashid,' Mirella said, some anger now slipping into her voice. 'I am just so happy he has found someone that he loves and wants for himself. He deserves the best. I could have wished it was someone other than Humayun, because of the life she has led in the past, but love chooses without looking forward or backward.'

'As true, no doubt, as it is sentimental. But you had better hear the rest.'

There had been something in his tone, a warning. Mirella was alerted at once to the fact that Moses, her good and dear Moses, was in trouble, whether he knew it or not. She scooped the remaining chocolates off her stomach. She took Rashid's hand by the wrist and wrenched it from between her legs and dropped the sweets into the moistened palm, clumsily scrambling away from him.

He hurled the chocolates across the room and grabbed her before she could get off the bed. She didn't fight him, simply sat with her back to him while he squatted on his haunches and fiercely caressed her naked shoulders and kissed the nape of her neck.

'I knew you would be angry and unrealistic about this. But no one could be sorrier than I am. And that's why we must do what we can to save the situation. Just hear me out.'

She took one of his hands from her shoulder and kissed it. She knew very well he meant what he was saying. And there was no point in getting angry, either with him or the situation. She slowly rose from the bed and stood to face him. For nearly a minute neither said anything. They were too busy looking at each other. Mirella was yet again taken aback at her tireless lusting after the handsome man naked on his knees before her. She marvelled that this beautiful man, this inveterate seducer of women, should be so much a part of her life, and that she could hand herself over to him erotically to do with as he wanted. Because whatever he wanted stimulated the search for more, always much more, the quest for a sexual oblivion. Standing naked before him in her present condition she could not but love him for the sexual excesses he shared with her. It was he who had destroyed sexual shame in her forever, accorded her sensual freedom.

'Okay, Rashid. Tell me about it while I dress.'

'It's quite simple. He fell in love with one of the world's most remarkable whores, who happens to be my sexual slave, but whom I will not free – not only because I want her, but because she would never be happy anywhere but where she is, with me. She may toy with the idea that she could love Moses enough to marry him, and play the good wife, but that's a fantasy. Humayun is a sexual adventuress with bizarre sexual appetites, and she lives the life of the most coveted sexual slave in the world. She is a famous and rare oddity, and in love with her life and me, and no one else. If Moses pursues this any further, it will be disastrous for both of them.

'I know that you don't want to hear this, Mirella, but already he is in trouble. She is turning him into her sexual slave, slowly destroying the man he is. It must be stopped and soon, so that he too is saved. Of the three of us, he is the most vulnerable.'

The telephone began to ring. It put an end to their conversation. Unimpressed by Rashid's apparent altruism, Mirella now knew a third thing that was making Rashid unhappy. He wasn't getting his way in breaking up Moses and Humayun. She would have to think about how to handle that and talk to Deena when she met up with her in town, perhaps even call Adam and ask his advice. She was very sad for both of them, mostly her dear Moses.

She could not help overhearing Rashid's conversation.

'It's been weeks since you were hired to find her. I told you to be subtle, but not ineffectual, man. I thought you were the best in the business. At least, that's what Interpol made me think.'

Mirella watched Rashid's face change expression several times while the person on the other end of the line spoke.

'Were you at least able to trace the call she made to me three days ago?'

Again Rashid listened and Mirella, now dressed, walked past him and through the sliding glass wall to stand outside near his swimming pool, not wanting to work herself into a jealous curiosity as to who the new woman was whom he chased.

'Look, my patience is running out. There is a bonus of $25,000 if you find her in the next three days. If not, you're fired.'

She heard him bang down the receiver, and noted a fourth frustration generating the undercurrent of anger she sensed in him.

Chapter 9

Moses swung Adam's 1937, cream-coloured Mercedes Benz convertible into Gin Lane. Throughout the drive from Easthampton the extraordinary events of the last few days had kept tumbling though his mind.

Mirella's baby had been born as she wished in the Easthampton house and with the least possible fuss. She had had a long and hard labour, thirty-eight hours. The infant, a girl, was particularly beautiful for a new-born baby. Masses of blonde hair. Eyes that kept changing from emerald green to deep violet so that no one was quite sure what colour they were. Long, dark brown lashes. Unlike some, this baby came out of her mother's womb with hardly a blemish on her creamy skin. Mirella tried to tell herself that the aura of light and specialness she sensed around her baby girl was what every mother imagined. But perhaps any descendant of the Kadin Roxelana Oujie was special, right down to her tiny slender finger tips. Neither doctor nor midwife, nurse nor nanny could help admiring her unusual baby, or resist touching her seductive baby lips with the tips of their fingers. A plump – dare Mirella admit, erotic looking? – happy and healthy baby, who won her mother's heart from the moment she was born. A seductress from birth. Both Moses and Deena found it almost impossible to stay away from her. And Adam in Istanbul, Rashid in Paris, seemed never to be off the telephone. Deena announced she wanted a baby. No, not one baby, many babies. Mirella opted for no more.

Moses's obligation to stay with Mirella until her baby was born had left him with no time to see Humayun. She was available to him because Rashid had left the Hamptons suddenly, almost at a minute's notice, after assuring Mirella he would be on the telephone to her every day. He had rattled off a series of telephone numbers to call as soon as she went into labour.

His exit and the knowledge of what was going on between Moses and Humayun had prompted Mirella and Deena to have a talk with Moses about the affair. That had all taken place the day before Mirella had gone into labour. She had not been feeling very well and a strange depression seemed to have overtaken her. Deena and Moses had put it down to her worry that the baby was more than three weeks late, and the doctor insisted she would have to go into the hospital and have a Caesarean delivery if labour didn't start within three days.

Having made up their minds to talk with Moses in a ruthlessly honest manner about his friendship with Humayun, the two women had invited him to join them as their guest for lunch, just the three of them in the Easthampton kitchen. Moses had sensed something was in the air when they announced that Deena was taking on the role of chef. Deena, though a gourmet, was not a happy cook; she was a culinary snob as well and had been known to leave a kitchen as if she had strafed it with a full clip from a machine gun.

188

The large rectangular pine table had been dressed beautifully. A massive display of the last of the summer flowers – a melange of faded pinks, purples, mauves, yellows and whites, mixed with poppy heads and long grasses in a low bowl – had filled the centre of the table handsomely and was set at one end for the three of them. Moses had been placed at the head of the table, the women on either side of him. Their meal, one course, the ingredients for Chinese pancakes stuffed with Peking duck, was laid out before them. On crisp, white linen place mats, edged with an inch of indigo blue Brussels lace, were several different blue and white, eighteenth-century Nanking dishes containing a stack of paper-thin pancakes, soy and bean paste, shredded crispy duck, slivers of cucumber, transparently thin rings of spring onion, ready for each of them to prepare their own pancakes just as they liked them. Ivory chopsticks lay neatly across the weeping cherry and lotus flower patterned plates. Large champagne cups of clear crystal on delicate long stems waited to be filled from two silver coolers proffering the best Krug champagne, from the cellars of the Easthampton house. One of Moses's favourite meals. So that was the parcel delivered by the helicopter when it had landed an hour before with the day's mail and shopping from the city.

The three had just taken their seats, and Moses was opening the wine. He looked at the two women with great affection and popped the question, 'What's this all about?'

'You and Humayun. Please don't be angry with us for putting you on the spot like this. We feel as family towards you. We care for your happiness. Rashid does too. He has asked me to speak to you about your relationship with Humayun.' Mirella's embarrassment showed, but she struggled on under it. 'We don't intend to do that, Moses. Not unless you want us to. All Deena and I care about is that you know we are here for you, friends, ready to lend an ear. And not only to listen. We want to share in your happiness, help you, if it's help that you need.'

Then Deena had added, 'Listen, Mose, you can tell us to mind our own business. We can live with that. But we can live better if you would take us into your confidence, because that's the only way we'll ever know all is well with you. And that, Mose, is important to us.'

A hundred yards before the entrance to Rashid's Southampton compound, Moses suddenly swerved off the road to one side, pulled up the hand brake and shut off the engine. His thoughts harked back to that lunch, and the relief and gratitude he had felt by the genuine concern and support Deena and Mirella and – as he was to learn later – Adam and Brindley were giving him. He had been overwhelmed by the understanding the women showed of him and of Humayun. They had given him straight out their case against him and Humayun being able to sustain a happy and constructive life together. Over and over during their four-hour lunch as they sat together drinking champagne and filling, rolling, and eating their pancakes, Moses opened up to himself and the two women as he had never allowed himself to do before.

Now he sat in the quiet of Gin Lane, thinking about things that had been said at lunch that day.

'I love her,' he had said to them. 'And I'm relieved that you know about it. I can see by the look on your faces what you're thinking: but does she love Moses?

Yes, I believe she does. How much? I can't answer that because I don't know. I can only hope, enough to marry me.'

'Moses, can we ask more? Will you allow us to talk about this with you?' That had been Mirella.

'Yes. Why not? There are no two other people I feel closer to. And when Humayun accepts my proposal, I hope that won't change. Or my job either, for that matter.'

'We should hope not,' answered Mirella, shocked by the very idea that he might leave them. To Moses she had also looked uncomfortable sitting so pregnantly on the dining chair. He had placed the champagne bottle down, having removed its wired cap. Before opening it he had gone to Mirella's aid, changing her chair for an old soft club chair, and an ottoman for under her feet, covered in a patterned glazed chintz of red and white cabbage roses that always stayed by the open fireplace in the kitchen. It was a scene etched in his mind for the loving care that these two privileged women took upon themselves in discussing with him the most shocking and intimate facts they knew about the woman he loved. At the same time they declared their homes open and ready to receive him and Humayun at any time.

He had returned to his place at the head of the table, filled the glasses, and, still standing, had addressed the women.

'Why are you looking sad for me? I am happier than I have ever been in my life. Until I met Humayun, I had no idea that there was something missing in my life, that I was a lonely man. Be happy for me, ladies. C'mon, we're not Romeo and Juliet: This is not the tragic unquestioning love of youth. Believe me,

191

because in those first weeks together with Humayun I was constantly questioning: "Is this love, or infatuation? Moses, is this intense happiness you feel, this bubbling over in sheer delight, is it nothing more than a moment of peak experience? What other woman has ever inspired in you the deep trust you feel? What other woman has inspired you to see yourself and accept yourself for what and who you are, no more, no less?" Loving Humayun has restored that essential courageousness in me to open myself up to whatever life throws at me, and experience it. She has reminded me to keep open to whatever comes up next, not get scared and enclosed and want to sweep it away. She has made me give up not wanting to be hurt any more. You know, she is a remarkable woman. She deserves more in life than being indentured to Rashid Lala Mustapha. I love her and I want to set her free, show her another kind of love that has nothing to do with being anyone's sexual slave.'

Deena's words smouldered in his mind. 'Maybe,' Deena had said, 'she doesn't want to be free. Her whole life has been dedicated to mastering the role of sexual slave to Rashid. I have seen her. She *is* erotic love, and passionately happy in that role. Moses, if you love her, then love her only in that way, because that's her life. And it just may be possible that the kind of love and freedom you want to give Humayun could destroy her.'

And then Moses thought about what Mirella had said. 'Moses, you must ask yourself more questions, my dear friend, face truths, deal in realities. Are you so sure the love you feel for Humayun is more than erotic love? Look, I don't denigrate that kind of love. It's as powerful as any. But it is what it is, and its demands and goals are anything but selfless. It claims pleasure at any price. And when that's the rule, true love does not exist. Not the kind I know you have in you, and want for others. Do you really want to pay any price, and fragment your life and your ideals for, well, sex? You have to think about those things, Moses, because love is whole, not to be broken up just because passion and desire take over and crowd out everything else. Obviously at those times there is no love. I should know. That's why I live with two loves, but have bound myself only to the real one I found in myself with Adam.'

Mirella's words had snapped him back to reality, and the reality of his situation confused him, yet he had said, 'I have no conflict of any kind in loving Humayun. That would be such a waste of energy.' Now, as he sat in the open car, only minutes away from lying in the arms of the woman he loved, he probed his passion and desire for Humayun, though he had not done so with Mirella and Deena.

He couldn't remember which woman had said, 'You always believed it was important to know oneself, not according to a formula, or through the eyes of some guru, but out of a natural awareness. You used to say, self-knowledge puts an end to illusions and hypocrisies. Are you so befuddled by carnal love for Humayun that you have forgotten your principles?'

Then he attached a face to the voice that had spoken those words to him. 'Believe me, Moses, it's me, Deena, telling you. I understand, I have been there, where you are now, moving in the dreamworld of what *I* want, what *I* must have. How many formulas and gurus and fads had you teased me out of before I was able to tap into my own self-awareness? More than I

193

want to remember. I can only repay your wise understanding and patience by pointing out to you that Humayun is an extraordinary sexual seductress. She gets men and women who come her way to lose themselves, wallow in self-abandonment. I can understand that that's why you love her, for that and sexual ecstasy. Oh, but, my old buddy, wake up and understand it, and love her for that. Only, remember, no illusions. Don't be a hypocrite. She is a sexual slave who battens on the dark side of men's erotic desires and fantasies.'

Mirella had added, 'My uncle Hyram always said of you, "Moses has a mind that is rich in its quietness. He is not a man to look beyond what is. He has the only treasure that a man can have, must have: innocence. That's something he'll never lose. It's grounded in his mind and in his soul. Moses, in spite of his thousand experiences, will always see what truth is. He is a learned man, our Moses, devout about his freedom, open in his vulnerability and his fullness of heart. There is innocence in him permitting him to know what truth is without even thinking about it. You can learn a lot from Moses. I have." '

Moses opened the car door and stepped into the road. He needed to walk. He had no idea when or where it had happened. Perhaps on the last curve in the road, or a thousand miles away, or in Easthampton while rolling a Chinese pancake. Truth is really a pathless land. He had kept going on love all these months, unaware that he had lost his way. Now, suddenly, here in the lane, he found it beside him again.

He walked under a bright sky and in the heat of the day down Gin Lane, grateful for every blade of grass or wild flower he saw, grateful for the sun that shone above him and warmed the very marrow of his bones, the whisper of the soft breeze rustling through the boxwood hedge, the song of a small bird. He sucked in the sweet scent of fresh air and let it out slowly. In his servitude he was free. In that moment he realised that Humayun had done with him what Rashid had done to her. The woman he loved had made of him her sexual slave.

With every stride he took, darkness lifted from his soul. His mind was lit by bright memories of the living care heaped upon him in childhood by a devoted mother and father, their friends.

Mirella Wingfield's Uncle Hyram, and Moses's father had been close since their days at Harvard when they were both students of medicine. What bound the two men even closer was their interest and belief in the Theosophical Society, which eventually became a pivot of Hyram Wingfield's and his black friend's lives.

Moses's father was Harding Jefferson, whose mother and father had been educated slaves on the Thomas Jefferson estate, Monticello. Once qualified, he became a renowned diagnostician. Hyram entered into medical research, and became a successful inventor, reclusive and eccentric. But, in Harding Jefferson's day, Negro doctors, no matter how educated they were, no matter how expert in their chosen field of medicine, found no offices on Park Avenue, or chief residencies in hospitals. Yet, before Dr Harding Jefferson's death, there were great medical centres in cities such as Boston, New York, Washington, Rochester, that had tried in vain to woo him from his offices on the fringe of black Harlem. There he started his practice as a young man, and there he remained until his death. Park Avenue came to Harlem. Need of the rich mingling with that of the poor.

Medicine, his wife, Charleen Tizzle, who had been his nurse, his son Moses, his friend Hyram, and the Theosophical Society, became the doctor's life. They had been Moses's world too, until the death of his mother when he was eight. The loss served to draw Hyram Wingfield and the two remaining Jeffersons even closer. When someone guessed there was a better upbringing to be had by a motherless boy among the female staff of the Wingfield household, more peace and quiet away from his father's thriving clinic, he was moved in there. So the two Jeffersons divided their time between Harlem and East 65th Street, the Wingfield brownstone house that Mirella now owned and where Moses still lived.

Moses saw a copper penny shining in the road. He scooped up the coin and flipped it high into the air off his thumb nail. He watched it twinkling in the sunlight as it flipped over itself and plummeted back to the palm of his hand.

He smiled to himself, recalling his father and Uncle Hyram and their stories about the old days among the hard-core Theosophists. Could any child have been so lucky as he, to be brought up with such bizarre but intelligent adults? His life was still rich and colourful with beliefs drawn from those the Theosophical Society was founded on – forming a nucleus of the Universal Brotherhood of Humanity where no discrimination of race, creed, sex, caste or colour existed. The Theosophists studied comparative religion, philosophy and science the way others read the Bible. They were dedicated to tracing the patterns in nature's activities and identifying powers latent in man.

The Society emerged from the vision of an American Civil War veteran in 1875, one Colonel Olcott, who was interested in spiritualism and mesmerism. Alongside him was Madame Helena Petrovna Blavatsky, a notorious Russian lady. Some wrote her off as a complete fraud. But she drew near-worship from others as a seer and miracle worker with occult powers derived from some exalted spiritual source. Madame Blavatsky put life into the eastern, esoteric heart of the society. Uncle Hyram and his father in their youth had been devout followers. But they were also men of science, who believed in the inherent inner teachings. These included a goal of ultimate perfection, when the ego, the soul, is released from the treadmill of reaping from life what it sows either of good or evil. That gave the men a problem with believing that they could get to Tibet to talk with a Master without leaving 165 East 65th Street. They might make contact on some astral plane. Or the Tibetan Masters might materialise themselves into ghost-like forms for those privileged enough to see them. A locked door or a wall was no bar to a visit. However, though they had their doubts, impressions of several visitations of a mystical kind removed a luxury of total disbelief. All their lives they accepted the possibilities. And all along they waited for them to be proved wrong.

Moses's grandmother and grandfather had been directly involved with Olcott and Blavatsky. His father and Uncle Hyram were taken up by the next most important people in the movement, Mrs Annie Besant and Mr Leadbeater and the Indian boy, Krishnamurti, whom they promoted as the world teacher that the Society had been seeking. By the time Moses finished his studies at Harvard and returned once again as a permanent resident to the house at 165 East 65th Street, he felt as strongly about the teachings of Krishnamurti as his father and Uncle Hyram did. And like them, he picked and chose among them.

The two doctors had been in Holland at the Ommen Camp in 1929 when Krishnamurti broke away from the Theosophists. As head of the Order of the Star, he dissolved the organisation with all its thousands upon thousands of members, and announced that it had become a crutch for the individual. It prevented him from growing and establishing his uniqueness, which lay in his discovering for himself absolute, unconditional truth. After this, though the two doctors remained until their deaths friends of the Theosophists, they assessed Krishnamurti's teachings for themselves. They freed themselves from dependence on any group or organisation to answer life questions.

Moses loved those very special men. They left a legacy of remarkable achievements behind them. For him as executor of both men's estates, new discoveries of their achievements were always surfacing to remind him of the spirit that had sustained them.

Humayun. He had never mentioned them to her. Now he realised that he must. How could she possibly know him, love him if she knew nothing about the men who helped shape his life, the philosophies he lived by? To tell Humayun about Hyram and his father, and growing up in a world where you didn't stop and trace out a path for another to follow or a master design for your own life suddenly made great sense.

She, wanting to know all about Moses, and faced with a wall of silence, had accused him of hanging back, of being too modest. And now, as he approached the entrance to the compound, he understood why he found it difficult to tell her about himself. What could it possibly mean to tell her he had a degree in philosophy from Harvard, that he was a first-rate chef, the Wingfield-Corey housekeeper, an archivist for two elderly eccentrics who loved him, that he had had several love affairs that never worked out? That he was a keep-fit addict who taught underprivileged children in Harlem? What did all that come to, in the face of knowing a man sexually down to the very marrow of his bones, to the ecstasy of his soul, the darkest and most depraved side of his nature, the way she knew him? It came to much, he decided. He had to tell her about his truth, about the light and the bright side of his nature, the wisdom he'd acquired at the elbows of thinkers and seekers and teachers who believed in the goodness of man.

The impressive black iron gates to Rashid's compound were open. All four Pharaoh hounds lying lazily in the sun sprang to life. One of the security guards appeared as if from nowhere. Moses, was it? he asked and called off the dogs. The hounds settled for prancing around the two men, snarling greedily for a bit of petting. Moses and Harold, the chief security man, shook hands. They walked together through the grounds towards the house. He presented Moses with a clipboard and Moses signed in.

'Moses, how did you get here? Where's your car?'

Moses put his hand to his head. The question surprised him. He looked and felt confused. He had forgotten about the car parked a few hundred yards up Gin Lane. He had been caught up in his memories, and in an awareness of himself and Humayun hitherto lost. With every step he took towards the house and

Humayun, he could feel her powerful pull on him. Passion and desire for her seemed to overwhelm him once again. He stopped and looked at Harold.

'You all right, Mose?'

'Fine, just fine, Harold. I needed to walk for a while. That's why I left the car on Gin Lane. I'd better go back for it.'

'Give me the keys. I'll have one of the boys drive it into the compound. We'll leave the keys in the car. It'll be okay because we're closing the gates. No other guests are comin'. It's a great day. The sun and the light, the air, it's kinda magic. And you got the whole place to yourself. There's only that Turkish lady, and one of them foreign bodyguards still hangin' around. Maybe some of the regular staff. See you, Mose.'

Humayun watched Moses shake hands with the security man and continue walking up the white, polished pebble drive towards her. She remained partially hidden behind a larger than life-size Henry Moore bronze sculpture, one of his reclining women, set on the blanket of perfectly clipped grass. The bronze lady was positioned to face both the compound and the sand dunes, the beach below and the ocean. She glistened in the sun, monumentally seductive and powerful, casting a spell of titanic femininity over the compound.

Humayun disliked the Southampton compound, and everything about it. Its modern, aesthetically perfect architecture, the American speedy, clean-cut atmosphere, the household staff, even her sexual encounters with Rashid and his friends. No matter how thrilling the sexual ecstasy, once she came down from those heights, she was uneasy in the surroundings.

She caressed the soft warm curve of the bronze, and

was soothed by the feel of the reclining goddess and the sight of Moses across the lawn and through the waist-high hedge of the full blooming, bright blue hydrangeas along the curving drive to the house. For the first time since Rashid left for Paris she felt some joy. His departure had been so sudden, and he had been so preoccupied with getting to Paris that he had left her only with instructions to remain in the house until his return. He had promised to call in a day, two. Five days now, and not a word.

The last thing he had said to her had been about Moses. 'Go to any lengths you have to,' Rashid had told her, 'but make sure he understands who you really belong to. Do it in a way that he knows he can have you when *we* want him to.'

Then he had gone to the wall safe behind a raunchy Picasso nude painting of Humayun in his dressing room. He had removed a jeweller's box from it and tossed it to her, saying, 'I bought this for you when I was in New York the other day at Harry Winston's ordering something. Think of it as a gift in celebration of our day together in Crete. Once I saw them, I knew they would suit you as they would no other woman in the world. I was going to give them to you at Christmas, but suddenly I want you to have them now. Enjoy them.'

Humayun wore the thirty-carat emeralds carved as doves on her ears. She brought her hands up to each of them, touched the earrings. She did that often when she was wearing them, as she had been doing since he gave them to her. He was right, as so often: they were exotic gems and suited her perfectly. The moment she saw them, she knew they would be her most treasured possession. They were also an affirmation of what she had thought: that Rashid and she would never love each other more than they had that day together in Crete. Nor love each other less.

There were several things that were odd about Rashid's departure from the house. He had no idea how long or where he would be. That was not like Rashid, who was always superbly well organised and did very little spontaneously. He was a plotter, a planner, a man who liked to control his movements and those of everyone around him. Yet, he had left her alone to fend for herself with only her bodyguard and her maid. And he left at a time when he wanted to be near Mirella, even though he was still smarting at his banishment from her experience of labour. Humayun had been with Rashid when the telephone call came that took him away. She understood that it had been for a liaison with a woman. Nothing unusual about that. The unusual thing was that at the very last minute he cancelled the visit of guests. And as for Humayun, with his being away, the norm would have been for him to offer Humayun's company to at least two or three of his friends. He had not done that. She had even heard him refuse her favours to a Supreme Court Justice who was besotted with her. Only Moses had been mentioned, and a couple they often invited to enhance their sexual games. They, he suggested, might be of use to discourage Moses's infatuation with her.

Humayun stepped out from behind the reclining bronze. She was dressed in a gaily hand-painted sarong: large, white lilies trumpeting their lifelike beauty in a design of long, pointed, emerald green leaves on a heliotrope-blue ground. She sported a large, glamorous bright pink straw hat. The emerald doves nestling on her ears showed magnificently against the pink of the hat and the red gold of her hair that she wore long and loose. The nudity of her smooth shoulders and arms, her long shapely legs and bare feet glistened in the sunlight like tawny polished marble. In her beautiful hands, whose slender fingers were tipped with glamorous, bright red enamel finger-nails and covered with rings of coloured stones: canary yellow diamonds, inky blue sapphires, red, red rubies and gem-green emeralds, she carried her sandals.

It was several minutes before Moses was aware that she was standing in his path. Until he saw her Humayun had studied him. How many times had she made love to him, devastated him with her sexual expertise and watched him respond and take her over, draw her into himself and surprise her by his cries for more, for him to be dragged down into a depth she made of sexual depravity. She had lost count. This huge and handsome, well-educated black man: his athletic body had excited her in ways that surprised even her. He had come to her naïve in the tactics of erotic love-making, starved of sexual ecstasy, familiar only with the basics of sexual gratification. Walking towards her was a man she had been moulding into a sexual slave. And the joy she felt for the power she had over him was boundless. There was something else that thrilled her, his love for her. She liked very much, maybe too much, his loving her. She adored seeing the light in his eyes when she demanded sexual acts and passions from him that he had hitherto only courted as depraved fantasy. She had caught that look before in other men's eyes. It was love for her courage in taking them with her where they dared not tread alone or with anyone but her. But there was something more in Moses's eyes. He touched her heart more than any of the others, and she liked the feeling.

There was a serenity in his face today . . . and a vulnerability more acute than usual. She liked that. She liked reaching down into his soul, especially his sexual soul, and probing it. Recently she had begun to feel something of his innocence rubbing off on her. She found it amusing and at the same time a trifle exciting. Often, when he had left her bed, she lay awake and mused that there was a wisp of a little boy in him that appealed to what scant maternal instinct she possessed. But there was more than a lick of the taciturn preacher dormant in him that she found most unappealing, even dangerous. What troubled her today was that of late she had grown to want to be more involved in his life. That day in Crete with Rashid had served to show her how feeble a feeling it was. Rashid was her life, Oda Lala's and who and what she was were her life, and she had been forced to face the truth: how much she enjoyed that life, how happy she was in it, and how she would never want to change it. Feeble though that feeling might be, she had it still. He had called it love, she had laughed. But she wasn't laughing now. Here he was, after some considerable time of absence, and still love was there.

Suddenly he saw her. He stopped to stare at her. Her sensitive and seductive beauty stunned him. He felt his heart begin to race, his mouth go dry. His body yearned for her. His loins ached with the pain of lust for her. For the first time since he had met her he saw her in truth, and for what she was, and loved her all the more for the seeing that replaced his blindness. They gazed into each other's eyes and tomorrow disappeared for them. No yesterdays were there to be remembered. There was only now. All his thoughts stopped and so did their sense of time.

The light that he saw on her face was like the light behind the eyes. He kept very still and unknowingly he went with it. The beauty of that light was love.

Humayun felt a strange quietness come over her and a feeling that everything about her had come to a standstill – though a car slid into the compound, Moses was walking towards her, somewhere a bird was singing in a tree, the waves were crashing on the beach. Her sense of aloofness was sublime. She never moved, just stood there and drew him to her. He placed his hands in hers. She slipped her fingers through his and was mesmerised by the interlocking of their tawny and black skins. She raised their fingers to her lips and kissed them.

She whispered huskily, 'You fill my soul.' He answered, 'I fill my soul with you.'

Destiny came to them most unexpectedly. A strange stillness and peace seemed to pour down from the clear blue above and the heavens beyond to cover the earth.

If they hadn't known it before, though they said not a word about it to each other, they knew now that their love had been born, that a voice had called from their terrified souls, and that they had to face it because there is no defence against the lure of love.

Tie first, then the cufflinks, one by one. Fingers slipped under the buttons of his shirt, feeling the warm hardness of his chest. A slow sensuous strip, down to the ebony buff of him. He stood there, rock still, watching her every movement and let her take him over. Each shed garment of his was answered by the soft shedding of one of hers. After his trousers he removed her sarong and began to devour her nakedness with his eyes and his hands.

She liked him nude. He shone like black marble in the sunshine. She enjoyed the firmness of his flesh, the roundness of his buttocks and his arms, shoulders and thighs. She took in the strength and muscle of his body, caressing it as she was now. And his phallus, the weight of it, and his testes in her hands. His body was perfect, seemed more than perfect when he was in the throes of lust with her. At those times he used his body alternately as athlete, ballet dancer, rampant man possessed, a submissive female, a glorious primitive animal capable of taking her roughly like any jungle beast. Only she could excite him into those roles with her magical hands and probing fingers as she was doing now. She felt the rise of her own passion as she let her jewelled fingers rove the dark silkiness of his skin. She took him by the hand, her eyes fixed on his thick, reaching penis. She led him to the Henry Moore reclining nude. So far, if he had tried to touch her she had not allowed it. But now she placed his hands upon the warm bronze of the sculpture and ordered him to caress it. She watched his hands pay their sensuous, tactile homage to the bronze figure as hers did to him. Then she took both his hands in hers and raised them to her mouth. She kissed them passionately.

A kind of wickedness came over her. She stood back a few steps so that he could take a good look at her. With her legs wide apart, she ran her hands over her breasts, squeezing them, fingers pulling on her large and tantalising nipples. Her back arched, she ran her hands over her beautiful mound, naked of all hair and so enticing with its tattooed arabesques of henna. Her body signalled, 'Take me,' begging with every gesture to be pulled open and probed by her lover.

Humayun rubbed herself roughly up against Moses,

206

like a cat in heat. She dropped to her knees slowly, just brushing with her cheek his yearning penis as she sank. Her hands in his, she pulled him down to the grass with her and made him assume the reclining position of the bronze lady. With her back to him, while resting on her haunches, she bent over, affording Moses one very sensual view of her. Her mass of red-gold hair was falling about her shoulders and over her bare back, accentuating the roundness of her exposed bottom and the shaded cleft between the cheeks. He pulled the cheeks apart, none too gently. He viewed her spread open from her anus to the sensuous moist lips of her cunt, which he swiftly opened with probing fingers to find her clitoris.

Moses sensed Humayun full of lust for him. Lust gave her voice its husky, sensual throb as she said, 'No, no more, not yet.'

She slithered in one sensuous movement onto her side and up against his body. 'Promise you will do everything that I tell you?'

'How could I not?' he answered, already lost to her in lust, alert to her every demand.

Her body tight against his, her arms around his neck, she kissed him. First an earlobe, then his mouth. Lightly, gently, soft as the whisper of a butterfly's wings. She caressed with her lips the other earlobe, and placed a more seductive kiss on his chin. She moved her lips to his neck and on one side to just under his ear, to kiss him there. She licked her wet, sensuous tongue across his neck and kissed him once again under the ear. She passed her pointed tongue across his shoulder to mouth him in the crack where his arm met the side of his body. When she lifted his arm and kissed him in its pit, she felt a spasm vibrate in his chest, heard a sob escape him, and a barely audible muttering, 'Oh, God, God.' She smiled to herself: he was lost to her. She would enslave him further.

She slid on top of him and moved her lips to one of his nipples and licked it. Around and around, lightly scarcely touching before she closed her teeth over the small tip and sucked. She hungered now for his cock. Huge and full, it throbbed between her legs. But she held back. No, she would not let him in. As she straddled the phallus she craved, she squeezed it tightly between her legs as she moved her mouth to the other nipple and sucked it sensuously.

Hungrily, greedily, she reached up and put her arms around his neck, and they kissed with open mouths. Just their tongues played with each other now, while all the time she felt what she really wanted pressed tight against her cunt.

Humayun roughly tore her lips from his to kiss him on his chest. She slid down his body and ran her tongue around the inside of his navel, moistening it with her saliva. Next her lips tracked a dewy trail down to the black mass of pubic hair. Humayun sighed and rubbed her lips and the snub of her nose in his crisp fluff. Oh, the wonderful, raunchy tang of him! Her lips found the base of his penis, and, taking his hot, hard phallus in her hands, she lifted it to kiss the under part. In spite of herself, she felt again the mystery of his dark masculinity. Moses had a fine scrotum which she adored. She began sucking. She took one ball in her mouth and rolled it around, sucked deep and hard on it. He was on the edge of coming, she knew.

She found his hands with hers, and as she stood she pulled him with her. 'Take me into the house,' she ordered huskily. And he swept her up in his dark, cradling arms.

Chapter 10

'Will you marry me? Will you come away with me and be my wife? If happiness can be promised anyone, I promise you we'll be happy. Your life needn't add up to being only a sexual slave to Rashid. I want to live with you and show you that there are other worlds to see and ways to live beyond the luxurious prison Rashid keeps you in.'

'No. Do you think I do not know already your other worlds?'

The coldness in her voice when she so emphatically rejected his offer surprised Moses.

'Why deny us a life together?' he asked. 'I know you love me, you can't tell me that you don't. I saw it in your eyes this morning in the garden. And how many times in these last hours together have you told me you loved me? Don't pretend that was merely lust speaking. I know better.'

'I don't deny I love you, Moses. But sexual slaves don't marry their masters, love or no love.'

'But you are not my sexual slave, Humayun,' he declared. Did she really think him capable of setting up such a bond?

She began to laugh, it was a wicked laugh. 'No, my dearest man, you have it wrong. It is you who are my sexual slave; I am the master.'

'That's not true, I have never been anyone's slave, sexual or otherwise,' he snapped back at her.

'Don't pursue this, Moses,' she said, a note of annoyance in her voice as she sat up in bed and switched on the lamp on the table next to her.

'Not pursue it? But I must. How can I allow you to think of me in that way? It's simply not true.'

Humayun rose from the bed and, taking him by the hand, pulled him across it. He rose reluctantly and stood next to her. She slid her arms around his waist and sensuously caressed his body with hers until he succumbed to her embraces and enfolded her in his arms. Only then did she speak.

'I love you, Moses, in ways I have denied other men. I have never known a better, kinder man, nor one I felt more drawn to. That's very special, but still not enough for me. The love you offer me is dim and ponderous in the light of the erotic love I feel for you, and the sexual excitement I gather from the life I lead. I love you far more profoundly as my sexual slave. Accept what you are in my life, and that it is all you can ever be.' He began to speak, but she silenced him with a finger over his lips. 'No, please, let me say what I have to say, and then you can speak.'

She walked him, still in her embrace, across the room to her dressing table, where she took a navy blue silk robe lying across the bench in front of it and held it up for him to slip into. She tied the sash and pressed her cheek against the side of his face. Then she slipped into a sheer, silver silk kimono; its sleeves were embroidered with cranes whose voluptuous outstretched wings were sewn in gold thread laced with diamond chips. She sat down at the dressing table and handed him a silver-backed hairbrush. He obediently began brushing her hair, all the while looking into her face in the mirror. She pulled the stopper from a bottle of Coco and dabbed the scent behind her ears. After replacing it, she clipped the emerald doves on her ears and spoke, surprising herself at the twinge of sadness she was feeling.

'I listened very carefully during dinner when you spoke to me about your life, your family, and the influences that have moulded you into the man you are. I understand now what makes you so different from most men I have met. You and I do not only live in different worlds and cultures. We are separated by basic beliefs, like the big truths and realities of life. We can love each other for a few hours on occasion in spite of our differences, because we are the other side of the coin, the complement to each other's souls. But more than that is asking too much. We have travelled too far down our different paths to change direction for each other, especially since we are very happy in the lives we live without each other. Moses, we must face that truth together, here and now, and go on happily in spite of it. Otherwise each of us will destroy the other. You must see that?'

'I can't agree that what we have together can't be built on, anymore than I can agree with being just your sexual slave.'

She felt the steady strokes of the silver-backed brush going through her hair and it soothed her ruffled feelings. There was something in his voice, a subtle change that she sensed. A lack of conviction. She had her moment, and she knew she must press on and do the deed.

'Of course it is true that we could never run away

together and make it work. Of course you are enslaved to me sexually, and you must face the fact that I have driven you slowly and methodically into that role.

'It is you who wants to take me away from Rashid and my life at Oda Lala's, not I. You who cannot understand that I can be happy as a sexual slave to Rashid and have no desire to be free. You see that as some sort of crime on Rashid's part. Maybe in law it is. Maybe most people would call it a crime. But not me, because I am a willing victim. I am amoral. I accept that my kind of slavery still exists. Why should I care even that there are victims of it who may not be willing? I believe it is up to them to find their way out of it, if that's what they want. I have seen that look of determination on your face to show me your better way to live as a free woman. It is what has driven me to enslave you sexually. You know now what it is to be bound. I've tapped into that vein of evil in you that tells you to submit, surrender, be mastered by oblivion. I have made you, while in the throes of sexual madness, drop every one of your moral stands and revel in the nothingness of sexual ecstasy. Exhibiting our sexual trysts before voyeurs. Orgies where you suddenly found yourself with other men, who helped themselves to you while I looked on. And the heterosexual ones that went on for days. The whip, the bonds. And the fire in your heart that showed in your eyes and your actions when you watched other men take command of me and deliver me into sexual oblivion. And always you came back for more. You have fallen in love with me for it. And you claim not to be my sexual slave?'

She said all this while staring hard at Moses in the mirror, and now she turned around on the bench and

212

wrenched the hairbrush from his hand. It flew across the room. With passionate strength she grabbed him by the wrists and pulled him to his knees in front of her.

'You have to accept that from the moment you came to me I saw love in you, and that some of it rubbed off on me. But it has not changed me in the least. I learned at once to accept you for what you are. I wondered about your sexuality. Were you pure? Celibate? You gave that appearance, and I thought it might be so. I asked nothing. I took you on wanting – as Rashid did – to give you the joy of sex, the fun, the ecstasy we sensed you needed and lacked.

'Oh, I have taken great sexual satisfaction with you. I enjoyed the love. But there have been many times when you have left my bed, late at night, lying there freshly bathed between the cool, smooth sheets, I have made love to myself. I would start by stroking my hair and then my shoulders. I would hold these full breasts,' she opened her kimono and with one hand fondled herself, while still clasping him tightly by the wrist with the other, 'in my hands and cup them, squeeze them, take the saliva from my mouth and spread it over my nipples with my fingers. I would squirm with desire and then masturbate. Come again and again, until the spasms were so great they exhausted me. Only then could I sleep.

'In the morning I would wake still wet and slippery between my legs and think how ridiculous it was. I knew that men wanted me, that you wanted me, and it didn't stop me wanting a stranger. One particular time, after a night such as that, and one when we had made love all the day before in that little hotel in Bodrum, and you had confessed that you loved me and

213

wanted to live with me, and had asked me to think about it, then reluctantly left for Istanbul, I was delighted, maybe even a little in love. But it never stilled my sexual craving, or stopped me from masturbating or from considering several sexy-looking men in the port who pursued me the following day. I was there waiting for Rashid, who was to arrive in three days' time. I accepted none of the strangers as lovers. The thought of picking up a stranger not at the behest of Rashid repelled me.

'During the lonely nights that followed I pleasured myself with fantasies. But not fantasies of a married life with you. You only figured in them when I wondered which new areas of sexuality we might trespass in together. Those nights I came so completely and achieved such release that I would call out into the dark. Often I had to stifle my passion by putting my fist in my mouth and biting hard on my knuckles. The scream still in my head, beads of perspiration on my forehead, my body taut like a violin string, I would continue, and come again and again.

'The second night after you had left me was no different. I came and the huge wet warmth flowed over my fingers and between my widespread legs. I writhed, jerking my head from side to side with the agony and the bliss of orgasm, moaning softly from the pleasure of it. Then I saw him bending over me. He was a tall, heavyset man. Turkish, about fifty years old. He had slipped into the room through the unlocked door. He had been watching me for I don't know how long. I reached for the sheet to cover my nakedness and, taking my clenched fist from my mouth, I began to speak.

'But he put his hand gently over my lips and said, "Don't be frightened. I have been watching you in the light of the open door. You are wonderful. I have never seen anyone like you. So beautiful, such craving. I have heard you for two nights from my room next door. I will make you much happier." '

'The man wore nothing but a pair of trousers. He undid the fly and dropped them. He was massively erect. I removed the sheet without thought or hesitation. He slid his hand between my legs. When he found me moist and ready for him, he mounted me with an urgency and violence that thrilled me. He said nothing more, just pulled my legs wide apart until they ached and they straddled his shoulders, and then he poun . . .'

'No, no more. I don't want to hear this,' Moses said in a voice of anguish. And he tried to struggle to his feet. But she was determined to be heard, and now, once again, her hands around his wrists forced him to remain where he was.

'I insist you hear me out. I listened to you and the story of your life without protest. This is only one small incident in my life and *you will* listen. I need you to know that he pounded mercilessly into me again and again before he came. Exhausted he lay down next to me, this rough, uncouth faceless man. He took me in his arms and rocked me back and forth, and stroked my hair and cried because he had come too quickly and wanted more for both of us. All that took place in the darkness of the room. I never really saw him, only his outline. I could hardly believe what had happened. It was outrageous yet thrilling. He had ignited in me the arid flame of sex. He was right, he wanted to give more cock, I to take it. For as long as it lasted his was

215

wonderful, even if it was over for him almost as soon as it began. I was caught up in the mystery of being violated by a man I could not know, and it was new and thrilling to me. He asked me to wait and not to move. I had to say I could hardly wait for his return. I found I was reaching inside myself with searching fingers, trying to simulate the thick cock I had had so briefly. Not many minutes later he returned and slid onto the bed next to me. Then the door opened and two more men slipped quietly into the room. Moses, I did not protest . . . not then, nor when they switched on the bedside lamp and threw a silk scarf over it to take the harshness of the light away. It was as if we had agreed on silence. The man who had fucked me was a huge man with a not unkind face; the other two men were in their twenties, with brooding, handsome, dark sexual looks. Women fantasise about being taken by such men. One went to the door and bolted it. They stripped. They were young and virile and hungry for a woman. I wasn't frightened. I only squirmed out of the arms of the older man, wanting to switch off the light. They mistook it for fright, and one of them caught me from behind. He held me by slipping his arms around me, and clasped me by the breasts. I felt him, his nakedness, his stiffness pressed between the cheeks of my bottom, and he whispered. "Please don't cry out. My father, my brother and I, we have been listening to you in the night, whimpering for love."

' "The light, turn off the light," was all I could reply to him. I don't think at that point they understood that there was to be no struggle on my part. The young man laid me on the bed next to the father. The other son went to the chest of drawers. With some of my own clothing they tied down my hands and fixed a gag

216

across my mouth. Then they did as I asked: they switched off the light.'

'I don't want to hear all this,' Moses cut in. 'I know what you will say of them. I know.'

'But I need to know I have told it all to you, Moses. You must hear it, all of it.'

'Humayun, I—' said Moses, but she silenced him.

'The father fondled my breasts, kissed them. He was randy. He pulled and bit into my nipples while the two sons took turns fucking me. They were marvellous young studs who did not brutalise me. The first young man was a long time at his task, and his constant thrusts in and out of me were all that I wanted then. I felt the father and the other son kissing and sucking my breasts and clitoris. It just enhanced the power of my orgasms and their steady flow. They understood, at last, that I was not resisting, but sharing their lust. The second son released the gag in my mouth. I had hardly gasped before he replaced it with his penis. He moved it in and out once or twice. That was all that was necessary for him to understand. He released the bonds on my hands and I felt myself take him wholly down my throat. I sucked him off as he had never believed possible, while his brother came. The father slipped on top of me, full of sperm again and rampant, while the brothers lay momentarily exhausted on either side of me.

'Just as daylight broke, the father rose from the bed and kissed me tenderly, tears brimming in his eyes and words on the tip of his tongue that were better unsaid. The emotion was there and told it all. Sometime later the two sons kissed me and cautiously slipped out of the room. That afternoon a large bouquet of flowers arrived without a card. And Rashid came back a few hours later.'

That Moses was shattered was so evident from the expression on his face that Humayun felt compelled to look away. She removed her hands from his wrists and then once again looked him straight in the eyes, as she had during her compulsive erotic confession. He rose from his knees and stood over her.

'Why did you have to tell me all that? It was so . . . sordid, so depraved,' he said.

Humayun heard his words and was disappointed. She had not expected a different reaction from Moses. Yet, in her heart she had hoped for something else. She rose from the dressing-table bench. Gathering her kimono around her, she slipped her arm through his and walked with him back to the foot of the bed, where they sat down together.

'There is a footnote to that tale, Moses. When Rashid arrived the very first thing I did was to tell him the story I have just told you. No more, no less. I had experienced something new and thrilling, and had learned something more about my own sexual nature. I wanted to share it with him. He no more found it sordid and depraved than I did. He simply called on the man and invited him and his sons to dinner. Of course, when they saw who Rashid was, they accepted at once. And after dinner we indulged the interest that had brought us together.

'You see, my dearest Moses, having you listen to my tale, one you didn't want to hear, has forced us both to face the truth. I am a sexual adventuress and I don't want to be anything else, and you see that as sordid and depraved. There is no future for us, Moses, except to be together at those times when your raw instincts

218

are set free, and you are prepared for a few hours to enjoy being my sexual slave. Times when we can love each other for who we are and what we are. Times when neither of us has to pretend to be something we are not.'

'Then you can only see ours as an impossible love.' Moses's question turned into a statement even as he framed it.

'Well, don't you?'

He hesitated before he answered, trying desperately to lie to himself. But it was far too late for lies. His soul was no longer so blinded by love that he saw nothing. Her tale had restored his sight. His eyes and his heart were open to the truth about Humayun and himself. He looked at her and his heart skipped a beat. He stroked her hair and traced her lips with his finger. He opened her kimono and caressed the tantalisingly pretty, henna-coloured designs tatooed around the nimbus of each nipple. Then he tilted her chin up, looked into the emerald green of her eyes and answered her.

'Yes, but something deep, something genuine, even if it has to be impossible love. I think you will have to agree with that.'

'Without doubt,' she answered.

Pierced to the quick, she winced somewhere deep inside. She was scarcely able to hold back the cry that gathered within her. No woman, she thought, had ever made a greater sacrifice for love than she had for Rashid and for Moses. She had done as Rashid asked, and prayed that she would never again have to suffer or inflict such pain.

She bit the inside of her lip until she felt a trickle of her blood on her tongue. The flow seemed to staunch

219

her acute emotional anguish.

They remained facing each other, still on the end of the bed. Life-like sculptures, a hollow man and woman whose souls had been whipped to death. An awkward silence followed. It lasted several minutes and seemed to Humayun to demand to be broken. They needed something to breathe life into them, to return them to the roles that, accepted now, they would play, she imagined, each to the other, for the remainder of their lives.

Humayun understood instinctively what she must do – entice him into a fresh and exciting sexual exploit. She remained silent but engaged him with demanding eyes. When she rose from the foot of the bed he followed. As she raised her arms, a seductive smile formed on her lips. She parted them and allowed her tongue slowly to trace on them a moist sensuous gloss. Her motions set up a voluptuous ripple in her sleeves of sparkling embroidered wings. She opened her kimono.

He sighed. Her majestic charisma slowly drew him to her. She was the most perfect voluptuary. Enchanted, he opened his robe to let it fall around his feet. She was a feast for his eyes. He began nibbling at her breasts, licking her mound. She teased him into action by slithering her body snake-like up against him. The scent of Coco, blending with the faint musk from her body, accosted his senses and made him dizzy with desire. He placed a hand around her neck and pulled her head to his, his lips upon hers. His other hand sought between her legs for her vaginal lips and caressed the moist slit he loved so passionately. She enveloped him in her winged sleeves and dressing gown. All thought evaporated from them. Lust ignited their skins. A sexual flame flickered into blazing life for them, and they were happy. Pleasure followed and yielded to bliss. They forgot the world, themselves, and passed a night suspended as if floating between sexual heaven and hell.

Rashid was more amused by this mysterious Ethiopian lady than he had been by anyone for a long time. He had seen her only once, under such bizarre circumstances. But when he had woken up and she was gone she had left behind a new sparkle in his life. Humayun, too, had often done the same for him, gladdened his heart. She still did. Mirella also was able to amuse him, but not in the same way as the other two women. There was an undercurrent of hatred he bore for Mirella's ancestors and her own reticence in not committing herself to him that made her more fascinating than amusing. He would always have his special relationship with Mirella. But she would never be totally his. She wore Adam's love for her like a protective vest, to stop herself from submitting completely to him. Rashid smiled to himself. Like his great-grandfather before him, who had been unable to tame the Kadin Roxelana Oujie, Mirella's great-grandmother and benefactress, he felt confined to an always tenuous and constantly changing part in Mirella's life. It was almost, though not quite, enough. Everything within him demanded that he try to bring her to a complete submission.

Concorde had started its long descent. Rashid was delighted by his own boyish enthusiasm at the prospect of seeing his exotic black beauty again. He smiled to himself, thinking of her voice on the telephone several hours before.

'Is this my Turkish delight?' had been her first words to him. He had replied with laughter. Though familiar with western habits of speech, Rashid delighted in the childish charm of her cheekily converting him into a box of candy. The literal meaning of her phrase tickled him. It was odd, an Ethiopian teasing a Turk in so thoroughly western a way.

Rashid had recognised her voice immediately.

'Oh, it's you,' he replied, 'I was beginning to think I hadn't given satisfaction.'

'And what made you think that?'

'Most women don't wait weeks before chasing after me.'

'I am not most women.'

'I had noticed. Now what can I do for you?'

'You know very well what you can do for me. But you would have to come to Paris to do it. Are you free?'

'That depends.'

'On money, I suppose.'

'You suppose right. On money. But there are other considerations.'

'Like what?'

'Like, how much you want me. And for how long, and when, and where.'

'Haven't you forgotten something? The "how much will you pay?"'

Rashid had snapped his fingers and thought it dumb to have slipped in playing his role of money-grabbing gigolo. He quickly retrieved the situation. 'Hardly. I make my price after I hear what you want. Had you forgotten?'

'Paris, tonight, for two days. A room at the Ritz,'she had declared. He had sensed a note of irritation in her voice and that had spurred him on.

'That's awfully short notice. I would have to disappoint someone here to satisfy you. That's poor business but I might do it if you make it worth my while.'

A moment of hesitation on her part. He had waited, and then finally she had answered him, 'Spoken like a perfect whore. Your arrogance, I assure you, is difficult to overlook, but it appears to come with the package.'

Rashid had raised an eyebrow at her bitchiness, but he relished every move in the game he was playing with her. He wondered what she would do when she found out who he was. Would she tolerate his stringing her along in her mistaken assumption that he was a toy boy?

'I'll pay the same as before,' she continued. 'A thousand dollars a day, and your air fare, economy class.'

He had begun to scoff at 'economy,' then stopped abruptly. She might hang up. 'Don't be ridiculous. I'll be on Concorde, the flight that leaves Kennedy at one o'clock this afternoon. It arrives at 22:45 Paris time. My price is $10,000 plus the Concorde round-trip air fare. You should arrange for the ticket to be paid for by the time I pick it up at the Concorde ticket counter at Kennedy Airport. My money is to be paid upon my arrival. For that you get me for three days. I come with a guarantee to make them memorable. Take it or leave it.'

'Room 921. Bring a dress suit,' had been her reply. He detected a tremor that was either in the electronics or in her voice, not there before, and then a click in his ear and the empty drone of the disconnected telephone.

Rashid looked at his reflection in Concorde's window, and was pleased by the excitement he saw in his face. He ran his fingers through his hair and was delighted by his own sensual good looks, surprised that he wanted her to want him beyond anything or anyone in the world, that he wanted her to be devastated by his beauty and his sexual prowess. He smiled at his image in the glass. How remarkable he thought, that he should be so smitten by this woman who wanted to pay for his sexual services. He reached up and switched off the small stream of light from the reading lamp above, and his image was swallowed into the blackness beyond the pane.

He sat in his pocket of darkness. How satisfying it would be when the mysterious unnamed woman he called Sheba would take him between her lips and slowly fill her mouth with every last centimetre of him. How she would come with every pull of her mouth on him. How he would go down deep into the small of her throat. Oh, the tightness of her lips around him, the wetness and softness of the inside of her mouth as she worked on him. She would leave him shiny, covered with her moistness, and have to draw back and admire the gleaming energy of his erection throbbing at her.

She would say things to him in admiration. 'If she placed him on a pedestal, he would be more beautiful than any Greek God. How she adored the very tang of his skin. How she wanted the ambrosia of his sperm.'

He imagined her returning to his penis, wanting to absorb him into her mouth. Her tongue would play with the open eye at the tip of his phallus. She would bring him to the exquisite edge of orgasm. He wanted her to love and adore him.

He thought of her body, the hardness of nipples that

ached to be sucked and kissed. How wet with come she would be between her legs, but how she would wait because she was not through making love to him. She would find his buttocks as sensual and as sexual as his phallus and she would spread them and after kissing, licking and caressing with all her passion on his testes she would find his anus and play with that secret, tight and puckered place. Kissing it and the inside of his cheeks, putting her tongue over it, she would lose herself in an animal tenderness for him. And still she would not be done with him.

He could bear such imaginings no longer. A stack of magazines had been lying on the chair next to him for hours but he had never bothered to look at them. Now, he picked them up as a distraction, something to cool down his sexual fantasies.

He looked through the pile of magazines. He was stunned. She figured on the covers of more than one of the seven coloured glossies. Her name was not Sheba, it was Tana Dabra Magdala Makoum. She was not, as he had imagined, one of the upper-class Ethiopians who, having robbed the treasury, escaped to the West before the coup, and now furnished herself with male lovers at the expense of some aged and impotent westerner. It was all there, page after page of her and a life story that was perfect magazine fodder.

'Mr Sharif, Mr Sharif. Excuse me but all the passengers have left the plane, and you must too, sir.'

Rashid finally acknowledged the steward when he tapped Rashid on the shoulder. 'Mr Sharif': he had forgotten that was the name he had been using, the one she had given him that he had pretended she had guessed correctly to be his. He had been so engrossed in the photographs and a profile and several short articles about her that he had missed the lights of Paris below him and had been unaware of their landing.

One fact about her had riveted his attention. She had been the Ethiopian woman who had been linked in business with Adam Corey. She was said to be indirectly responsible for the magnificent financial coup which launched him into the Dr Armand Hammar league vis-à-vis geopolitics in business. Well aware of Adam's influence and connection with Ethiopia, he had toyed with the idea of asking Adam to help him find the mysterious woman he called Sheba when the detectives he had hired had failed. Something had prevented the appeal to Adam. He had wanted to find her himself.

It was coincidence on a grand scale now to have been picked up by her. To have been taken for a male prostitute, a successful gigolo, he had found amusing, and nothing more – until he had bedded her. Then feelings had invaded his performance as paid stud. She fascinated him, and when she reversed roles with him and took his body over and made love to it, she ran the gamut of passion and gave everything she had. In the final hours of their sexual encounter he had once again taken over. He tamed her wild, pagan, sometimes primitive sexuality with his polished sexual performance. As he did so, he had begun to sense that something more than sex was happening to them. When he awakened, she was gone. He was disappointed. He had found it doubly amusing when he had counted the money and found she had left him an extra hundred dollars. A tip. At the time he had simply slotted her into his pigeon hole for special one night stands – until several days passed by and he realised that he had been waiting for the telephone to ring. When she did not call the charity of his choice was deprived of the money she had paid him. He gave it instead to the best detective agency in Paris, instructing them to find her.

Rashid thanked the steward. Walking through the plane towards the exit he found it difficult to blot out the photographs of his Sheba. 'No,' he said to himself, 'not my Sheba, but my Tana.' She was far more magnificent than he had remembered. The intelligence, fire and passion in her face were far more pronounced and enthralling. The body, long and lean like that of a young boy, yet utterly feminine, was all cunt and lips and mouth, modest breasts crowned by large and luscious black nipples. All of this he had made love to, with the bravado of a young buck, aiming to be reckoned worth the thousand dollars she had paid him to play stud to her hungry, frustrated lady.

He bypassed the other passengers on his flight waiting for luggage. He almost never travelled with the burden of baggage. He was greeted by several of the Customs men and waved through without even stopping. He was recognised at once by the immigration man and his passport was stamped. He had escaped ordeal by airport. He was on his way to her, at the Ritz. His chauffeur was waiting for him. Rashid gravitated towards the man, until he saw Tana Dabra Ras Magdala Makoum about a hundred yards away, regally walking in his direction. She was scanning the dwindling crowd for him. Was that his heart missing a beat? She was so splendid looking. His friend the Princess Eirene had warned him often enough. 'It only takes a minute, just one little minute, to fall truly in love, and find the other side of yourself.' It had caught up with him, his moment, his one minute, was upon him.

He waved his chauffeur away, realising he must not yield her his real identity . . . not yet. He walked towards her. She looked very chic, far more so than the night she had picked him up. Her hair was pulled back severely into a glamorous twist at the nape of her neck. Large gold loops in her ears added a glow to the stunning features of her face. She wore a sludge grey silk blouse with large pointed revers, the V neckline plunging between her small breasts nearly to her waist. Voluptuous and alluring balloon sleeves softened her look. The huge and magnificent ruby surrounded by sapphires upon her slender neck gleamed in its price-less beauty and elegance. With every long stride she took, her hip hugging, wide, grey silk trousers swirled rakishly around her legs.

He raised his arm and waved, trying for her atten-tion, and quickened his step. She saw him, and he caught the relief in her face, and the joy. She raised a hand and placed it over her heart as if to still its beating, and her smile broadened as she waved back at him. They hurried towards each other weaving around other passengers who stood between them in the noisy, brightly lit terminal. Then they stood in front of each other, face to face. He almost swept her into his arms, wanting to kiss and crush her into himself. He hesitated.

'I didn't expect to be met,' he murmured.

'It was a spur of the moment decision to come.'

Further words failed them both. He took her in his arms and kissed her with passion and tenderness. She gave in to his kisses and, when they parted, the urgency in his voice said it all for both of them.

'You have a car? Good.'

With arms around each other's shoulders they hurried into the waiting car, a rather vulgar, stretch limousine with black tinted glass. Neither one of them could wait. They kissed and cuddled, but when he began to open her blouse, she stopped him with a hand placed gently on his wrist. She took an envelope from her handbag and slid it into his jacket pocket lying on the footrest in front of them.

'As promised. It's best to get the business part out of the way and forget about it.'

Again, Rashid had almost forgotten his role, so impassioned by her was he. His heart was touched, not by the direction she tried to apply to the situation, but by her looking away from him while she did it, yet continuing to stroke the hair at the nape of his neck, seemingly unable to let him out of her hands.

'I couldn't agree more,' was all he answered, as he ran the zipper on the side of her bony hip slowly down and raised her off the seat enough to slide the soft silk to her thighs. He kissed and caressed, licked and teased her lovingly, and she answered him with whimpers of pleasure until he dressed her again and held her in his arms and they sat in silence. Now, with the windows down, they watched the lights of Paris flash by while they waited impatiently to arrive at the Ritz.

As they rounded the Place Vendôme, he tapped the window dividing the chauffeur from them. It slid down noiselessly, and he asked the driver to stop the car.

'You go up ahead of me,' he then told Tana Dabra. 'There is something I want to pick up.'

'If it's your clothes, a valise arrived with your things late this afternoon.'

'Oh, good. No, just a few special things for us.' And he was gone before she could say another word.

A half hour later, when she opened the door to the suite, he took her quite by surprise. He made his entry, attended by several pageboys carrying beautifully wrapped parcels stacked one upon the other and several flower arrangements, including four dozen white roses in a Lalique vase, two dozen sprays of white moth orchids in a rock crystal bowl. One boy bore a silver urn chilling two bottles of Roederer Cristal, and a kilo of the best Beluga chilling on ice in a large bowl of ornate silver.

She was unable to speak until he had shooed all the pages from the room. He picked up one box and, taking her by the hand, led her to the Louis Phillipe settee where he sat her down next to him. He opened a five pound box of white Belgian chocolates. He offered her one, which she took, and then he spoke.

'My greatest vice. But I am beginning to think you could become an even greater threat to my virtue than these.' He then ate two of the chocolates with emphatic delight.

He placed the box on the settee and pulled her along by the hand towards the bedroom. She had changed into a black silk kaftan that opened down the front in a series of small suchet braid buttons. Slowly, one by one, he opened them and savoured what he saw.

In turn she undressed him slowly, touched and caressed him, trembled at the sight of his complete nudity, the passion for him released in her.

'I am going to take that bowl of flowers off the table, and then I want you to stand up on it.'

He did as he was told and, when he was up on the round pedestal table set in the centre of the all-white bedroom, his rampant penis was in a direct line with Tana Dabra's mouth. He was magnificent, so handsome. He had so much charismatic power over her she found it difficult to hold back from making love to him. But that was not after all what he was there for. She had to remind herself that she was paying for his services, she was in command, he was nothing more than a male prostitute, a human machine hired to provide love making.

She walked around the table admiring him lustily. His penis responded to her beauty. Her long black hair was hanging loose over her shoulders; she stalked around the table in nothing but high-heeled shoes, black stockings and garter belt. Her long dusky limbs, slimness, hard and pointed nipples with their large black aureole against the glowing darkness of her body, seemed to ooze depraved sexuality. Even her face, with its perfectly chiselled, symmetrical features, tantalised him erotically. His memory of her voluptuous fleshy vaginal lips, mutilated by the series of evenly spaced holes pierced through them long ago, aroused anticipation of the erotic games the future would hold for them. The enlarged clitoris, what joy it would give him to make love to her there. Make love – those were strange words for him, he realised – but they were jettisoned from his mind when she gripped his ankles and prised his legs further apart.

'Oh, my girl, the things I am going to do to you before this day is over. I shall whip you with sex until you beg for mercy.'

He was there to do just that, and that was what she wanted, what she had imported him from New York to do. Then why did she resent him? Was it his slight impudence, the self-assured attitude he exuded? He was hers to command, and yet there were moments when she felt he was in control of their liaison. And there was a look in his eyes, at one moment a softness, a generosity of spirit towards her, and in the next moment possession and lust. He was a lady killer, a supreme seducer of women, she thought. Worth his price, so long as love was left out of it.

Chapter 11

She walked around the bedroom as if seeing it for the first time. It appeared to her in the midday sunlight as much larger, the sculpted plasterwork ceiling much higher. She had thought the all-white room bathed in soft lamplight the night before seductively beautiful, a perfect background to soften the intense carnal hunger she felt for her paid lover. Not so in daylight. The room was something much more than just beautiful. And might not she and her gigolo be much more than a pair of libertines devouring each other in the name of Eros?

Tana Dabra touched the white damask patterned silk of the walls, ran her hand across the polished, tinted oak of the wainscoting below it. She touched the silk of a lampshade, switched the lamp on and then off, and ran her hand languidly across the marble table top it rested upon. She opened the French windows and the noise of the traffic whirling around the Place Vendôme thundered into the room. She closed it at once: why should the essence of the room and what had passed there the night before be disturbed by the reality of the world beyond? She drew back the sheer white, silk chiffon curtain with one hand and for a few minutes peered through the glass at the monument opposite her windows, the elegant round of eighteenth-century buildings in the Place Vendôme, and at the more affluent citizens, rushing from rendez-vous to rendezvous.

She let the curtain fall and turned her back to the window. She viewed the room, wanting every detail of it etched unforgettably in her mind. Something had awakened in Tana Dabra in that room during the night. She had sensed a hint of something similar with the man she called Sharif the other time she had been with him. But only sensed. This was real, a genuine feeling of sublime wholeness. For a woman who had, all her adult life, been doing a high-wire balancing act by shifting from being controlled to being in control, and who had as a result always felt fragmented, this new feeling of wholeness was inexplicably joyous and fulfilling. She felt free, easy and uncomplicated, full of physical pleasure for everything she could see and hear and smell and touch. He had triggered it, Sharif, from the moment she had seen him in the air terminal. All this was implicit in their erotic relationship, this and her wholeness. If something more were to grow out of the relationship, that was fine. If not, that was fine too. How could it be otherwise, given their positions and the circumstances of the relationship?

Tana Dabra walked across the room, and the scent of white roses, faint and romantic, inspired a smile. At the foot of the bed she scrunched up in her hands some of the rumpled white linen sheets and the white silk bed cover whose satiny tulip pattern seemed to bloom in her hands. She pressed her face into them. The faint aromas mingled: his Armani cologne, rumpled linen, her Coco perfume, the musk of sex, and the sweetness of chocolate, that made her extend her tongue as if to lick a satin tulip. She threw her head back and gave an enchanting throaty laugh. She turned around and, with the bed clothes straggling behind her from one hand, she moved across the floor to stand in front of the round pedestal table where she had had her lover stand like the living replica of God. How liberatingly 'wicked' she had felt walking around the table admiring him as a man, sexual machine, beauty. She dropped the bed linen to the floor and spanned the table with her arms till her hands gripped the far edges of it. She bent forward and laid her cheek gently on the table and remained thus for a few seconds.

Standing now, in the centre of the room, she crossed her arms over her breasts and ran her hands up and down her arms ever so gently in a kind of hugging of herself. It felt so good to be alive. As she turned to walk towards the black and white marble fireplace and pluck one of the white orchids from its arrangement in the rock crystal bowl on the mantel to pin in her hair, she saw him leaning against the door jamb of the sitting room. Tana Dabra felt suddenly embarrassed that he should catch her so romantically involved with the room and her feelings.

He remained silent and waited for her to say something. She watched him walk towards her, savouring him, handsome and elegant in his white crew neck jersey and casual Armani suit of putty-coloured cotton poplin, its sleeves pushed up above his wrists. She noted the yellow and white polka dot silk hankie decoratively flopping out of the breast pocket, the woven yellow canvas belt, silver-buckled, around his waist, the well-polished black shoes.

And now, after last night, she knew him to be more than elegant, a wit more than witty even, a connoisseur alike of women, sex, food and wine. The world of the gigolo was new to her: and she found it amazing that a man in that sort of work should be so princely and display such gallantry towards women as the man walking towards her had. It suddenly occurred to her that he must be a famous and extremely sought-after middle-aged toy boy. The scale of his fee should have told her that.

He slid one arm under hers and around her waist and pulled her deliberately, slowly into his arms. She felt herself melting into the embrace. She touched his cheeks with her fingertips. An Asiatic allure was in his eyes, along with mischief and something quite dangerous. Sexual ecstasy and promiscuity were trapped in the shape of his lips. Every feature was perfect and sensual, so handsome that any woman must fall for him. She was aware of that, just as she sensed in him a brave man, skilled, wily, charming and ruthless, a man who lived beyond the rules. It was all there in his face, that side of him that aspired to achievement, to ideals, but was controlled by a spirit working furiously within him. The way he moved from ferocity to charm and back, even that showed in his face. She found him scary – at once seductive and threatening – and imagined there were few women who would not succumb to the erotic about him, bound up as it was with menace.

He kissed her, eased her lips apart with his tongue, and crushed her to him until she lay weak and nearly limp in his arms. Then he carefully released her and, placing an arm around her, walked with her to the telephone and rang for their breakfast. He placed the receiver back in its rocker and his first words to her were, 'After breakfast we'll go shopping, Cartier's or

Van Cleef's, whichever you prefer. Then we'll parade around Paris like the lovers we are, and show off the lust and happiness we share in each other. Then we'll come back here and make love – passionate, erotic love that will make last night seem just an overture to paradise.'

They walked from the bedroom through to the sitting room, where there was a round table covered in snowy white damask, a bowl of white lilies in its centre. Placed in front of the French windows, overlooking the same view of the Place Vendôme she had seen from the bedroom windows, it was set for breakfast with silver and crystal, and white Limoges china. He picked up a tall, slender Lalique champagne flute stuffed to the brim with small, white pitted Italian peaches, and poured chilled champagne over them. Handing one to Tana Dabra, he remarked in a curious tone, 'You are very quiet this morning, have you nothing to say to me? Are you not as happy with me as I am with you? Have I displeased you in some way? What have I done to dull the love I saw in your face when you were memorising the bedroom where we discovered each other?'

His anxiety over her feelings calmed the disappointment she felt in him. The wholeness and love she was feeling for herself and for life in general included him – for the moment. She had no problem admitting that to herself or to him. She answered him frankly.

'I have a lot to say to you, and you make me very happy. And not even your greed can shatter what you saw in my face and I feel in my heart. It simply left me speechless to think that you should want me to reward you with a present for last night. Diamond studs, sapphire cufflinks, how many women have had to

237

reward you with a tip like that? I must be forgiven for my silence and my naïvety. You are the first man I have ever paid for, and I simply don't know the form.'

She touched the rim of her glass to his, and he began to laugh. He carefully removed the flute from her hand and placed it with his own on the table. Taking her hands in his, he held them while he calmed his mirth. And then an extraordinary change came over him: he found it difficult to hold back tears. He struggled with them for a few seconds before he smiled at her and said, 'I was not asking you to take me to the jeweller's. It is *I* who want to take you there. I am the one who feels humbled – by the love I feel for you. And I want to shower you with all that's beautiful in this world, in celebration of what we discovered together last night under the spell of Eros. My feeling for you is very strong, I thought you understood that.'

Tana Dabra had lowered her head in embarrassment, unable to look into his eyes while he confessed his love for her. When she raised it again, she smiled at him and said, 'I came to life in your arms as I have never done before. It was more than I could hope for, that you should feel the same and we should have a romance. When you mentioned the jeweller, I could only think that, if we were having a spellbound romance, it was my fantasy and your business. How was I to know otherwise?'

'This should be enough to tell you,' was his answer. The urgency and roughness with which he pulled her into his arms, and the passion with which he kissed her, did just that.

They drank their peach-flavoured champagne, and another glass and another, and he seduced Tana Dabra again with his appetite for sex. He double

238

locked the door before he laid her on the floor of the sitting room and teased her warm pink slit with the coolness of the white peaches as he slid them into her during their passionate kisses. One by one he sucked them from her, now covered in her own juices. They ate them while he told her of the many ways they would come together that night. She was out of control, his sexual protégée now, wanting everything he offered. He delighted in her lust, but he was a master seducer of women, able to transform the erotic seduction of Tana Dabra into a romantic affair, and hold her right where he wanted her.

Rashid was in love and wanted to marry her on impulse. He was dazzled by the feminine energy she exuded. Their love affair had begun compulsively as his love affairs always did. But this one had started out as no other ever had, and he was certain it would end in a happy marriage between them. Before Tana Dabra, and with the exception of Mirella, he had ensured that his affairs had always been short lived. Preoccupied with escaping, he believed that no matter how durable an affair might appear to be, the sooner it ended the better.

He draped the skirt of her mocha-coloured linen dress back down over her legs and helped her up off the cushions he had thrown from the sofa to the floor.

'Say you love me, Sheba,' he demanded.

'My name is Tana Dabra Ras Magdala Makoum, not Sheba. That is a lot of name, but I think there are other things, too, that you should know about me.'

'Fine. I want to know everything about you, just as I want you to know everything about me. But for the moment, just say you love me, and then we'll talk.'

239

'No. I don't think I dare do that,' she answered hesitantly.

'Why are you being sensible? That's not enough. We're two people who have got to run risks. Our being here together today proves you are a risk taker. You know how to throw over apple carts and leap off cliffs, and are as wild and free as I am. Commitments of the heart don't come easily to me. I don't know how to live inside a relationship, how to say I love you, how to open up and let you into my life. But my defences are down. Goddamn it, woman, say you love me, because I am going to marry you, Tana Dabra Ras Magdala Makoum, so you had better get used to the idea as quickly as I have got used to your name.'

They heard the key in the lock, and then a knock at the door. Rashid ran his fingers nervously through his thick, straight black hair. The knock came again. And the pair of lovers began to smile and then laugh at the timing of the intrusion. 'The bell has saved you, but not for long. Well, you just keep in mind what I have told you.' He gave her a quick hug on his way to unlocking the door, laughed good-humouredly at himself, and thought, 'Here I am at a moment of truth, and it's turning out more like some second-rate romantic farce. But this scene isn't played out yet, my girl.' He turned to her just before he opened the door to a brigade of waiters about to roll in the breakfast under silver-covered dishes, on portable tables covered in crisp white damask, and announced, 'My name is not Sharif. It's Rashid Lala Mustapha. Try that for size.' Then he pulled open the door. He turned back, glanced at her to see if his name had had any effect on her. It hadn't. The name meant nothing to her, and he realised that she thought she had had a proposal of

240

marriage from a gigolo. Yet again, in spite of the seriousness of his intentions, he smiled wryly at their situation.

They sat opposite each other and ate luscious, fresh, skinned, ripe purple figs. The waiters put the finishing touches to their Oeufs Carême before serving them: scrambled eggs mixed with diced goose liver, white chicken meat and truffles, filled in a flat puff pastry shell and garnished with lashings of sliced truffle, surrounded with a fine *demi-glace*. It was one of Rashid's favourite breakfast dishes. They shared that egg dish and another: lightly poached quails' eggs on a bed of thick, creamy spinach and long thin strips of crispy bacon. They ate their way through a pyramid of fresh, hot croissants, rich with butter, melting on the tongue. Their fruit preserve was raspberry and kirsch, which Rashid spooned out copiously on his croissant, and they drank cups not of coffee, but of steaming hot exquisitely blended China tea. They were ravenous and ate with gusto. Tana Dabra was yet again dazzled by the man sitting opposite her. She was trying to keep a cool head and stay in control, but she felt herself slipping further and further under his romantic spell.

Their conversation settled on Paris and the things and places they favoured most about the city. Waiters hovering over their meal denied them intimate speech with one another. Not a bad thing, she thought. Not so, he. Until she acknowledged love and agreed to marry him, nothing else in his life would be quite right. That seductive sweet laughter with which the Princess Eirene used to enchant her friends tinkled in his ear. Or so he imagined. How the Princess would laugh to see him smitten, longing for marital commitment, having to beg the woman of his choice to marry him.

241

Well, for years she had warned him that some woman might, one day, dangle him on the end of a long string. Yet still he would suffer only a fraction of the pain of unrequited love that he had inflicted on so many women.

At last they were alone, the table cleared except for a fresh pot of hot tea and a plate of thin, rich, dark chocolate-covered peppermint cream leaves, and a pedestal dish neatly draped with bunches of lightly caramelised white grapes. Rashid placed several chocolate leaves on a plate, and with the ornate silver grape scissors cut a small branch of grapes and placed it prettily by the leaves. Then he rose from his chair and walked around the table to Tana Dabra, kissed her lightly on the head and set it on the table in front of her. She reached up to touch his arm. A look of love flickered for a moment in her eyes. He avoided her hand discreetly. But she was aware that he had avoided it. Rashid had done that to provoke fear of loss in her, so that she might realise how important he already was in her life, hoping that fear would spur her on to say, yes, she loved him, she wanted to be his wife. Returning to his chair he placed several of the chocolate leaves on a plate in front of him. He placed a leaf on his tongue and then drank from the teacup, allowing the flavours to melt together. He ate several of the chocolates in that manner, never taking his eyes from Tana Dabra.

There should have been a kind of awkwardness about the silence that lay between them across the table, but there wasn't. That surprised him. He sensed at once that a magnificent silence was flowing through the veins of this most sensual and exotic woman, a silence such as he had rarely felt in any other living soul. He felt it extending to him, becoming as if another skin. And, instead of it oppressing him, he found it sexual and uplifting. It exuded a quality that was exciting yet peaceful. Mystery and intrigue, the ethereal, all these elements inhabited the profound silence of Tana Dabra. And Rashid knew he would never let her go: she was already an essential part of his life.

The silence had no effect on Tana Dabra, although she was grateful for it. It afforded her the opportunity of staying close to Rashid, and not having to explain her enormous attraction to this most beautiful yet menacing man. Not to him or to herself. She was still pained by his little ploy of not allowing her to make physical contact with him, pained and aware of how much more pain he could inflict upon her. Tana Dabra wished that she was more experienced and worldly in the ways of love, if for no other reason than to get it right with Rashid. Pain or not, in spite of his less than admirable way of living and working the life of the paid escort, there was something important going on between them. For the first time, she was in love, at last.

She pondered, 'Is this, then, what your life has been reduced to? That of a poseur for the world and its cameras, a black clothes hanger on a catwalk for haute-couture? A sex object to be ogled by the masses, kept safely in the public eye to preserve yourself from political revenge by your own countrymen? The only man ever to love you for yourself, and who wants to marry you, a paid lover? How can I say, yes, I love you, Rashid, when I don't even love myself or the life I'm leading? How can I say to a man I have just paid ten thousand dollars to make love to me for three days, that something is very wrong? We *are* better than this. We *can* use our minds as well as our bodies. We *can* rise above what and who we have become. But how, when I hardly understand what and who we are?' With his charismatic presence before her, and in the wake of the profound erotic ecstasy she was certain was shared by both of them, all those questions vanished. She was happy with him. They were happy. What could be the point of questioning what they had, or looking beyond the three days they were committed to?

She rose from her chair and took a small bunch of grapes from the pedestal dish on the table and walked around to Rashid. He pushed his chair back and she slipped onto his lap. She fed him a grape, then one to herself. The sweet, caramelised glaze crunched between her teeth, and then the succulent grape split and was delicious. She plucked another for Rashid and placed it between his lips. When it vanished into his mouth, she stole a kiss from him.

'What shall we do today?' she asked, a lovely happy smile playing on her lips.

'Make love, have more sex, see Paris, talk to each other, make more love. Behave the way Parisians are supposed to, just as we have been doing since you picked me up at the airport. Does that appeal to you?'

'Fine, just fine.' She plucked another grape and fed it to him, then whispered in his ear, 'I can feel myself becoming more Parisian every moment.'

'Then say you love me.'

She threw her head back and gave her seductive, light-hearted laugh. Her eyes twinkled, and she said in a throaty whisper, 'I love you.'

'Louder,' he demanded. She repeated the words

louder, and again, even louder, and threw her head back and gave him that same seductive laugh once more. He removed the bunch of grapes from her hand and placed them on the plate in front of him. Then he kissed both her hands and eased her off his lap, saying, 'I knew it. I knew you loved me. Come on, I want all Paris to know it.' And, taking her by the hand, he started for the door. He hardly gave her the time to get her jacket and her handbag. Once out of the suite of rooms, he pinned her against the wall in the corridor, and said, 'I promise you the most wonderful wedding any woman ever had.' He kissed her passionately.

She placed a hand on his arm: 'Did I say I would marry you? I said I loved you, and I do, and I don't say that lightly. In fact, you're the first man I have said that to. We have two more days together, and I don't want to think beyond that. I want to live and enjoy every minute of these three days we agreed to have together. I don't even know if a committed love is for me, whether I could be happy in a marriage. Let's take it as it comes, and let it go if we have to let it go.'

'But you do love me?'

'Yes, I do, that's what I told you.'

'Then you will marry me. You'll see. I am as sure of that as I am of anything.' He gathered her up in his arms and kissed her, pressing her to him until she went limp, dropping her handbag, the black and mocha checked linen jacket slipping off her shoulders.

Rashid retrieved her bag for her and, barely giving her time to recover, helped her on with her jacket and pulled her along by the hand. He laughingly turned around and said, 'That old, beat-up cliché, "There's no fool like an old fool", is getting to me. I feel almost

245

as young as you are, younger even. You're good for me, Tana Dabra, my Sheba.'

At last he slowed down to her pace and, with his arm through hers, they walked down the stairs and into the lobby of the Ritz. The concierge greeted Rashid effusively. The manager saw him and the two men shook hands. He snapped his fingers and, as from nowhere, the housekeeper materialised. Rashid exchanged greetings with her, while the manager asked, 'I had heard that you were a guest, sir. I hope all is to your satisfaction? May I offer you a *boutonnière*?' and the housekeeper presented a tiny exquisite white gardenia, which she pinned to his lapel. 'And for the lady, if it pleases her?' Tana Dabra accepted a small bunch of white violets, and allowed the housekeeper to pin it to her jacket. Tana Dabra watched the obvious fuss that was being made of Rashid, and was both puzzled and amused. She thought he was behaving more like a spoiled and pampered VIP than a handsome gigolo whose room was being paid for by a woman, in this case herself, and who was more than eclipsed by her escort.

Several guests turned to watch the couple as they walked towards the door. Tana Dabra suddenly felt vulnerable to the eyes of strangers, one of the things she could not get used to and enjoyed the least in her new role as celebrity mannequin.

'A telephone. I must get to a telephone for just a few minutes.' The manager offered to have one brought for Rashid. Or would he graciously use the manager's office? Rashid chose a settee in a secluded corner in the lobby, and he and Tana sat down.

'Do you mind?' he asked, kissing her hand that he seemed determined not to let go of.

'No, of course not. You're not my prisoner, you know. Just my lover. You seem very well known here, Rashid. Do you often stay at this hotel?'

'Sometimes. Yes, I suppose I do use the Ritz often.'

'Where else do your ladies keep you, Rashid?'

'In bed. Mostly in bed. The way you do,' he teased, and then laughed. He felt her bristle.

'Jealous of those other women?' he asked. 'You needn't be. I never asked one of them to marry me.'

Before she could answer, the telephone was brought to them. Rashid made his first call.

'How is she?'

Tana Dabra watched the change in his expression while he listened to the person on the end of the line.

'Why are you letting her suffer like that? All these hours in labour, she must be exhausted and in terrible pain. Can I speak to her? I am desolated not to be able to be with her.'

There was a long pause, and then his face lit up. 'My darling, what can I do to make this birth easier for you? I wish I could bear the pain for you. I wish I could hold you in my arms, caress your breasts and kiss you, and make love to you, ease your pain with ecstasy.'

Tana Dabra was shocked by what she heard. He was seducing a woman in labour, and with such panache that she herself was beginning to feel randy. She tried to pull away from him. He held her tight by the wrist. For several erotic minutes he continued his telephonic seduction. She blocked everything she was hearing from her mind and was forced to sit where she was, seething with anger for having been taken in by her lover, for believing that he loved her.

He replaced the receiver on its rocker and sat quietly for a few seconds. When he turned back to

Tana Dabra, she saw a sadness in his eyes. 'It's not my baby. She's not my wife. But she is an important woman in my life, and always will be. You'll have to learn to live with that. There are others. There will always be others, monogamy is not possible for me. But I don't believe it is for you either. I never thought marriage was for me until I met you. It never ever occurred to me to marry any of them. They know that. And now so do you. Did you hear her begin to scream? I find even the pain of giving birth erotic. I wanted so much to share this birth with her. She wouldn't have it, and I can understand why. I made love to her all through her pregnancy and found it thrilling. So did she, and so will we when you are carrying our baby. Why do you look so askance?'

'You were sexually seducing a woman in labour without realising it was natural to you, a part of your whole being. Being a whore comes naturally to you, and you will never give up wanting to seduce.'

'That's very astute of you, Tana Dabra. Except for one thing. It is being a libertine that is second nature to me, and the most important thing in my life. A libertine, dear, not a whore or a gigolo. I don't believe you have that quite worked out yet. You show me a man or a woman of any age who wants to surrender the urge to seduce, and I'll show you a dead person. The act of seduction is something I enjoy doing, whether it comes to anything or not. I had my first sexual experience at the age of ten, and it left me hungry for more, and women of all types, and it made me the libertine who is sitting here with you now, who is not afraid to tell you that I am grateful – and so should you be – that I am what I am. One more phone call, and we're off to conquer Paris.'

With that he drew her hand to his lips and kissed her fingers. Then he quickly grazed her cheek with his lips and whispered, 'It won't be easy, our life together, but it will always be new and fresh and an adventure, and we will build something wonderful out of our years together. Just you wait and see. My God, I can hardly believe my own words. Destiny has caught up with us, Tana Dabra. I pray to God we're strong enough to ride it out together.'

Oh, he was marvellous, thought Tana Dabra. Worth every penny. To live and make love, enter the world of sexual ravishment and depravity with. And to have him throw in romance for three days as well. A woman's dream, a fantasy come true. The gods must be blessing her for her riggishness and protecting her. Otherwise she might have met a man like Rashid and not seen him for what he was, and not paid him for her weakness. If he were not a middle-aged gigolo, she might fall in love with him and give herself hope for the open-ended future he had sketched for them. Where would she be then? Broken hearted, and at the mercy of his whims and fancies. Never. Three days would do just fine for her, thank you.

'I don't know about you,'she said, 'but I know I am strong enough for anything with you.' Then they both smiled at each other, and he dialled a telephone number.

'*Bonjour. Monsieur Orloffsky, s'il vous plaît.*' Then he switched into English. 'Serge, it's Rashid. Are we all set?' There was a pause in the conversation, and then Rashid spoke again, 'Do you think it's possible to bring our schedule forward to sometime this evening?' Another pause, then Rashid spoke again. 'That's just fine. Great. I assume you will be waiting in the usual place. Thanks, Serge.' After Rashid hung up, he turned to Tana Dabra, excitement and pleasure shining in his eyes.

'A surprise for you, for us.'

'Rashid, that's sweet of you, but one of the reasons that I hired you was to escort me to a black-tie affair this evening. We don't have to stay long, but we do have to make a spectacular entrance. I don't want to go, but I must.'

'It's a long time till this evening. Let's just see how our day goes.' Before she could say anything more, he had her on her feet and across the Ritz lobby.

At the entrance of the hotel, two chic French women greeted Rashid, and he introduced them to Tana Dabra. Then, for the first time, Tana Dabra wanted to know more about this man she had picked up. They were far from the sort of women who would ever know a gigolo, no matter how chic, successful and discreet he might be.

She was relieved when she and Rashid glanced only briefly in Cartier's and Van Cleef & Arpels' windows, and Rashid made no attempt to enter the shops. She was not surprised when both doormen greeted Rashid, but then, a few minutes later, was puzzled when he left her on the pavement to dash back and have a word with one of them. When he returned to her, all he said was, 'Just checking on closing time. If they are still open when we return, I might buy you a bauble. I like buying jewels for the women in my life.'

She didn't believe him. Well, she did and she didn't. She believed that he would select something for her, but wondered who would get the bill. He was all too generous and grand with his obsession for shopping and beautiful things. He was, after all, a gigolo, not a multimillionaire.

On the Rue de Rivoli they window shopped, and, just as they were about to cross the road to the Tuileries gardens, he left her once again on the pavement, this time to enter a small shop. He reappeared almost immediately and handed her, one by one, copies of the magazines he had seen on the plane with covers and articles about her prominently featured.

'I think you should tell me all about these, and how much this new career means to you, don't you? Come, we can sit on a bench in the gardens. A synopsis will do. But before you tell me one word about yourself, I think you should know that whatever your life has been can make no difference to me, except that I might love you more.'

He disarmed her completely. Confronting her with the magazines was one thing. But the manner in which he did it was another. He was demanding that she reveal herself to him. How could he possibly know how difficult that was for a woman who was used to holding back and giving nothing to a man? What he asked of her knocked her off balance. But what he promised her – the possibility of an even greater love than he claimed he already felt for her – cracked her protective armour against him. It was not just the words that did it. There was something in the voice, a look in his eye, the strength and bearing she felt when he directed her across the road, the warmth and energy, something akin to a healing power, she felt coursing through her from his hand on her elbow.

They found a bench overlooking the Seine, almost

opposite the place where she had met Adam Corey and handed over to him the last shipment she had smuggled out of Ethiopia. She unconsciously placed her hand over the ruby she always wore, Adam's gift to her, and she knew that she could fool herself no longer. Being a celebrity clotheshorse might keep her safe, might even be fun, but it would never be enough for her. Her country, the highlands of Ethiopia, the peasants who loved her and depended on her, wheeling and dealing in the money and high stakes business world suddenly meant more than being safe from the poisoned tip of an umbrella, or a blast from a sawn-off shotgun fired at her from a fast-moving car.

And now there was Rashid and what he had to offer her. Love, romance, an erotic, adventurous sex life second to none, marriage. No man had ever offered her more. Was what he offered her true or false? How would she know? Experience was hardly on her side. Twice in her life Tana Dabra Ras Magdala Makoum had met men who had made her feel she was more than a business asset, more than a sexual cripple, a mutilated female. And now, she had met one who instilled in her a sense of wholeness she had never known before. Though that could never compensate for the men who had exploited her mind and deprived her of a normal sexual life, it was something. More than something.

She looked at Rashid, and then at the glossy photograph of herself on the cover of the most famous of the fashion magazines. She suddenly could admit to herself that the ultra slim, extraordinarily long-armed and long-legged, dusky woman, wearing a strapless black satin dress with a puff-ball miniskirt, standing in high heel, black satin shoes, was by anyone's standards an unusually beautiful and erotic creature. She placed that in his lap, with the *Time* magazine, whose cover showed her dressed in her indigo blue shift, her hair pulled back off her face and plaited, looking every inch a royal Ethiopian with only hints of her erotic beauty. She remained silent for a few minutes as she thumbed through the other magazines. Then, moving away from Rashid on the bench, she placed the periodicals between them. She turned on the bench to face him, and without another thought she told him her story.

Afterwards she rose from the bench with a powerful need to walk, to feel the movement of her body, her arms and her legs swinging free, to feel her heart pump, and the oxygen flow through her brain.

'Love? Marriage?' she asked suddenly. 'What do a woman such as I and a luxury-loving paid lover such as you, a pair of adventurous libertines seeking the ultimate in sexual oblivion, know about such things?'

She smiled down at Rashid, who had not said a word during the telling of her story or after. She could read nothing in his face, what he thought or how he felt about her. She waited for a question, a reaction at least. Nothing. She turned on her heel and, ramrod straight, walked proudly and regally away from him.

She walked under a late afternoon sun through the garden, taking great long strides, and for a few minutes he was mesmerised by the way she moved. He could feel his heart beating and that stirred him to move. He was on his feet, his heart swelling with love for this most extraordinary woman, the woman he would soon call wife. He caught up with her and placed an arm around her shoulder. They walked a few paces, and then he stopped her and said, 'I would say we know nothing about love and marriage. But what I do know is that we'll find our way, and we are going to have it . . . together . . . you and I.'

Chapter 12

They crossed the Seine, walking over the Pont Neuf to the Left Bank, not stopping till they arrived at the Café Lipp. With every step they took, the thin thread that bound them to each other strengthened. They drank in the beauty of the city as if they were trying to quench some dreadful thirst. Every street, every house, every detail of architecture enchanted them, as if they had never seen the city before. And, with every step, a desire to be closer, to feel, touch one another kept building in them. On the Rue de Seine, Rashid pulled her into a narrow doorway. Slipping his hands under her jacket, he searched out her breasts and sighed with relief at being able to caress her. He placed his lips upon hers and they kissed, and he knew her need was as great as his when he felt her slender fingers intent below his belt. The sound of someone hurriedly descending the stairs behind the door was all that saved them from losing themselves to an embarrassing public display. They laughed as young lovers will at their boldness in love.

'There's no fool like an old fool, that great cliché,' Rashid exclaimed. And they laughed at themselves and knew that it was a good sign that they could.

Over Kir Royales, sitting outside the Café Lipp and

watching all of St Germain des Prés go by, he surprised her with, 'I, too, know Adam Corey. We're friends. I am particularly close to his wife. I gave her away in marriage to him.'

There was a certain look that came into her eyes, and Rashid knew instinctively that there had been more than a business relationship. He was grateful to her that she had not mentioned that. It somehow made the coincidence that their lives should be intertwined easier to handle, especially since he had no intention of letting his wife to be know that he, Adam, and Mirella were involved in a three-sided relationship that he most certainly would not give up or turn into a cheery foursome.

'You know, you have rarely asked me a single question about myself,' he commented.

'Yes, I know.'

'I like that in you. What I like most is to be understood without having to talk about my feelings. That's the way most men are, and there are very few women who understand it. You, like only a few other women I have met, make no demands for intimacy. I find the trait comfortable and easy to live with, and it makes me want to give the intimate side of myself to you.'

He kissed her hand, and she bent in towards him and kissed him on the cheek. She did understand. He wanted to say more to her about his admiration for the relaxed way in which she exposed herself to seeking sexual fulfilment, how together they would capitalise on her interest in eroticism, the qualities he sensed they shared. But there was no need. Their relationship was already ordained. They had identified themselves as sexy and fun. They recognised each other's freedom, acknowledged flaws as well as perfections. They were two people fascinated with being sexual, who wanted to get the best out of life. It suddenly came to him that here was a woman who understood evil, one who would allow him that streak of evil he cherished in himself. Tana Dabra was not a woman to shrink from walking the dangerous edge of things with him. He would never feel threatened, confused or assailed by demands for honesty and openness from Tana Dabra, nor would she be insistent on some kind of fluent emotional exchange. It was the startling stoic silence of soul she possessed that told him.

'Is there something you want to tell me, Rashid?'

'Not tell you, show you. Come on, let's go.'

He clicked his fingers for several waiters, whom he greeted by name. Then, leaving a large banknote on the table, he rose, bringing Tana Dabra up with him. Almost before she realised it, she was swept into the back seat of a black Rolls Royce, and it purred into the St Germain des Prés traffic and headed for the *rive droite*.

'Van Cleef & Arpels, Ahmed,' he ordered the driver, all the time keeping his gaze on Tana Dabra. 'I really do want to buy you a bauble. Allow me, give me that pleasure.'

'Rashid, every woman likes to receive a present. But can you afford it? Just please remember I can't. I have heard that in the world of the toy boy, the lady is usually made to pay the bills.' Suspicion glinted in her eyes. 'The car and the driver, how did you manage them?' she asked.

'The doorman at Van Cleef's.'

'Oh! For a moment I had the idea that the car and driver were yours.' She snuggled up close to Rashid, lifted his arm up and draped it over her shoulder.

257

'Hiring cars, top cars and drivers, to wander around Paris all day waiting for you, no wonder you have to charge such exorbitant fees.'

'I didn't hire this car.'

'Oh!' she said distractedly as she slid her hands under his white silk-knit jersey and caressed the hard, flat expanse of his stomach, his strong chest. He reacted at once to her touch and unbuckled his belt. Taking her hand by the wrist he slid it slowly down his body under the jersey until her fingers found his phallus. She wrapped them around it and caressed it, petted it. Slowly and sweetly they both enjoyed her admiration of him. They saw it in each other's eyes, and felt it by the peace and calm they enjoyed in each other's presence, the little extra race of passion that beat in their hearts.

'I didn't have to, it's mine.'

'And the driver?'

'Yes, and the driver.'

'Next you will be telling me that you're not a gigolo, just another multimillionaire playboy.'

'Turkish playboy.'

She was only half paying attention to him and their conversation; he could tell because of the sexual tension in her voice and the caressing, always caressing fingers between his thighs. He suspected she was trying to hide the tiny orgasms she was achieving by the mere touch of him in her hands out of embarrassment for her hungry need for him.

'I stand corrected.'

'I'm afraid you haven't got that quite right either. It is I who am standing, you who have been corrected.' She squeezed him lightly in lazy recognition of his boyish joke. Slowly he removed her hands from him and kissed the palm of one and then the other. 'Marvellous as that feels we had better stop now, or I will not be able to stop, and we are only several minutes from the Place Vendôme and Van Cleef's.'

He lowered his head to kiss her passionately on the neck. Then he ran his hands up and down her long slender legs sheathed in sheer black stockings. He lifted one up into the air and extended it fully to kiss the ankle, and then he said, 'I tried to find you. All those weeks since that night when you picked me up over a plate of *escargots* and were gone in the morning, leaving me with no way of finding you. I only *thought* I had fallen in love with you then. In the weeks when you vanished from my life, I *knew* it to be true. You confirmed it for me when I saw you at the air terminal. I carried on with my life when I couldn't find you, but there was always a corner of my heart waiting for you to reappear, as I knew you would. Have no fear of the regime. They will never harm you. It was clever of you and Adam to protect you by making you a public figure. And, of course, as my wife you will be doubly protected. I am a very wealthy and powerful man, Tana Dabra, with an international reputation, and the means to keep you safe, even though you have never heard of me. How could you have? We have lived in different kinds of worlds. Now that we are together, I will help you in yours. All you have to do is love me and be happy in mine.'

Tana Dabra sat up and tried to unscramble her confusion about Rashid Lala Mustapha's claims. She smiled at this handsome charismatic figure sitting next to her, and grazed his cheek with her hand affectionately, unable to miss any opportunity to touch him.

'Very well, Rashid, we can pretend that's what you

are for the remainder of the three days we have together, if it makes you happy, so long as you can afford such an extravagant fantasy. But it doesn't matter.' He began to laugh. 'I am not a gigolo, Tana Dabra.'

'No, and you didn't take ten thousand dollars from me on the way from the air terminal to service me for three days. If you want to play that game, I'll go along with you, why not? But really, you don't have to make out you're something you are not for my sake. I am having too good a time to care.'

Rashid rang Mirella from the car telephone as the Rolls crossed the Pont de La Concorde, and spoke to her until the car drew up at the jeweller's door. Rashid watched Tana Dabra's face while he spoke to Mirella, and when he had completed his call was not surprised when she asked if the baby had been born. It hadn't.

'You love that woman, Rashid, don't you?'

'Yes, very much. She and one other. But I love them differently from the way I love you. And those relationships will never interfere with the one you and I will have. Are you going to be able to understand that, and learn to live with it? They need never cause us harm.'

'Strange as this may seem to you, yes, I believe I can.'

It was she who claimed Rashid's hand now and kissed it and placed it over her heart. They were seated thus when the doorman opened the car door.

Tana Dabra was swept along on a wave of luxury and power that only the very rich are privy to. They walked through the shop dazzled by the jewels, and yet those were nothing, mere baubles. She learned quite quickly that anything under five hundred dollars was termed a bauble by Rashid. In a private salon of eighteenth-century *boiserie*, sitting in comfortable Louis XIV chairs, out came the treasures for them.

Only then did she begin to understand that Rashid really might not be a gigolo. It had not occurred to her yet that she had made an embarrassing mistake that he chose to go along with, all the time relishing her error. For the moment all she could see was that Rashid intended her to be his sparkling and glamorous wife.

She protested nervously as he selected some of the most beautiful jewels available in the world for his African beauty, falling more in love with her with every protestation she made.

'Rashid, I don't have a wardrobe to warrant wearing such jewellery. All I have are a few good dresses, I don't even have a winter coat.'

'Must I supply a wardrobe to match these stones? Then we shall be here longer than I anticipated. We must first of all buy you the right earrings to go with Adam's gift.'

'How did you know Adam gave me the ruby?'

'Adam and I have the same taste in many things. There are few men who would have purchased that necklace for you. He is one, and I am another.'

'You are not a gigolo,' she whispered.

'That's what I have been telling you.'

'Rashid, what are you involving me in? Are you a master thief? Do you do movie-type scams? Oh, dear God, are we about to be arrested?' She was torn between anxiety and amusement.

'Don't be ridiculous. I'll prove it to you.' When the managing director appeared and shook hands with Rashid, Rashid asked him, 'What is my credit standing with this company?' The man looked puzzled. He smiled and said, 'Well, Rashid, I don't think we ever thought about amounts. I suppose I would have to say "unlimited". Yes, with us here, Rashid Lala Mustapha would have unlimited credit.'

A gold wine cooler was brought in at this point. Chilled champagne was poured into antique gold and crystal champagne flutes.

The interruption afford Tana Dabra a moment to deal with the recognition that he really was a fabulously wealthy Turkish playboy. And that he had made a fool of her not once but twice. Rashid saw the fury come into her eyes. Her body tensed as she sat taller and straighter. Slowly she raised her chin and a regal haughtiness appeared. The cultivated, chic mannequin look dissolved into the touchy stare of an empress such as he had always wanted as part of his life.

Rashid saw the warmth Tana Dabra had for him evaporating, and an icy hardness crystallising over the erotic fire that had burned in her for him. He could not allow that, and knew he must do something at once.

'Pierre, would you mind bringing the Dalrymple diamond up from the vault, along with anything else you think we might like? Only your most important stones, that's what I want for this special occasion.'

As soon as the man was out of the room, Rashid went to Tana Dabra and sat on the end of the Boulle desk next to her. He placed a finger under her chin to turn her face to him as he said. 'Your anger is a formidable thing, Tana Dabra, which is good, but not if it's directed at me.'

She snapped her head away from his touch. In a flash he was off the desk and he pulled her out of the chair and into his arms. Inches apart they stared into each other's eyes. Tears of anger filled hers, and she began to breathe rapidly. He grabbed a fistful of her hair and held her by it. She saw tears coming into his eyes, and she sensed the aura of the passion he felt for her surrounding them like an invisible sheer silk scarf. 'Don't ice me out. Don't do this to us, kill what we have, out of petty pride and anger. We will never, either of us, do better than being together.' She felt his warmth and love melting her anger. She blinked back tears and listened to him tell her, 'I'll give you myself, and I'll give you the world. But I'll never ask forgiveness. I have always operated by the maxim, "never complain, never explain".'

Then he pulled her by the hair. His hand grasped gently, drawing her closer, closer until he saw the coldness in her eyes dissolve and he recognised once again erotic passion. He ever so lightly placed his lips upon hers. Slowly her arms went up over his shoulders and around his neck. She was helplessly slipping away from her proud self and back towards love. He was wrong to have taken advantage of her mistake. Her pride should demand that she crush him into the ground with insults and walk away from him, never to look back. But where was her pride? Being erotically besotted kills pride. Romantic seduction murders it. Tana Dabra forgot herself. From that moment on she helplessly concentrated on Rashid and persevered in making him happy by using him to satisfy her sexual hunger. Her attentions made him feel he was important. She was making the surest cast a woman can to net and keep her man, and she hardly recognised it. She sacrificed her ego and won the man who haunted her dreams. He waited, still as a stone, until *her* lips pressed his and *her* kisses opened his lips. They found, yet again, a sexual hunger for each other that filled them with joy.

They parted and she said, 'All right, you never ask for forgiveness. Do you perhaps return money obtained under false pretences? Say, one thousand one hundred dollars, plus ten thousand dollars, plus a round trip flight to New York on Concorde.'

Rashid began to laugh, loudly, joyously, and the note of relief in his laughter was not lost on Tana Dabra. 'Certainly not. I usually hold with the policy that a deal is a deal, but it can always be negotiated or broken, if that is to my advantage. However, not this one. It means too much to me.'

'You are a hard man, not always fair, I think. But I will say nothing more about your deception because both of us now operate under the same guideline. I never complain and never explain either. You might remember that.'

It was dark, long after the regular closing time, when they left Van Cleef & Arpels with a collection of jewellery and gems worth several fortunes. They went directly to their rooms and made love, romantically at first, but then with an intensity of unleashed passion. The telephone cut sharply into their ferocious idyll with an incessant ringing. Tana Dabra fumbled for it. When she replaced the receiver she was looking aghast at Rashid.

'What's the matter?' he asked with genuine concern.

'I can't believe it. One of the reasons I paid you to come to Paris was to escort me to a charity fashion show and ball that I promised to attend, as I told you earlier today. We're late and I am one of the ladies on the catwalk. That was Karl Lagerfeld. He's furious. Rashid, you made me forget the world.' She rose from the bed, but he caught her by the arm and pulled her down next to him.

'Forget it.'

'*Forget it*? I can't forget it. Come on, let's go. We must at least make an appearance.'

He responded only with intimate caresses and kisses on her breasts. She closed her eyes in an agony of desire to stay with him and dive deeper into the sexual excesses he promised. It took all her strength of character to push him away and order him to dress.

'Don't be ridiculous.'

'Don't you be ridiculous. I paid you for three days, and, by God you will give me those three days. For so long as I paid, you will service me the way I want. And, right now, I want you to get dressed and take me to that ball.'

He began to laugh. 'You don't want to go any more than I do.'

'That's true, but we're going. Now, please, Rashid, get dressed.'

She turned and was walking away from him. He watched her stride proud and naked towards the bathroom. He leapt off the bed and swept her off her feet and into his arms.

'I'll give you back your money. A complete refund.'

'Too late, you had your chance. Now, as my paid lover, my middle-aged toy boy, accept it, you have no choice. We are going to the ball.'

She couldn't help tilting her head back and giving that sexy throaty little laugh that so enchanted him. Still carrying her, he kissed her and then put her down to sit on the edge of the marble bath. He opened the taps and the bath began to fill. He poured a bottle of her perfume into the swirling water, then added bath flakes that burst into clouds of fine bubbles. He picked her up in his arms once more and stepped into the tub with her and lowered them both into the water.

'I love you,' he whispered in her ear.

'You are going to smell like a lady,' she warned.

'I'll shower the scent away.'

They kissed and their mutual need took over. She felt him enter her slowly. And they took their time fucking in the steamy, soapy water. Afterwards, as he was washing her with a large sponge, he said, 'All right, you win, we will go to that ball and I will show them how much I love you.'

The mirror within the walnut frame tilted at a slight angle on its pedestal and she saw herself looking very beautiful in a sable coat. One furrier adjusted the set of the sleeve, the other, on one knee, was checking that the hem was even. The master furrier of the Bergdorf Goodman Fur Salon was checking that the ivory carved buttons of the double breasted coat were sewn on properly. As he ran one hand down the rolled collar of the coat, he told her the style reminded him of his first raccoon coat in the Thirties, so long before she was born. She saw Rashid, reflected behind herself and the furriers, sitting in a small grey velvet love seat. Appreciation of Tana Dabra's pleasure in her new fur coat suffused his handsome face.

She caught glimpses in the mirror behind him of the thick grey carpets, the heavy crystal chandeliers, the occasional mannequin moving around. Here in a floor-length silver fox, there in a four hundred thousand dollar floor-length sable, a chinchilla, beyond in a black diamond mink jacket. They floated through the room between free-standing mirrors, small love seats and deep bergères covered in cream-coloured silk damask. Past rich and elegant women they modelled their wares.

The enveloping scent of fur, Jolie Madame, Joy, Mitsouko, Norell and, lurking beneath, mothballs of camphor filled the air. Tana Dabra looked away from the mirror and the luxury that it reflected towards the window. There was a cold, grey, foggy November day. The Plaza fountain was etched in frost but still able to bubble and dribble slow cascades of water. Beyond that, she could see the horse-and-carriages parked nearby, waiting for susceptible tourists to come along. Her gaze passed on over the tops of the trees of Central Park to where it was ringed by concrete and glass residential towers of the rich and the famous.

Tana Dabra heard Rashid complimenting the furrier. Her attention returned to the mirror, to herself in her new fur coat. The reflection showed her celebrating her own appearance and, grouped beyond, the trinity of furriers glorying in her as their creation. There was scope here for a reflective Mannerist painter, she mused, as Rashid rose from the love seat and walked into the composition framed by the mirror. She turned to him and he held out his hands to her. She took them in hers and, as always with Rashid, a warmth from him seemed to run through her fingertips down her body right to her toes.

He squeezed her hands and turned away from her to thank the furrier and his assistants. Quite pleased with himself, he put his arm around Tana Dabra and they smiled at each other. Rashid asked that they send the lynx coat she had worn into the department around to the Carlisle. As the pair left the salon, every eye in the room was on them.

And why not? Today Tana Dabra was wearing her long hair off her face and knotted high up close to the crown of her head, framing that magnificent face and long, slender neck. A pair of large square-cut diamonds on her ears sparkled above her new sable coat. Over her shoulder she had casually slung a large black alligator bag. She walked with a kind of clothesless freedom, almost loping like a gazelle. Yet, under her coat, she wore a black silk jersey Jean Muir dress with balloon sleeves that were tight at the wrist. It had a high simple round neck, and the material draped seductively over her breasts. Several strands of priceless pearls of different lengths seemed to give a glow to her face. As usual, she wore her ruby at her throat.

Though there still had not been a ceremony, on her wedding finger were three rings: two platinum bands holding a single eight-carat, square-cut diamond, and between them a platinum ring holding a twelve carat ruby. Rashid had given them to her instead of a wedding band. On her left wrist several slim bangles were solid with diamonds, dancing in the light. If people rated the elusive and somewhat mysterious constant companion of Rashid Lala Mustapha among the most beautiful women in the world, they had reason.

Just a few steps from the elevator Rashid turned to Tana Dabra and told her, 'I wanted you so much when I was sitting there in the velvet chair watching those men fondling your coat. I was wishing you were naked underneath that soft, downy fur. Those high heeled, shiny black alligator shoes, those trim ankles, your shapely legs in their sheer stockings . . . I could only think of stripping them off you, having you naked, maybe just draped in your jewels, and taking you ruthlessly the way I did when I swept you away from that ball in Paris and onto my plane. How long is it now, a month, six weeks, since we have been prisoners of our infatuation? I've lost track of time since we met again in Paris. That flight to Dominica seems to me to be only yesterday.'

He whispered softly in her ear, while he stroked the arm of her sable coat. 'Dominica, remember Dominica? What joy it was to introduce you to something as depraved as we shared there, and to discover you enjoyed it so completely. The more I discover you the more I love you. Put me out of my misery, Tana Dabra, marry me. You have only to say when and where.'

Yes, she would marry him, but in her own time, not his. And she had no idea when that would be. She was in love, but not blinded by it. She was committed to him till death might part them, but still she held back from naming the date. She didn't quite know why, but she was sure that it had to do with him and not her. She was waiting for him to reveal to her something he was holding back. She had no idea what it was, but, when he did reveal it, she would know it instantly, and then she would marry him.

'Hello, Rashid,' came a voice behind them. 'I never thought I would see you again. I don't suppose you even remember my name.'

'Cynthia Cohen. How could I be so careless as to forget a beautiful woman who was as generous to me as you were?'

Tana Dabra watched the girl flush crimson, and she felt sorry for her. Rashid was seducing Cynthia even as he recalled her previous seduction. He had obviously

269

discarded her. How she must have suffered. He introduced Cynthia, then turned his attention from Tana back to Cynthia.

In the weeks they had been together, Tana Dabra had watched numerous women encountered as casually as this girl, watched them cling to him with a kind of controlled desperation for his attention. He had charmed and seduced in minutes, as he was doing right now, only to leave them with nothing more than hope, as he would do to this poor Cynthia.

There were so many facets to the man. She had learned so much about him through his behaviour. Not all of it good, but then not all of it bad either. There was the woman who finally had the baby. When she was in labour they spoke every few hours until the baby was born. Afterwards he spoke to her every day. Rashid never talked about her to Tana Dabra. He didn't have to, she understood that he loved the woman. And he was right, it made no difference in their relationship.

Then there was the woman he called Humayun. He had flown her down to Dominica for four days of sex with them. Tana Dabra had never seen a sexual slave before, yet recognised it in Humayun at once. She had also been in awe of Humayun, her beauty, her apparent enslavement. Tana Dabra could hardly believe any woman could be as sensual and sexual as Humayun. There was something else Tana Dabra had seen for the first time: Rashid being sexually seduced by Humayun. It released a range of emotions in Tana Dabra that both thrilled and frightened her. And watching Rashid direct Humayun in a night of sexual debauchery nearly drove her mad with desire to be a part of their experience. She half fell in love with Humayun herself during the days and nights of sexual abandonment in Dominica.

There was the strange way he behaved about Adam. He had called him from the plane en route to Dominica. She recalled his words and puzzled over the meaning hidden in them. He had reached Adam in Istanbul, while they were in bed in the master bedroom, she sitting naked astride him, lost in her own lasciviousness. They were facing each other. He was savouring her obvious pleasure in taking the dominant role by impaling herself upon him. Lying passively he allowed her to make all the moves that gave her so much pleasure. Hers was the posture of sexual victory, her hands on her hips, a subtle but sensual animal quality in the way she moved up and down and round and round upon him with her pelvis, the tilt of her head, the twist and turn of her shoulders. She thought of those words now, 'Adam. It's Rashid. Just a quick call. I've met a most extraordinary lady. She claims to know you. Tana Dabra Ras Magdala Makoum. Strange name, mysterious woman. I took her to a ball a few hours ago, and am whisking her away for a while. Know that she is safe with me. I find it is you I have to be grateful to for all you have done for her. Adam, just now, only you should know I intend to marry Tana Dabra. I don't think this has to alter my other long-time relationships. I just need time to prove that to the others involved. You have my word, the last thing I will ever do is hurt the ones I love. Tana Dabra, if she marries me, will understand that our marriage will not change the secret aspects of my life. No illusions about that for her.'

Adam had said something in reply. At a more respectable time a few hours later, when she had asked

Rashid to get Adam back on the line, she was surprised when he refused. His candour about his reasons surprised her yet more.

'No. Not until we have announced our wedding plans. Am I going to let him tell you that I am a ruthless womaniser, a depraved man – bad material for a husband – a morally obtuse businessman? Do I want you to learn from him that I am obsessed with a past that has vanished? All of which is true, but I would rather have you discover on your own with me.'

While Cynthia and Rashid flirted, Tana Dabra's mind wandered back to those days in Dominica.

Rashid's jet was too large for the landing strip on Dominica and they had to change to a small plane in Antigua. The four-seater that took them to Dominica flew low over the Caribbean, and zoomed down to follow the shoreline, its wheels skimming the tops of the waves, shaving the undergrowth by the rocks and road before bumping down on the short runway laid out in the middle of a forest of coconut palms. The plane skidded erratically to a halt.

Several vehicles, a Range Rover, two beach-buggies and a Chrysler convertible, met them on the runway. They were swept off to the other side of the island, almost all of which was owned by Rashid. She had suddenly felt happier than she had been about any place since her last dangerous moments in Ethiopia.

The island, with its three hundred and sixty-five rivers, surrounded by a warm sea, sizzled under the tropical sun. It was a paradise within a rain forest. Its native dark-skinned Dominicans, its primitive simplicity, reminded her of home. A life of opulent uselessness in a European capital, trying to fit in with its radical chic, suddenly became impossible for her. She turned to look at Rashid and confirmed to herself what she had already known: they were meant for each other. He returned her gaze with a knowing look. It brought an instant reaction from her. She spoke up with a voice alive with feeling.

'I will want to do what I have always done: play with big business for the benefit of my country, and in opposition to the present regime. It will be dangerous and thrilling and rewarding, just like being married to you. Will you support me in all that, if I tell you that it will come second in my life only to loving you and being your wife?'

He nodded his consent. Her heart beat faster with an excitement felt in herself and mirrored in Rashid's eyes. She let go of the hand-grip she had been clinging to, bounced free and then slipped into Rashid's arms.

'How sure your instincts are! How could you have known how much I would feel for this place, what it would do for us? I don't have your quick responses. I'm not half the accomplished seducer you are. I will make a terrible wife. I have no domestic skills. I don't know how to run a house that would please you, I—'

He had interrupted her saying, 'I don't want to marry you for your domestic skills! Love, friendship, intimacy, sex, and personal fulfilment – those are the things I want to marry you for. Give me all that, and I'll never let you down. Then you will be free to pursue your own interests. Now shut up and kiss me, because for the moment my needs are narrowed to just one: sex with you, getting inside you and giving you more and more of myself.'

These memories were interrupted by Rashid's laughter. He took her hand and said to Cynthia, 'Tana Dabra has not yet seen the Southampton compound.

You have given me an idea. I will take her to see it. Care to join us? Be our guest.'

Tana Dabra disengaged herself from Rashid to look at a display of accessories, unwilling to confront the beautiful but unhappy face of Rashid's victim. How callous he could be when he found a weakness. He instinctively toyed with it. Tana Dabra wondered why any woman invited such treatment. She could never become one of his victims. She thought of Humayun whose role as Rashid's sexual slave was a world away from the role of the victim. The difference was that Humayun spontaneously renewed her assent to servitude. Cynthia's bondage was sudden, involuntary.

Pretending to be distracted by the display of handbags and silk scarves and doveskin leather gloves, a fur hat and gigantic bottles of French perfumes, she watched Rashid as he assumed the guise of the wealthy international playboy. Again her thoughts drifted back to Dominica.

His compound comprised seven square miles. One mile was white sandy beach that dipped in and out of coves where, on the long and straight parts, great white-capped Caribbean waves rolled slowly in to a palm-fringed shore of idyllic beauty. Point sur la Mer, he called it. What joy she had felt when she first saw the houses, each a different size, round with thatched roofs and not too different from the *Tukuls* of her own country: the cook house, the dining house, the living house, the master bedroom and bath house, the guest houses, linked together by paths of crushed sea shells, cut through the natural jungle. Wild parrots and orchids, rare wild flowers and trees, the sea and sex were their entertainment.

Staff members, assembled from all over the world

mixed happily with the locals who worked for Rashid. Descendants of the Caribe Indians who had once populated the island, and several black people who could trace back their ancestors on Dominica through two hundred years, made up a colony all their own. They remained faithful, silently condoning the sexual excesses practised at Point sur la Mer.

There she had found another Rashid, who wore only shorts and sandals, when he wore anything, and who swam naked in the rough sea. A Rashid who, day and night, furnished them with sexual games and entertainments that dazed her with their power to excite, tease and tantalise. He taught her, revelled in her naîvety. She saw he was enchanted by the way she rose to every sexual occasion, every corruption he afflicted her with. He had declared that there was no woman he could not lure to the brink of sexual abandon. After Humayun arrived with several men to join them Tana Dabra had realised he wasn't teasing He was raising a devil in her, she was certain, to mate with the devil in him. He wanted it all, and so did she. And it was there on the island that, strangely, he enticed her closer to becoming his wife.

But other, less disturbing bonds were created between them. She was a woman of the highlands of Ethiopia as well as the financial capitals of the West. She taught Rashid how to walk great distances with ease, to track in the rain forest, to live off the jungle. She found certain leaves and flowers with healing properties, and others that, rubbed in, sensitised the genitals. She revealed some nuances of African sexual practice that refined even his cosmopolitan repertoire.

There had been the excitement he felt on news of the birth of the baby of the woman he called each day.

But slowly, as days passed, they forgot the world beyond their present paradise.

Now she felt Rashid come up behind her, and together they walked back to the elevator. Cynthia had vanished.

Chapter 13

The elevator bell pinged. Seconds later the door slid open. The two of them smiled as they squeezed themselves in among the other New Yorkers. On the ground floor they wove their way through the people and counters towards the main exit. Tana Dabra spotted a cashmere scarf woven in a rich paisley pattern of deep reds and greys. She quickly broke away from Rashid and went to the counter and took it. Reaching into her handbag she paid the young woman. Not even waiting for it to be wrapped, she caught up with Rashid at the door to the street and draped the scarf around his neck saying, 'Thank you for my coat. I love you.'

He took the scarf in his hands. The cashmere was soft, even softer than the precious sable furs she wore. He looked at it, then at Tana Dabra. He gave her one of his more sexy yet wry smiles, and said, 'You thank me, and you love me. Yet still you will not marry me.' He put his arms around her. The fur felt sensuous against the palms of his hands. Once again, as so often in the weeks they had been together, an instantaneous spark caught and flared. He kissed her, and while looking over her shoulder he whispered, 'I still wish you were naked under your new fur coat, and I still want to fuck you, naked in nothing but jewels, spread out on your Russian furs. And maybe I will, very soon.'

She gave him her teasing throaty laugh with a tilt of her head, and said softly as he released her, 'And I, Rashid, will bind you with your new cashmere scarf and whip you into a sexual stupor with my tongue.'

He gave her a smack on her bottom, a reproach lost in all the fur he had just purchased, watched by a bevy of ladies shopping, who shot envious glances at the lovers. The two of them burst hand in hand out into the crowd milling up and down Fifth Avenue.

Near the front entrance their chauffeur Ahmed was waiting by the open door of Rashid's maroon-coloured Rolls Royce. Settled comfortably, they sped away from the world of Bergdorf Goodman, themselves again, unfettered by the pampering the luxury store's staff had given their egos.

That morning, when the call had come through to Rashid that Tana Dabra's gift, the sable coat, was ready, they were having breakfast in bed together. He offered her a day out in the city, and a surprise gift. The offer included a sumptuous lunch, to which they were now speeding through the midtown traffic.

Rashid was sitting close to Tana Dabra in the back seat of the car. He ran his hands with her fingers spread wide apart through the thick, luscious fur. He whispered, 'It is so soft. Nothing softer. Except maybe you.'

He kissed her, and Tana Dabra unbuttoned her coat and arranged her legs seductively. Rashid slipped his hand under her dress. His right hand kept fondling the sable sleeve of her coat as his left hand traced the fleshy line of her thigh. He kissed her deeply. She opened to him easily and moaned softly. He felt the slight tremor that went through her body. A satin wetness flowed over his fingers. His delight in pleasuring her was evident in his eyes.

He kissed her deeply again, and then withdrew his hand reluctantly from under her dress. Tana Dabra took that hand in both of hers and, turning it palm up, raised it to her lips and kissed it tenderly. Rashid licked his fingers then kissed her once more. Gently releasing her he sat back and said, 'How can it be I still want you all the time? The look of you, the scent of you, and, oh, the taste of you. Incredibly sexual. You still have the power to seduce me. And that is something I give thanks for, every day.'

Tana Dabra buttoned her coat, adjusted the collar and smiled at him. 'Since you first seduced me – and the seduction has been non-stop – all that time I have never stopped wanting you.'

With that she bent forward, kissed him passionately and touched his cheek tenderly with the back of her hand. 'Now, where are you taking me to lunch?'

Rashid was taking Tana Dabra to the newest restaurant in the city. Chez Mon Amie Lulu promised to be the best French restaurant in Manhattan, certainly the most elegant and chic. Wilsden Van Allen created the restaurant because he loved French cooking. An ardent Francophile, a multimillionaire, as accomplished a snob as he was an art collector, darling of the millionaire dowagers of Palm Beach, he threw them as sublime a crêpe suzette as the best chefs of France. For his adoring patronesses, sex with him was not on the menu, only the crêpes. He was a notorious closet queen for rough trade.

Everything about Chez Mon Amie Lulu was of the

best. Location perfect: midtown Upper East Side. Doorman pinched from twenty-three years' service at the St Régis. Entrance even more discreet and elegant than the old Colony Club's ever was. Interior decorations combining elegance and simplicity, not unlike the once famous Le Pavillon and a small section of the Louvre in Paris. Monet, Renoir and Picasso took turns on the walls with Turner, Manet, Pisarro, Dali and Gauguin. If one of the diners complimented Wilsden Van Allen on his paintings he came on revoltingly gallant, 'Oh, it delights me, your delight in my little pictures. It is my pleasure to be able to share them with you.'

Without visible effort he tantalised with the most exquisite food imaginable. He had stolen the pastry chef from the Connaught in London, whither he had fled from his native France as one of the finest chefs in the country. The wine steward had been weaned away from many years at Le Grand Vefour in Paris. From Lyons, the gourmet paradise, he snitched the best vegetable chef. An offer the master chef had found himself unable to refuse closed the shutters on that man's restaurant in Paris, then considered one of the five best in the world, and he the doyen of French chefs. The maitre d' and the waiters, who ran the restaurant to utter perfection and style, had been hijacked from the best restaurants in Manhattan and Los Angeles.

Chez Mon Amie Lulu matched promises to money. All in all, not a bad buy if you wanted an exquisite meal in privacy, with a wallpaper of great paintings. Wilsden Van Allen might, through the small hours of the night, expend himself at fashionable night spots, or cruise the grottiest of steam baths for a trick. But you could be sure that none of that part of his life darkened the door of his restaurant.

With Wilsden, the strict apartheid of a classic closet queen operated; entertainment with the masses, disco dancing at a gay place, a trick, S and M, kinky sex, were one thing; society, culture and business another. Snobbery halted at the frontier of his sex life. From there on, even the roughest who could debase him the most was never sex low enough for Wilsden.

He was dining with his guests a few tables away from Rashid and Tana Dabra. Wilsden was delighted that they had found their way to his restaurant. Occasionally and most discreetly he looked over to their table. Tana Dabra, the newest love in Rashid Lala Mustapha's life, was wondrous looking. She was a new but instantly famous face. Rashid was in the jet-set society world as well as the international cultural world. These were the sort of people he liked to see in the restaurant. He knew Rashid's houses around the world were choc-a-bloc with rare and beautiful objects. After the Kennedys at Hyannis Port, and Camp David, Rashid's compound at Southampton was a retreat high on the list of sought-after invitations. He as yet had not received one.

Wilsden remembered the couple from a few weeks before when he had been the guest of a Greek millionaire, Christos Mavrodakis, a friend of Rashid. A yachting trip through the Greek islands to Side on the Mediterranean coast of Turkey had been extended to his society dowager of the moment. He was invited as her escort. He and Rashid had met many times in society, but this was the first time he had met Tana Dabra. He noted that they made an extraordinarily good-looking couple. Presumably she was his mistress.

They had been aloof, and kept more or less to themselves and their host. Something about them made him feel superficial, small. He did not know why. They had certainly been more than civil to him. Now they were in his restaurant. It occurred to him to send a bottle of rare wine with his compliments, but he thought better of it. Instinct whispered to him that this would be wrong. It was accepted wisdom to tread carefully around Rashid Lala Mustapha. He turned back to his friends, content that at least they were dining in Chez Mon Amie Lulu. But not before he recalled something strange that had happened.

It was in the ancient port of Side. They had all gone ashore and were roaming over the amphitheatre. Rashid had been made a great fuss of by the locals. He was standing among some of them engrossed in conversation. His woman, the Ethiopian, had climbed to the uppermost tier of seats and was sitting there alone contemplating the wonders of the marble architecture and the sea beyond, when shots, rifle shots, resounded. Everyone scattered or took cover, except Rashid. He sprinted like a young athlete and bounded up over the seats to his woman. He took her in his arms, she was unhurt. Their anguish had been acute, and they had promptly had a row. Had she been the target for the sniper? No one knew. Several hours later two Turkish bodyguards arrived to watch over her. Rashid disappeared for twenty-four hours, and on his return the cruise continued as if nothing had happened.

Tana Dabra and Rashid were having a happy time together. The food was fantastic. Not since the years when Monsieur Point presided at La Pyramide, his world-famous restaurant in the French countryside, had Rashid dined so well. On the taste of such food, memories flooded back. Reminiscences merged into each other, and he laughed and loved Tana more because their memories were few, their history almost non-existent, because it was yet to be created by them, and they had years ahead to do it in.

Rashid raised her hand to kiss it. 'I have not sent for the car. Why not walk home? We could do some window shopping on the way. If you feel up to it, we might step into a gallery or two.'

'Lovely idea, Rashid.'

Walking smothered in furs through the streets of Manhattan on a cold November afternoon with a man she was madly attracted to . . . An absolutely marvellous day out with her husband-to-be, though he was still not sure of that . . . Happiness felt within her grasp. Tana Dabra Ras Magdala Makoum was happy.

They peered into the windows that tempted the rich with marvellous goodies all along Upper Fifth Avenue. Occasionally they would stop and Rashid would take out a slim black crocodile-skin-backed notepad and write something down. An object to enquire about, something to have sent around to his rooms, the possibility of a gift for someone. They walked among the crowds of people until suddenly Tana Dabra had had enough. She stopped in the middle of the pavement. They faced each other and Rashid put his arm around her. Crowds of people were passing around them, crossing to the other side of the street.

'Rashid, I never dreamed I would like New York so much. It's the fastest, most exciting city in the world. The adrenaline seems to run off the skyscraper walls and down the streets. Those streets, they're more like manmade canyons. And the people, what a cross section of humanity, or inhumanity, maybe. It's mind bending. And the sex. From what you have shown me, it's the best equipped sex shop in the world. As someone I met, though I can't remember who, said, "Ya puts your money down, babes, and ya gets what ya pays for. That's sex and love in the Big Apple." ' She began to laugh. 'Ah's putting ma body down, man, so let's get home quickly. I don't wanna be out here any more. I want to go home and make love to you, really thank you for the coat. I have wanted to all day.'

He began to laugh. 'I don't have a problem with that. Let's go. And if you are very good I'll put *my* money down on a spicy little something to amuse you, and *we'll* see what we get, babe!'

Often when Tana Dabra made love to Rashid, he would, in a delirium of lust, question her as to who had taught her to make love the way she did. At those times she thought of Adam Corey, so thankful for his being the first man to take her and to teach her how to excite lust in men. That was her secret, and she would never tell Rashid. It was that expertise and a base animal rutting that she emanated that excited Rashid. She was different from any woman he had ever had, and he often admitted to himself that her mutilated genitalia, and the bizarre ways in which she was able to excite with them, were especially depraved. And depravity was something that triggered in Rashid that streak of evil he so relished in sex. What made her different from other women he had involved himself with in casual affairs was that they chose to turn a blind eye to his evil. Mirella accepted it, and loved him in spite of it. Humayun accepted, nurtured, and loved even that in him. But only Tana Dabra Ras

Magdala Makoum, understood it and, understanding, became a part of it.

He lay now under her tongue, her probing fingers and her seductive sucking. He watched her. He was on the edge, about to yield to the spasm of release. But he was a master of control, and he knew the longer he waited, the greater their pleasure. Overcome with lust she asked him to take her, begged him. She could bear it no longer, she had to feel the spurt of him inside her. He taunted her with his passivity a little while longer, until there was no love or affection left in their movements. Nothing but raw lust. Then he took her.

Without interrupting his rhythm he pushed pillows under her back and, pulling her even tighter up against him, and her legs even further apart, he paced his thrusts with such power and timing that she came again and again between gasps of infinite pleasure. A stream of flattering dialogue was peppered with sexual obscenities that spurred him on. He fucked her not only with his phallus, but with his mouth and then his hands, leaving none of her erogenous places unserved. Tana Dabra was barely able to catch her breath between thrusts and orgasms.

Her come, the sweet smell of sex . . . He let go and gave himself to her in an orgasm that seemed to him to go on for ever. They sighed and whimpered, unable to speak, and stayed locked together for a few minutes, exhausted from treading on the edge of oblivion.

Reluctantly he withdrew, and with his hand he scooped up their lust, and together they licked it out of his palm and from her fingertips. Lying on their sides facing each other, with a passionate voice on the edge of cracking, she said, 'With sex you take me out of this world.' Rashid raised her up and made her lie flat over

285

his body. Their skins touched across the width and
length of their bodies. He reached out and poured a
glass of champagne for them, and they drank from the
same vessel.

Some time later, still in bed, without saying a word
about it, each knew that their afternoon of sex was far
from over. It was therefore no surprise to them when
the door bell of the suite rang.

The young man introduced himself as Richard Ram.
He was a twenty-four year old Cuban refugee, whose
real name was Ricardo Ramirez. Richard Ram was of
average height, but his averageness ended at the waist.
He was a super stud who was paid super fees by rich
sexualists like Rashid Lala Mustapha to perform with a
young lady, or a young man, or, on occasion, something more bizarre. He seemed to adore new people to
fuck with, and was therefore perfect for foursomes. He
was even better at large orgies. Richard Ram loved his
work and managed to take it seriously at seven hundred dollars an hour, with bonuses for special devia-
tions. He was into everything, a real pro.

Not only was he a super stud but he was also super
good looking, mildly intelligent, and undemandingly
honest. With his dark hair and olive-coloured skin he
was not just handsome, but beautiful. If he were
adorned in a long wig, he could have been a most
sensual-looking girl. Not only his face was beautiful;
he had gorgeous hands and elegant feet. All in all, his
was a dark, delicate beauty, endowed with the gift of
ten inches of phallus to pack into his underpants.

He wore a Brooks Brothers suit of dark grey
herring-bone tweed, a button-down shirt of pale blue
cotton and a tie that could have passed for old school.
A navy blue cashmere overcoat was draped over his

shoulders, and he carried a smart Gucci briefcase.

The girl was wearing a floor-length, expensive, red fox coat and black leather boots. Under the coat she wore a smart, black suede shirtwaist dress. She had one of those faces that could only come out of California, with the right nose, cheekbones and chin, with big innocent blue eyes. She was pretty with her long, straight, blonder than blonde hair and an ever-so-light make-up. No jewellery was needed.

Richard Ram introduced her to Rashid as Mary Littlelamb, her real name was Shirley Wizsnitsky. Mary Littlelamb put down the oversized Louis Vuitton shoulder bag she carried and took off her coat. Rashid, of course, did not give his name. Johns never did, unless it was John. This couple would never know about Rashid and Tana Dabra, unless they read the gossip columns. They only would know they had serviced two clients in room 2211 at the Carlisle.

Mary sat down while the two men settled the matter of money, and the sexual menu. Richard understood at once that it was to be a no-holds-barred sex session. Rashid picked up Tana Dabra's sable coat that had been lying over the back of a chair and started for the bedroom where she was waiting, having told them to come through when they were ready.

Tana Dabra and Rashid showered together. She went to the dressing-room table in the bathroom and made herself up. Wanting to please Rashid she draped herself in some of the jewels he had bought her and snapped the Adam ruby around her neck. With nothing more to cover her nakedness she walked into the bedroom. He took the dressing gown trailing from her hand and held out her sable coat for her. She laughed and slipped her arms through the sleeves. Together, he in his silk robe and nothing else, she naked under her sable coat, they lay down side by side on the chaise longue and waited for Richard and Mary to appear.

Mary was astonishing, tall and very fair skinned with the face of an angel. One could hardly expect what happened from the neck down. Below the face that made her look like the eternal preppy from Berkeley, Bryn Mawr, Smith or Mount Holoyoke, was an extraordinary and erotic full, curvaceous body. Mary Littlelamb was clever, she knew well how to make herself look availably debauched, utterly ready to be used.

Her long but shapely arms and legs seemed to accentuate her full breasts. Around her long, slim neck she wore a tight choker of black enamel chain. On the centre of it was a ring, and suspended from the ring were a pair of long black enamel chains that hung down between her breasts to her ankles. They jangled as she walked into the room.

Her breasts were large and firm, and though heavy as if bursting with milk, tilted upwards, the long nipples coloured with a pale pink ointment that made them shine like satin, stiff and open as if begging to be sucked. She had an extremely narrow waist and a flat stomach, but was wide in the hips and the bottom. Around each of her ankles was a chain made like the one around her neck. She walked on long, slim, bare feet. There was more tinkling of chains because she had, high up on her thighs, close to her groin, black enamel chains that dug into her flesh. Because she had been shaved smoothly the slit between her legs was clearly visible. It gashed her voluptuous mound that shone satiny as her nipples did. She smelled of fresh cut freesias.

First she went to Tana Dabra and gave her the innocent smile of a child, bent over and kissed her on one cheek and then on the other. Seductively she opened Tana Dabra's fur coat and looked at her. Then it was Rashid's turn. She took him by the hand. He stood up and she opened his sash and removed his robe. She kissed him, and he reacted at once, returning her kiss hungrily, while he draped the chains around her breasts.

It was then that Richard Ram came into the room. Handsome, beautiful, downright pretty, but all macho man. Naked except for a wide leather belt with a huge gold sculptured buckle that only added to the effect of the fearsomely thick, flaccid penis reaching so low on his thigh that Tana Dabra's heart beat a little faster.

Around each of his wrists were buckled wide leather bands with gold studs. Masses of black curly hair on groin and chest only added to the animal quality of his body, an odd contrast to the almost delicate face. In his right hand he gripped an ivory-handled whip. He smiled seductively at the other three people in the room.

Richard took Tana Dabra by the hands and had her stand, removing her sable coat by using the handle of the whip to edge it off her shoulders. It fell and draped over the chaise behind her. Richard Ram's eyes seemed to eat right into her body. He placed his hands on her waist and pulled her close to him. He held her that way and kissed her on the forehead, then on her cheek, and she felt him rise between her thighs . . .

When they had taken their satisfaction, Rashid and Tana Dabra left their private world behind them and went down to the bar. The New York drinks hour is like every city's cocktail hour. In smart bars like this one all over the city people were fortifying their egos with alcohol and bonhomie – wives, lovers, husbands, mistresses, businessmen, tricks and friends. It was the transitional hour between one kind of work and another, business to social. The restoration hour, the revitalising hour when the adrenaline of the day, all used up, was replaced by the Martini, dry with a twist of lemon, and the Manhattan, with its slice of orange and red cherry. An hour when Rashid chose to parade, like so many others in the city, at the smart bars along the Upper East Side. It was another mild wonder of New York city life he was introducing to Tana Dabra.

The room buzzed with chic-looking people drinking the right drink at the right hour, bound for the right place and to the right dinner with select friends, unless they were going to the concert, play or musical of the moment, and then on to one of the best restaurants for irresistible food.

The atmosphere was heavy with success, money, chic and amusement. This kind of place set you up and on your way for the evening. Tana Dabra and Rashid were enjoying it tonight.

'What shall we drink?'

'Try me with something wicked!'

'Haven't you been wicked enough for today?'

'With a ring master like you. I want to get the night off to a wicked start.'

'Alright then, what's your idea of wicked liquid? No, don't tell me, I can guess . . . you want a Margarita.'

'Right.'

Halfway through their Margaritas they settled back comfortably to eye the people in the bar.

Smart, chic, knowing all the right things and doing

them, is how they appeared as a group. Within the group, sub-types detached themselves. There were the ultra slim, almost frail, exquisitely jewelled, millionaire widows from Chicago, Cleveland and San Francisco, Dallas and Palm Beach, up for their winter shopping, and now hitting the New York social circuit. They invariably had an escort, usually the old homosexual friend, or perhaps the smooth antique dealer/ adviser directing their funds in order to bring them culture, prestige and status, and himself money. Unless, of course, it was the shockingly young whizz-kid museum director hustling for a wing to his museum. The beautiful, ageing ballet master, who needed funds for the latest ethnic group he worked with in his spare time, was another favourite escort – so sensitive.

The pretty boy escorts, once called gigolos, today's toy boys, all homosexuals with the occasional bisexual who played it straight, waited on and amused the rich dowagers. These were svelte, cultured young men who were vastly entertaining and mad about heavy and old money. They escorted the good, lonely ladies starved for masculine attention, fawned over them, pampered them, and in return were slipped money under the table by them, and kept most discreetly in cashmere sweaters and gold cufflinks with large sapphires.

Tana Dabra giggled, and bending forward across the table she whispered to Rashid, 'And to think I thought you were one of those, and I was a younger version of them.' She raised an eyebrow in the direction of a table not far from them. 'I don't know what madness made me think that was all I was fit to have in my life.' Then she returned her attention to bar watching.

In this room one could see the so-called lucky ones,

those who still had husbands, even older than themselves, and more wrinkled, frail and rich. These sat like pairs of wooden dummies, nothing exchanged between them except another drink, offered or politely accepted. The well-preserved husbands, condescending and charming to their wives, eyed the delectable younger women in the room, while their drinks washed down fantasies of what they would do to one, or several, of them.

Then there were the men without their wives. Older, rich, secure, attractive, sometimes handsome. Some were with beautiful girls who were gratifyingly young: thirty, twenty-five, twenty years younger than themselves. These were men with age on their faces, youth still in their eyes and uncertainty in their limbs, longing to love and adore the beautiful girl of the night, to charm and seduce, vampires in well-cut suits, eager to suck youth back into their old bones.

Old Ivy Leaguers from Boston, Westchester County, New Haven, in town on business, were matching themselves alongside the handsome younger men in their mid-thirties or forties. All were well-dressed, well-read, cultured, hustling businessmen. Some had beautiful young wives on their arms, others were with luscious girls. Intelligent, well-schooled, dressed-up couples were on the town after a day of being in town. Some were real Manhattanites, others were just there for a few days to absorb the city, the life, the adrenaline, the excitement of the Big Apple to winter on, back at Hartford, Springfield, Bangor or Fall River. Home they would go to their humdrum upper-middle-class lives, replete from their big city fix.

Somewhere among these people, was the odd solitary, serious drinker, or unaccompanied, middle-aged, very good-looking woman, the divorcee on a handsome pay off. Sculpted about equally by money and loneliness, she would be rationalising herself into some kind of a life, awaiting her currently married friends' arrival to cheerfully underscore her isolation. Tana noticed the occasional pair of handsome, wealthy homosexuals, cock and hen, clucking kindness and charm to each other.

The social mix was topped off by the foreigners. There were ambassadors from Spain, Portugal, or Latin America, with beautiful young men or women on their arms, free for an hour from the diplomatic circuit. Then there was the old Italian industrialist with the beautiful blonde, chic French actress; the eccentric fifty-five year old Englishman, still sporting uncertainly a monocle and his original school tie. Or the elegant blue-black African, unidentifiable because uncelebrated by the media for not having practised genocide in his country, lacking the tyrant's kudos, but felt to be important because drinking with the token black representatives from the White House and two white senators from the Mid-West. Or the three Arabs (so rarely one Arab: so often in groups), impeccably dressed, eyes cruising the women, and faces dead straight; trying to put a southern governor in their pockets while the young Californian, old school friend and associate, plays sycophant and pimp.

What stood out among them in the room were the couples that sat by themselves emanating some sort of peace and contentment, the occasional couple who were attractive rather than beautiful, and quietly interesting. They seemed to exude a kind of loving togetherness without the label of relationship. Yes, the ones who stood out in the room were the ones who were still without labels to identify them. Labelless people might score high in the bar this evening. They were rare, but present. There were always one or two couples like that.

Tana Dabra was laughing at Rashid. He amused her by zeroing in on a person or a couple in the bar and making up a story about them. He etched out a life for them in diluted acid, and made his little vignettes seem possible, believable.

He had just finished one about an upper-crust dowager-type and her gigolo when the waiter arrived with their third round of Margaritas. Tana Dabra, well on her way to being tipsy, picked up her glass and clinked it to Rashid's.

'To you, Rashid. How can I ever say thank you enough for Paris, and Dominica, and New York and for today? For all the things you keep adding to my life. Where do we go from here?'

'To the altar.'

'You make it sound like a sacrifice.'

'It is, for some, the ultimate sacrifice. And I am beginning to think that's the way you see it. You're not going to die, you know. I am not going to take you like some vestal virgin to the block to have your throat slit and draw your blood to appease some pagan god. I am going to marry you, and our lives will be rich and full as they have been these many days. I warn you, Tana Dabra, I am going to stop asking, and I might even do something drastic.'

She began to laugh, too happy and sated with his seduction of her to take him seriously. 'That sounds thrilling. Like what?'

'I'll kidnap you. Run off with you, and keep you locked up in a wooden palace in Turkey, where no one will ever find you. Until you come to your senses and marry me.'

She asked for another drink in between spurts of laughter.

'Oh, I suppose you think me too civilised to do such a thing. What a surprise I have for you! No, I've changed my mind. Before I would lock you up in my wooden palace, I would take you to a marvellous place, Oda Lala, it's called, for a month. Yes, I would lock you up in Oda Lala's, a house created for nothing but lovemaking and sexual bliss. And *not* allow you to participate. I'll torture you with celibacy until you set the day for our wedding.'

Then they both began to laugh, and Rashid suddenly realised it was not a bad idea at all; in fact it was a very good idea.

Rashid woke Tana Dabra with a cup of strong Fortnum & Mason, Royal Blend tea at six in the morning. One of her great assets as far as Rashid was concerned was that Tana Dabra was a morning person: once awake, she was alert and invariably ready to move in on her day – one of the many things they had in common. He attributed her sharpness in the morning to having been on the run in Ethiopia. You do, after all, have to be quick to save your life.

She sat up in bed drinking her tea. He kissed her naked shoulder, and then asked, 'I have two questions for you, and I want you to answer them with absolute honesty. And then promise me to remember your answer, no matter what happens between us after that. Okay?'

This was something new. She smiled, and then said, 'Okay.'

295

'Do you love me enough to forgive me anything? And, please, my dear, think well before you answer. And the other question is: are you courageous enough to follow the dictates of your heart, no matter what?'

Tana Dabra looked away from Rashid, lowered her eyes, and sipped her tea. She took her time in answering, and when she did she raised her eyes and looked into his.

'Yes, would have to be my answer to both.'

Rashid was quite overcome. It was more than he had hoped for. He covered his emotions well enough, removed the cup from her hands and placed it on the table next to the bed. Then he raised her hands to his lips and kissed her fingers.

They were dressed and at the heliport by 7.15 am where they were surprised by a photographer and a reporter, both of whom Rashid knew well. They started off with that well worn line, 'Rumour has it, Rashid . . .'

Rashid cut in and said, 'Rumour is right this time. I have asked her, and she still hasn't said yes, and I will keep asking until she does. Now, one picture and we must be off. I have promised Tana Dabra a day at the beach.'

The gossip columnist and her photographer pressed no further. They had a scoop, and a photograph of the world's newest, most sought-after glamour couple. They shot the picture of Tana Dabra dressed in a jump suit of fine amber-coloured cashmere and a waist-length, sleeveless chinchilla jacket, her hair tucked under a tight turban of black silk. Rashid appeared in a pair of worn jeans, black leather cowboy boots and a black leather Armani jacket.

Whirling over Long Island Sound Rashid produced

a breakfast basket. He never ceased to amaze her with the lengths he would go to surprise, please and enchant. Once again he seduced her, only this time with hot black coffee and the American doughnut: glazed, chocolate-dipped, jellied and just plain, to satisfy another of her passions. He watched her dunking and eating them, and licking her fingers, and he knew he had come to the end of his tether, waiting for her to set the date of their marriage. A plan was quickly taking shape in his mind.

The moment she placed her feet on the ground of Rashid's Southampton compound she had a good feeling about the place. Everything about it appealed to her. It was for Tana Dabra a Hollywood version of what a contemporary millionaire's Long Island house should look like.

After a full tour of the premises and introductions to the staff they went together to the garage. 'Can you drive?' he asked.

'Well, of course I can drive. I don't have a licence, but I can drive. Don't look so frightened. If you can drive in the highlands of my country, you can drive anywhere. Get in,' she ordered.

She slipped behind the wheel of one of the beach buggies. 'Just lead the way,' she insisted. They drove down a small road that followed the perimeter of the compound. At the far end, near one of the pavilions, was a dirt track that led to the dunes. Tana Dabra zigzagged down over the sand to the beach.

She stopped, and they watched the waves breaking on the shore line, dissolving and pulling back hard out to sea again. There were many whitecaps, and there was a chill in the air that the morning sun had not seen off. There was that feeling one gets by the ocean that the day is clear but rain is on its way and the night will be a wet one. It had the smell of rain at the beach.

Rashid hopped out, 'Alright, my lady, let's see what you can do. And try not to get stuck in the sand.'

She laughed. The sound of her laughter seemed to ride on the wind. She shifted gears and drove along the beach, the tyres skimming the water's edge. She went into top gear and placed her foot hard on the gas pedal. The car shot forward, and the wind pushed the turban-wrapped scarf off her head down around her neck. Her black hair danced in the air and the soft chinchilla fur of her jacket was flattened by the force of the wind swirling in the open beach buggy.

There wasn't a soul on the beach. It was rough, wild and glorious. This was the only way Tana Dabra liked to drive: in open, lonely places at top speed. She never sat behind a wheel any other time. She was a good distance down the beach from where she had left Rashid standing. So she shifted down and turned around in a flash, raising a great spray of sand, and then shot ahead.

She drove up and down the beach several times, and then rode over the sand dunes back towards Rashid and the compound. She liked to charge up one sand dune and then spin off it and crash down on to the beach with a bump, change gears and drive up along the rim of a dune, riding the length of it as far as the dirt road that led back to the house. Rashid walked up to the sandy track and sat on top of a dune watching her. He waved to her with thumbs up. She laughed and pulled the car up next to him.

'Hello, do you want to have a go with the buggy, or me?'

'Move over, showoff. No wonder you don't have a licence.'

They burst into the kitchen, happy but chilled from their beach buggying. The aroma of fresh, exquisite food, newly cut herbs, roasting meats and baking bread filled the kitchen.

'I am going to cook lunch for us. Jean and Li are busy getting on with a feast I have ordered for our dinner. This evening we will dine on steamed clams served in their natural broth, soft shell crabs sautéed in black butter and lemon and hot turtle consommé. We'll follow with lobster boiled in ocean water and seaweed, served hot and shelled on a bed of wild rice; roasted ears of corn just dripping with butter, and a really crisp celery salad. Then for dessert, we'll have fresh raspberry sorbet and genuine home-made, wafer thin, dark chocolate mints. Real New England fare, something else new in your life. I have selected the wines you have particularly enjoyed – a Muscadet with the clams, Grand Cru Chablis '75 with the soft shell crabs, and for the lobster a Pouilly Fumé '76.

'With all that going on the table for an early dinner, I thought I'd offer you a lunch of something light and difficult to master, to impress you with. To show you yet another side of Rashid Lala Mustapha.'

'You can cook? I am impressed. I would never have guessed it.'

'Well, just you wait around to see.'

'Would it burst your bubble if I said I think I would rather have a lie down and have you surprise me with lunch?'

'Yes,' was his unexpected answer. And pulling up a kitchen chair for her, he sat her down and handed her a stack of backdated *Gourmet* magazines to thumb through. 'Please don't rain on my parade.'

She grabbed his arm as he was about to turn away from her, and she said, 'I never want to do that. I just didn't realise that cooking was so important to you.'

'It's not the cooking that's so important to me, it's having you near me to admire my expertise. I'm a show off, like you are driving the beach buggy,' he answered with another of his wry smiles.

'*Touché*,' was her reply.

He occupied himself for the next hour in the kitchen, making lunch for Tana Dabra and himself – artichoke hearts with an especially light vinaigrette, individual cheese soufflés and a crisp, green salad in a lemon and walnut oil dressing. For dessert there were slices of stem ginger preserve and pineapple, and chocolate-covered Brazil nuts with Turkish coffee.

Jean would do the artichokes, and he would do the soufflés, the salad and dessert. He rolled up his sleeves and Li, the Chinese cook, who was in the kitchen, brought him a white chef's apron and helped Rashid put it over his head, tying it behind him. One of the chef's assistants, a local girl called Mary Miles, brought the ingredients out and placed them on the huge, old, white marble-top table in the centre of the kitchen.

Rashid began cracking eggs and separating them. The kitchen was buzzing. Rashid had a quality in him of creating energy wherever he worked or played.

A heavy baroque French silver tray, with a fine white linen and lace cloth on it, held several short-stemmed Waterford crystal glasses filled with a sparkling red wine. It was carried over to Rashid. He offered Tana Dabra a glass. He raised his own and said, 'To you, my black empress, welcome home.' She raised her glass and drank, then turned her back to him to stare out of the window, wondering how she could achieve her escape.

The feeling of being trapped by Rashid was not new to her. It had been surfacing on and off since Paris, but had always been dispelled because being with Rashid and in love overrode all such feelings. Tana Dabra had time to contemplate her anxieties about marrying Rashid while she watched him prepare their lunch. She was most certainly in love and happy with him. The idea of marriage with him seemed right and inevitable to her. Yet she stubbornly would not set a date. Was it a trapped feeling, or was it fear of making a commitment to share her life with another human being? She would have to work that out. And soon, because Rashid was showing signs of annoyance with her about it. Tana Dabra resolved not to push Rashid too far. She sensed danger there.

They had their lunch in the all-glass building with a sliding roof off among the trees on the other side of the compound. The pool was Olympic size, with hard white marble stairs all around it that seemed to dissolve as they descended under the water. It was surrounded by a tropical jungle of the most exotic trees: date, fan and kenitia palms almost twenty feet high, papyrus in blossom, yukkas, mimosa all in flower and flame trees. There were bushes of hibiscus in flower and a myriad of bougainvillea colours everywhere, vines of stephanotis and orchids copious in size and variety. There was even a vast patch of arum lilies. Under the sliding roof a fine, almost invisible, silk net was stretched. It gently restrained the tropical birds and parrots that lived in the pool house from flying away. Here freedom was confined.

Lunch was a seduction of the palate. Afterwards they swam and talked away the afternoon, filling each other with visions of all they wanted to see and do in the world together. They dressed and walked along the beach once more and watched the helicopter that was to fly them back to New York that evening return across the ocean to land again on the beach.

Back in the living room of the house, awaiting dinner, they drank champagne while lolling among cushions in front of an open fire. From an imperial jade box Rashid slid out a small, flat slab of jade and placed it on the floor next to him. From a drawer in the box he took a small jade pick. It was flat on both sides and had one edge that was sharp. He scooped up cocaine on the end of the pick, and with the blade of jade he prepared half a dozen lines for himself and Tana Dabra. Lifting the small jade tray and a jade snorting straw, he offered it to Tana Dabra. She took a deep sniff and got a hit almost at once. The two sniffed all the coke before they sat down to dinner.

It was with infinite joy that Rashid watched Tana Dabra all through the delectable meal. Everything approached perfection. She ate and drank with gusto, and afterwards admitted to being extremely high, happy and replete not only with food but with love.

They returned to the living room and as they stood together in front of the stone fireplace wall, Rashid served her the hot and sweet Turkish coffee himself. He saw to it that she drank it all down in one swallow, insisting that it would sober her. And then he caught the tiny cup and saucer as it fell from her hand, and her, in one adept movement.

'When next you wake, you will be in Istanbul, my lovely.' He whispered in her ear as he bore her in his arms across the room and through the front door to the helicopter waiting on the grass in the centre of the compound.

Chapter 14

It was not unusual for Adam and his son Joshua to have a casual business meeting in the Peramabahce Palace. But it was unusual for Joshua to bring with him an associate. The Peramabahce Palace was home to the Corey clan. A visitor who was not in the clan signalled 'intruder', no matter how welcome the guest was made.

Mirella looked down from the first-floor balcony into the three-storey, white marble great hall. The three men sat at a round marble table under a giant acacia tree. Her curiosity was aroused when servants brought three telephones and placed one before each of the men.

She walked along the gallery that ringed the room, and started down the long staircase. Looking through the huge window walls that faced the garden and the Bosporus beyond, she hoped to see the clan arrive from their own house, the *yali*, some distance up the river, where they lived. Instead she caught sight of a Russian cruiser passing an enormous American cruise ship. For several minutes, the gigantic ships blotted the other river traffic from her view: the working *caiques*, the ferry boats, the speedboats and yachts, the merchant ships on the way to Galata and the

Golden Horn to unload their supplies.

The tinkling sound of water, played by the antique Arab fountain in the middle of the hall, was like soothing music. The shabby palm and date trees of great age and size distracted Mirella from thinking winter would soon be upon them. They would once again be on the move to New York for the Christmas holidays. But the hall's other greenhouse inhabitants – mimosa, and azalea, magnolia, orange and cherry trees without a blossom – told the time of year. She could not ignore it.

It was an unusually warm day and the sun high-lighted the garden between the great hall and the river's edge with contrasting patches of brightness and shadow. The garden was still beautiful with beds of white chrysanthemums, dozens of varieties, without a blem-ish of rust upon them. The many shades of green – dark and foresty, bright and grassy, olive, limey and soft and pale against the white marble palace – were still, at this time in November, one of the finest sights on the Bosporus.

In the triple-domed, seventeenth-century pavilion in the garden sat the Princess Eirene, flanked by her two eunuchs, playing a game of cards with Marlo Channing and Rashid. Little Alice was running around the pavilion playing house with several of her favourite dolls. Servants carried things to and from the pavilion and the garden in preparation for tea.

Mirella looked guiltily up the stairs from where she had come, her study. She thought of what momentous manoeuvres were being set in motion there. But Brindley had it all in hand. She had made the deci-sions, signed the documents, and at this very moment the writs were being issued. Within hours, every piece of skulduggery Rashid had practised upon her estates would be challenged in the Turkish, Greek, English, and American courts. She would tell him, not now in front of the others, but tonight in the love pavilion his great-grandfather had built for her great-grandmother and that Rashid had restored for Mirella.

His surprise arrival that morning in Istanbul could not have been more timely. The writs: she had worried how she would tell Rashid about them over the telephone. Now that problem was solved. Adam was leaving after tea for an archaeological expedition. That too was timely. Since the baby had been born, she had seen less of Rashid than ever before. Both of them had expressed dissatisfaction with that.

The first time she had seen him was a few days after arriving from the States at the Peramabahce Palace with the baby. He had flown in to Istanbul for only a few hours, just to see her and the infant. It had been the child's name day. They were having only the clan, Princess Eirene, Brindley and Deena, and Rashid present for the ceremony. It was to be conducted by a long-time friend of Adam, an orthodox monk from Mount Athos, who was on his way to Bethlehem for a conference with the patriarch.

It had been only a few weeks since Mirella and Rashid had been together. Yet both had, in very different ways, been through tremendous emotional changes. She had given birth to a child. He had found love and the woman he wanted for his wife. Mirella at that stage had known nothing about Tana Dabra and Rashid. Her concern had been with her own feelings. Might she react differently to him? Not want him erotically anymore? Might he not want her? Those had been her anxieties, until he had entered the sitting

307

room and they had come face to face.

It had been magic. Nothing, no one, neither distance nor time could dispel what they felt for each other. Mirella's heart had pounded so hard on seeing him that she had feared someone in the room would hear it. She had wanted him. She had been in an agony of passion until he had walked up to her, taken her hands in his, and kissed them. Then he kissed her first on one cheek, then on the other, and then a third time on the lips, sweetly, tenderly, to cover his own wild desires for her. She had calmed down the moment they made physical contact, their mutual chemistry casting its familiar spell. Composure had been maintained. No one in the room saw them as other than they always were: the closest of friends, happy to see each other, thrilled to be in each other's company.

Adam had been in the room too, with Deena and Moses. All the others were downstairs milling around in the great hall, or en route from the *yali*. Rashid had shaken Adam's hand, slapped him on the back, and, after greeting the others, insisted he must see the baby at once. The nurse and nanny were sent for and the child produced.

Rashid had fallen in love with her at once. They formed an immediate bond, there was no doubt about that. It was not the itchy-kitchy-koo thing adults do with newborn babies. This was love. He kissed and caressed the baby and played with her fingers and looked for her toes. It could have been embarrassing, had not Rashid kept saying to Adam how proud he was to be the baby's godfather, how grateful he was for the honour, how happy for them both.

When at last he could be diverted and the little girl was taken away, Rashid had produced a gift for

Mirella in honour of the birth of her first child: a pair of perfect, dazzlingly beautiful, icy pink pearls, each the size of a child's glass marble, set in a circle of diamonds. She had placed them on her ears at once. The lustre of the pearls was a marvel of natural beauty. For Adam he had produced six boxes of the finest vintage Havana cigars to accompany his ruminations on fatherhood.

The baby had been named and blessed next to the fountain Mirella was looking at now. But that day the room had been filled with fresh white flowers, lilies and tulips, large branches of lilacs, orchids, poppies and hundreds of white, full-blown roses, whose scent had hung upon the air. In the fountain had floated white gardenias, dozens of them.

As godfather, Rashid would hold her at the christening, which was to come a few weeks later. But on this day it was Joshua, the infant's half-brother, number two godfather, who had held the baby. Mirella had stood behind him dressed in a heavy, white silk wrap-around blouse that crossed over in a low V between her full breasts and was tied at the side on her waist. Its long and voluptuous, billowing pleated sleeves closed tight over her wrists just above her diamond cuff bracelets. The long, black silk, crepe skirt clung sensuously to her now nearly trim figure.

At her neck were the three diamond link necklaces, with the seal of her great-grandmother carved into the huge single jewel hanging from each. These were the famous Oujie necklaces that had once belonged to Rashid's great-grandfather's two brothers. They had been stripped of them when the two men fell from grace for plotting against the sultan's great love, the Kadin Roxelana Oujie, the Jewess, the most powerful woman at court during the last opulent years of the Ottoman Empire. She was Mirella's great-grandmother, her benefactress, the ancestor who had lately materialised in the form of a legacy. The seal of her influence was on Mirella's life as surely as her seal now hung threefold upon Mirella's neck.

She had worn no other jewels, not even her wedding band. And that should have told Rashid something. It should have been an indication to him of how serious she was about this name day, of why she had refused to tell anyone but Adam her choice of name for her baby.

But Rashid was Rashid. When he saw them he took no warning. He could only think that soon, one day soon, just as he had taken back so much of the Oujie legacy, those too would be his. That, much as he loved Mirella, she would be stripped of them as once his family had been. He would replace them, compensate her with even finer necklaces, but those she could not have. They would pass back to the Lala Mustapha family. And, for the first time since he left her in bed that morning, he thought of Tana Dabra, and what a happy day it would be for him when he draped each of them over her head and around her neck.

When the old monk had asked Joshua the baby's name, Joshua turned to Mirella. She hesitated for a few seconds while she slipped her arms through those of Rashid and Adam who were standing on either side of her. Then she had announced very clearly to Joshua and the clan standing behind them, 'We name the baby Kadin Roxelana Oujie Wingfield Corey, in honour of my great-grandmother. And with her name goes a vow to restore the Oujie legacy to all that it once was, when my great-grandmother was in power. This is my gift to our first daughter.'

Joshua was quick to understand the significance of the baby's name, and Mirella's vow. He was so proud of his stepmother. The fight against Rashid's treachery was on. He loved Mirella more than ever for going after what was hers, and the style with which she had fired the first shot. He had repeated the name at once to the monk. The brief ceremony was over.

Rashid could not remember any time, ever, that he had been more surprised by Mirella. He had waited and waited for some reaction after he had successfully master-minded, with the help of Christos and the business syndicate, his vast property take-over on the Oujie legacy. When not only she but Adam too had chosen to ignore what he had done, Rashid could only assume that Mirella might not have liked it, but did not want to lose Rashid over it. So maybe she would take her losses in silence and like a lady. Probably Adam was furious with Rashid for pulling off the coup, and with Mirella for allowing him to get away with it.

Mirella, at the moment of the naming, had waited for some reaction from Rashid, for his body to tense, a look of anger to flash in his eye, even for him to walk out. There had been nothing. Not one indication that he was angry, or even aware that it had been a declaration of war, a new vendetta in the age-old saga of two Turkish dynasties. Had he not caught the significance of her action?

In fact fury gripped Rashid, impassive as he had seemed. She was hurtful. She was devious. Ever since she had received the legacy she had vacillated: proud one minute to be involved with something so momentous, overwhelmed the next, and anxious simply to liquidate, to cast off such responsibility.

For himself, it was clear cut. Strictly a passionate

hatred and vendetta of the Lala Mustaphas against Roxelana Oujie. Yet she had given her beautiful baby those dreadful names, Kadin – how could she take the gross liberty of changing a title into a given name? – Roxelana Oujie. She knew how he despised them and the woman who had borne them. The only thing that made it easier for him to accept what she had done was that he had really had no idea that she could be such a vindictive bitch. And he rather liked that. He had found something new in Mirella to play with.

As the monk intoned his blessings, Rashid had to ask himself, 'Why did she do it?' The only motive he could come up with was some kind of revenge for his latest coup. With that in mind, and disappointed that she had not given the infant at least one of his names, as he had expected, he nonetheless exerted every bit of his willpower to conceal his anger.

She had seen him alone for only a few minutes that afternoon. During the party Mirella had quietly retreated to the nursery to feed the baby. Rashid had bided his time, and then found a moment to slip away unnoticed. He had entered the nursery very quietly, Mirella was sitting in a rocking chair, one breast fully exposed and offered to her baby, her arms cradling Kadin, while Kadin sucked voraciously.

Mirella had smiled at Rashid. He had turned around and twisted the key in the door lock. Then he had gone to her, knelt down on his knees, and watched the baby take her milk. She was the most beautiful, seductive infant he had ever seen and he loved her. He felt he would always love her. No matter how many children he might himself father, he would never love any one of them more than this one. Mother and child brought a tear to his eye. He had slipped his hand under

Mirella's blouse. Without disturbing Kadin, he had exposed the other breast, and cupped it in his hands. He saw Mirella react to his caresses, sensed the change in her breathing. He rolled the enlarged nipple between his fingers and watched the rich milk ooze from it. He lowered his lips to it, took the breast as fully as he could in his mouth and sucked.

It had been a moment of near-sexual excitement for both. When he had released the nipple, milk kept spurting and ran over Mirella's breast. Rashid had taken a hankie from his pocket and wiped her breast. He kept dabbing the nipple in the hope of staunching the flow of milk. He had placed the silk hankie over it, and then Mirella's hand to keep it in place. He had said no word to her until after he kissed her passionately on the lips. Overcome with desire for her, all he could whisper was, 'I will always want you, and have you, and it would be good for you to remember that it is your love for me that has broken down my resistance to commitment and an enduring love. I love our baby, yours, Adam's, and mine. You have done so well for all of us. I have to go now. I'll call in the morning, as usual.'

The next time she saw him, he had done it again, flown in for just a short visit for the christening, a small but magnificent affair he arranged by telephone from various parts of the world. And he had arrived with a christening gown fit for a princess.

The Princess Eirene had offered the material for the dress, an antique piece of dark ivory silk satin, still perfect, although it dated from the early eighteenth-century. Its fifty-two exquisite lace flowers were antique as well. Each one of them had been hand-stitched onto the christening robe, likewise a hundred

313

and fifty-eight small but perfect, icy pink pearls. The hem was an inch deep of rose cut diamonds. The baby's cap matched the long, flowing dress.

By that time the papers were full of gossip and speculation about Rashid and Tana Dabra. Adam had persisted with questions about the couple's relationship. Once he had the answers, and after Rashid had admitted that the exotic and clever Tana Dabra was stringing him along without giving him any commitments about the future, he was satisfied that his white knight and friend, Tana Dabra Ras Magdala Makoum, could take care of herself. She would come to no harm in the hands of Rashid. He had met his match, at last. The signs were there. Rashid was truly in love. Adam noted the symptoms. It had also been Adam and not Rashid who had given the assurance Mirella was seeking that, whatever happened between Rashid and Tana Dabra, hers and Rashid's relationship would never change. His words had been, 'I guess it takes one well-worn reprobate who has succumbed to marriage to spot another who is about to. I am sure that Rashid would be a great deal more relaxed about it if he was not so busy assuring Tana Dabra that their marriage will never change his other attachments and relationships. Surely Tana Dabra rumbled that straight out and took it in her shapely stride!'

Sensing Mirella's anxiety that their *ménage à trois* might suffer a drastic change, he had of course said it to dispel her nagging anxiety that Rashid would leave her. The pain and fear of losing Rashid lifted from her heart at once. They had been lying in bed ready for sleep. Mirella reached out and squeezed his hand, and he slowly pulled her close into his arms.

'You don't miss much, Adam,' she whispered,

recognising the same subtlety with which he always made the point, but never referred directly to the subject of their unusual three-way relationship. She was happy he could not see the expression of relief on her face in the darkness of their bedroom.

'I keep half an eye open.'

'And I love you as I could never love any other man.'

'I'll open both eyes to that.'

And then they had made love, had sex for the first time since the birth of the baby. They slipped into their own erotic world, renewing every aspect of their raunchy intercourse, and at dawn fell asleep, happy in themselves and the life they had made.

The third time Mirella and Rashid met after the birth of Kadin had been when Adam had gone off on business for a few days. During that time Rashid had been on a cruise with Tana Dabra off the coast of Turkey. Rashid had been making his usual daily calls to her during this time from the yacht. Then suddenly one day there had been a second call. He wanted her, had waited long enough. Was it too early after the birth of the baby? He could stay with her for twenty-four hours, no more. He wanted her, he needed her, he had to have her. They had met in the love pavilion. She had thought they would talk then. There was a great deal to talk about. But as soon as they saw each other, words were superfluous. The sexual chemistry frothed between them. They divided their time between the pavilion and the House of Oda Lala, steeped in their own passionate lust and nothing more. Mirella had known he had abandoned Tana Dabra to two bodyguards and the other guests on the yacht, to re-establish what they meant to each other, and to prove to her that nothing need change for them. She was abundantly joyful.

As for Rashid, being with Mirella and Humayun at Oda Lala's, the house where he sexually enslaved all his women, tried to enslave Mirella, and in his house, the pavilion, in his beloved Istanbul, only whetted his appetite to seal his relationship with Tana Dabra, to bring her home. He would make her a part of his household, his world, the place where he was close to his ancestors, and where he hoped they would create a new dynasty to perpetuate the line of the Lala Mustaphas. It is good thus, he had thought then. What had these women, Mirella and Tana Dabra, in common, that they should have such power as to make him want to be one with them throughout their lives?

Adam watched his wife walking down the last few stairs and towards him. The men rose. Joshua kissed Mirella in greeting, while Adam introduced her to Wendell Beezely, a man very high up in Adam's company, the Corey Trust.

'I'm sorry about this, Mirella,' Adam apologised. 'What with the clan arriving to say goodbye, my archaeologist friends' coming and goings before we leave for this dig, and now this little emergency, I'm afraid the place is a bit like a three-ring circus.'

She began to laugh as she took a seat with the men. 'It's not a problem,' she said, 'it's exciting. There's always excitement living in this house. You attend to what you have to. I'll see – or rather Moses and I will see – that everyone is comfortable. What's happening, by the way?'

The three men looked at each other, and Mirella

could sense the excitement of their quick, intelligent minds. They were able to cut through preliminaries to the heart of what concerned them. It was Adam who spoke.

'Joshua is having a frustrating time over a very important bill he is trying to get passed in the US Senate. He has had trouble with several state representatives. He wanted to catch me before I drop out of the present for a while and go back in time, at that Hittite mound we're excavating.'

'I welcome Dad's and Wendell's suggestions,' Joshua added. 'They'll be useful. They might give a point or two that would help me get the bill passed when I go in front of the Senate committee in a few days' time. It's damned important for the Corey Trust. And a hell of a lot of other conglomerates, too.'

'And I, Mrs Corey,' said Wendell Beezely, 'have been working with Joshua, setting up an enormous deal involving an oil exchange with an Arab country. Josh and I felt we were mishandling it somehow, because it's not moving fast enough. We got a hunch we should push for immediate completion. We reckon the deal is getting sloppy. And we're not going to lose that deal. So we have flown in to see Adam and hear what he thinks. Sorry about the intrusion.'

'Not at all, Mr Beezely. I'm fascinated. May I sit in on this for a while, Adam?'

'Of course,' he answered, delighted by her interest. 'Okay, how do we stand at present?' he asked, turning his attention back to the men and the problem at hand.

'We sent a telex two days ago. An ultimatum that the deal must be closed on or before a certain date. Otherwise we drop the negotiations. That date was today. They're going to ask for another extension. We

want to know what you think, Adam,' Wendell Beezely said.

Adam had been aware of the impending deal for
some time. He wanted a few more details. Within ten
minutes the three men were hyped up over the deal.
They backed Wendell and Joshua's hunch. They were
determined now to solve the problem to their advantage as soon as possible.

Joshua rang through to his father's secretary and
two assistants in the study. He had them bring to the
great hall the latest data on the project, together with
their private telephone directories, on Adam's instructions.

Adam said to Joshua, 'Okay, the form is we sell at
once to the highest bidder. Only we select the
buyers. We have been good guys long enough,
keeping the deal warm for just one buyer. Wendell,
I'll handle the call to China. You take the Saudis.
You Josh, get the US Agricultural Department on
the line. A guy called Pope. It's your deal. We'll
play the other bidders to get what you want.
Remember we lay the pressure on for that and only
that. Whatever happens, we cannot lose. Now, how
do you want to play it with your man, guys?'

Joshua took over, 'Simple, Dad. With all three
buyers we deal directly with the man at the top. The
guy who makes the real decisions. Unless the Saudis
come through within the hour, we sell to the highest
bidder. If they lose, they'll have to wait for another
commodity oil package to be put together.'

'That sounds fine to me.'

'And me,' asserted Wendell.

Mirella remained silent but intrigued. She just
hoped the family would not descend upon the great

318

hall and force the men to retreat into Adam's study. Not for a while at least.

The three men picked up their telephones. The dealing started. Adam spoke to his man in China. An offer resulted at once. Joshua held up a piece of paper for the others to see the offer made by the State Department man. Wendell, dealing directly with an Arab prince, shocked him into action by pushing for a decision within the hour. He then passed him over to Adam. Adam knew the prince from way back.

'Look, old friend, you people have been sitting on this deal far too long. We close in forty minutes, with or without you. Wendell was right when he told you he holds back nothing. Your men should have moved faster. Now you're facing competition. You bid against China and the US. We take the best offer. I'm passing you back to Wendell. This is his deal. And, old friend, can I just say that if I were in your place heads would roll for what this delay is going to cost you? Nice to have spoken with you. I'll see you in a few weeks' time anyway, in Paris.'

The bids were in. What should have been a simple sale was now a scramble. Adam had turned it in minutes into a delicate geo-political game. The three were hooked, and the Corey Trust was going to do better even than expected as a result. They now had a choice to sell for gold, silver, or oil.

Ten minutes before the hour was up, Mirella had to leave them. The clan had arrived by boat and were descending on the garden and the pavilion. She could not bear them to interrupt Adam in the great hall.

The separate strands of her life now kept intertwining, maybe too much. But that was how things seemed to be most of the time. Everything had changed from that moment she had learned about her legacy. Had it really been only two years before?

She took Kadin from Muhsine, who carried her from the *yali*, where the baby had a nursery as well as in the Peramabahce Palace. But she did not have the child for long because Rashid left the card game to play with the pretty, good-natured baby. As soon as Mirella could settle everyone in the garden she excused herself for a few minutes. She'd be back right away. Then she rushed into the house, eager to know what had happened.

Champagne glass in hand. Adam was giving a toast. The men drained their glasses. All were laughing and talking at once, congratulating each other on the amazing deal that had been made. It was a businessman's dream, a deal headed for the record books once it was out, a vast fortune made in less then an hour.

Adam suggested that Joshua and Wendell get in touch with their assistants and with their stockbrokers, at once, before the news hit the market. Might as well put some icing on the cake. The three issued instructions, what to buy and what not to sell. Then Adam turned the company's portfolio over to Joshua and Wendell and a squadron of assistants, secretaries and public relations men. Adam, of course, would not be available for comment when the news broke.

Mirella stood silently watching them. Adam saw her first, went to her with a bottle and a glass and poured her champagne.

'Join the toast. We have just had a terrific time.'

'What happened?' she asked, avid for the details. She savoured the swift, knifelike jabs the men had needed to make their deal. She wanted to learn ruthlessness, such as Adam surprised her with in winning his deal. She would have a use for it in handling the Oujie legacy affairs.

'To put it simply, Wendell and Joshua have been working for months on a commodities package: coffee, rice and wheat from all our own holdings. They had an instinct to move fast. For all sorts of financial and political reasons they were right. The Corey Trust did not want paper money for this particular deal. We were looking for a trade. We'd have settled for oil, gold or silver. Our preference was for oil, but the Saudis were playing a waiting game with us. They didn't want to give up the deal, nor the oil either. Greed. Hating to pay up until the last minute. There are times you can make millions that way. But that's not the way we do business at the Corey Trust. They gave their word; they should have completed. Instead they kept asking for extended completion dates. They were playing their own waiting game with rising prices. Their manipulations have cost them a bomb: in round figures, nine hundred million dollars more in oil than originally negotiated for.'

'But even that's not the best part,' continued Joshua, reliving his excitement. 'In order to satisfy the losers, Wendell has sold next year's output for the market value at that time. It increases proportionately with inflation. On top of that, there's a 30 per cent fee for handling, to the Chinese. Payment is half now, half on delivery, in gold bullion.

'That just about pushes the Corey Trust into number two, possibly even number one place for the wealthiest conglomerate trading in the world.'

Mirella sat down at the table for a moment, dazed by what she had just heard. Adam sat down next to her, all smiles.

'It's the deal that's the excitement, making the kill. There is nothing like the big kill, the big win. But the thrill only lasts such a short time. It's good to remember that part of wheeling and dealing: fast-lane, fast-changing finance is in a world all its own, where men like us are powerful enough to manipulate the world's currencies and influence the politics of entire nations. Fast-lane traffic like that can just as easily leave you bruised. I guess the secret is never to allow it to leave you bloodied or bowed. A good rule of thumb for your own protection is, stay always true to yourself, no matter what.

'Okay, fellas, shop's closed. Tea, family and friends. And then I'm going digging. I wish you were coming with us, Mirella. You were invited, remember, and it's going to be a thrilling excavation. I have good feelings about it. There is an area a few miles from the mound that may throw up some of those distinctive monumental rock sculptures. And to think they are on your land, land that has been the Oujies' as long as anyone can remember. Think again about joining us. You'd never be bored. My guess would be that the Anatolian plateau holds many of your ancestors' secrets. You can travel and discover, while I dig.' Adam said this as he placed his arm around her. They walked away from Joshua and Wendell, who were about to retreat to Adam's library to make more calls to New York about their deal.

'I know. It's just that the baby is too young. I don't want to leave her for three weeks, not now. She won't stay a baby for long. And, that aside, with all Kadin's other surrogate mothers, Aysha, Giuliana, and even Marlo to love her, and Muhsine and Moses to spoil her, she might forget me. They love Kadin so much.

We are very attached to each other's children. Sometimes I can hardly believe this extended family of ours works so well.'

She punched him playfully on the arm, then added,'You've got it all, haven't you?'

'A fair amount of it, yes. It only takes courage to live by your own inner truth to get it all.' He began to laugh at his own words. 'And luck, and hard work. And inherited wealth to start you off with. And great parents. And, and, and.'

'Oh, shit, he's parading some of those inner truths of his. A slice of the Adam Corey philosophy. I can't keep up with the intellectual walkabout,' said Marlo teasingly, coming up behind them. 'I can't stay, I'm on the run. I've a million things to do before I leave for London,' she continued as she lured Adam away from Mirella and entwined her arms around his neck to kiss him.

It was a friendly kiss. A teasing kiss. It still made Mirella bristle, and jealousy almost flare into a flame, until Marlo turned to her, and whispered in her ear as she went to kiss Mirella on the cheek, 'Don't be a ninny, I only do it to see you bristle.' As she looked Mirella in the eyes, the two women laughed.

They had become good friends, in spite of Mirella's still believing that Marlo Channing, the Katharine Hepburn of the photo journalist world, was the only woman as close to Adam as she was. She watched and listened to her now, and saw a light come in Adam's eyes that was never there for anyone but Marlo. The romance between them and the frenetic sexual relationship were long since gone, but the love lingered. That was perhaps the most remarkable thing about all Adam's former mistresses who lived in his *yali*. The love was still there, on their side and on his. And that was what Marlo was talking about to Adam just then.

The three of them walked past the pavilion and waved to the Princess and Rashid and the others inside. Adam excused himself for a few minutes longer. They sat on a white marble bench and Mirella listened to the sophisticated Marlo who preferred war to peace, the passion of the moment to love. The world's newspapers and magazines labelled Marlo Channing 'trouble', and pursued her for coverage of the stories she chose. The beautiful, aggressive, clever Marlo, who wore out men as most women wear out shoes, and discarded them without a thought, was winning Mirella's heart to her, yet again, with her plea to Adam. Even more so when Mirella tried discreetly to leave the pair of them, lest she intrude on their privacy.

'No, don't leave, Mirella. This concerns you as well as all of us at the *yali*. It's about life after Adam, life after he has taken a wife and had another baby, a legitimate one in the eyes of the law. It's about we women in Adam's unusual household who have lived happily as in a modern-day harem for so many years.'

'All my children are legitimate, and are my heirs. I've seen to that, and you know it, Marlo.'

'That's not what this is about, Adam. This is about you and your wife, the way you live and love each other, your marriage. It's touched us deeply and changed the lives of everyone around you. Because you are no longer terrified of the power of that kind of love, you've matured and added more to yourself, and consequently to those closest to you – us women in your life, and our children.

'The whole point of what I am trying to say is that Muhsine, Giuliana, Aysha and I have begun to understand in these last two years that we owe our own maturity not only to ourselves but to you as well. You loved and cared for us, and in a sense we all grew up together, and you love us still. There's a lot to be said for that. Not much on my part, because you know how ungrateful I can be. But the others, well, they have worn me down pointing out that life after Adam does not necessarily mean we cannot remain an extended family. They all have plans for their futures outside the *yali*, me included. But we have all agreed we want to add our outside lives, our after-Adam lives, into the family. That is, of course, if you and Mirella agree to have us.

'I never thought about it much before, but since you and Mirella have married, I have come to realise that the pair of you are dynasty builders. I myself think dynasties are trouble and bullshit. But I have a daughter whom I love, and you, Adam, are her father. I want her to grow up as part of the dynasty that is yours and Mirella's and our extended family's, until she is ready to think and choose for herself. Maybe Alice will grow up with the same belief in continuity, and the necessity for family and roots, that the pair of you have. Me, I'm not ashamed to say I want to be able to sponge off it, be a part of it on my terms, whatever those terms may be, or however they may change. That's all I have to say. Except that I expect my future to be no different from my past. So you know what to expect from me. As for the others, I agreed to do the groundwork for them to come and discuss their future plans with you, each of them on their own. In the end, all we really want is to stay as we are always, and bring our fortunes home, and have them integrated into the Corey dynasty.

'Now is it on, or is it off? Because if it's on, we need another *yali* close to ours, for the lovers, and husbands, and more babies. Not any more of mine, thank you, I'll never do that again. But for the others who *will* do that again, if the right man or husband is found.'

Mirella began to laugh. Marlo and Adam looked at her and were puzzled. Marlo interrupted her laughter, 'You don't want us.'

'No, no, you misunderstand. Less than an hour ago I walked out of my study and down the stairs into the great hall. I'd just taken on the fight of a lifetime to get back every last vestige of the Oujie estate for our daughter. All my life I have worked for the good of humanity, and here I was ready for the first time to fight for family and heritage. I looked around, anxiously waiting for you all to arrive from the *yali*, thrilled at the excitement of being part of all this,' she waved her arm to encompass everyone in the pavilion and sitting in the garden, 'and a part of me worried about what would happen if I didn't have you all to share in the burden and responsibility of raising Kadin. Not want you? I don't think I could live without you.'

Both women then turned their attention to Adam. His face had become flushed. He had listened almost without reaction to Marlo's plea and Mirella's words. He had never had any intention of doing anything about the women and the children in the *yali* other than what Marlo had asked him just now on their behalf. He had hoped so many times that they would want to stay within their unorthodox family and add to it. He had never expressed that wish, wanting it to

326

come from them. Now that it had, he was overwhelmed with joy at what had happened and at
Mirella's more than generous consent. The only words
he could find to say were, 'As it happens, I bought the
two wooden palaces on either side of the one we have
years ago, for our privacy and protection, in the hope
that one day we would expand into them. Which, it
seems, is what is going to happen.'

He rose from the bench and excused himself. The
two women watched him walk through the garden,
collecting by the hand Muhsine, Aysha and Giuliana.

'Christ. Some guy. No wonder we love him,' said
Marlo. There was sadness in her eyes and voice.

'Yes, no wonder,' echoed Mirella.

At last everyone left and the house was quiet. But
the excitement was still here. Mirella changed into a
black chiffon dress with a halter top that plunged
between her breasts to the waist, where a wide sash of
the same material was wound tightly. The dress flared
out over her hips and fell softly and voluptuously to
just above her knees. She wore diamond cuff bracelets
and diamonds on her ears and pinned above her left
breast. She slung an evening bag of black satin over
her shoulder and grabbed her black mink coat from
the coat cupboard.

She hurried from her bedroom, through the great
hall and the garden to the boathouse on the dock and
picked up a large flashlight. Rashid's motor launch and
one of the sailors she recognised from his schooner the
Aziz, were waiting for her at the wheel, another on the
dock. One of the men took her by the waist, swung her
over the side and lowered her slowly into the arms of
the other. Then he leaped after her, before she could

even slip her arms into the sleeves of her coat. The pilot revved the motors and slammed his foot on the accelerator. The sleek, black and silver launch shot forward and carved a deep arc in the water as it swung away from the house.

The night was very black; a sliver of white moon was as if pasted on the night sky. They bumped and bounced through the waves up the Bosporus. Mirella could see the lights of the love pavilion just faintly on top of the hill, through the trees. He was there waiting for her. Her heart raced, goaded by the thought of violent sexual intercourse. She felt a rush of warmth through her. She took her shoes off and walked as fast as she could up towards her rendezvous with her lover. A third of the way up the path that wound through the trees, she abandoned her coat on a bench, finding it easier to climb the steep hill without it. She hurried, faster and faster.

Rashid saw her flashlight bobbing and weaving through the trees. He was hungry for her, desperate to feel himself buried deep inside her. He had been filled with sexual tension for her since the afternoon. When he held Kadin in his arms and played with her, he could barely put out of his mind the thrill of his last encounter with Mirella, having the breast in his mouth and drinking her milk. Not that he wanted more of that, but it had given an edge to his half-jaded sexual appetite that a man like him should drink like a baby from a woman he longed to subdue totally, fulfilling his every erotic fantasy. And there was something else. Giving Mirella sexual satisfaction as no other man could, and holding back from the still-sleeping Tana Dabra, was all part of his excitement. Time had run out for Tana's game playing. If she wanted him she

328

would have to answer his demands. Marry him, and soon.

He flung open the door of the pavilion and ran down the hill to meet Mirella. He took no flashlight. The white moon, the lights from the pavilion, and the yellow beam of her light showed him the way.

At last he had her in his arms.

Chapter 15

Tana Dabra fought her way out of a fog of sleep. Before she opened her eyes she knew that she had been drugged. Her tongue felt woolly, her mouth dry. The first thing she did was to move her hands. No handcuffs. Then her feet. Not bound either. The sheets were soft and silky: she had not been kidnapped by enemies. Her mind was now clear and rational and she had no headache. Having taken this inventory, she thought of two things simultaneously: to sit up, open her eyes and make sure she wasn't dead; and Rashid Lala Mustapha.

She sat up like a shot and opened her eyes, and surprised the huge Turkish wrestler standing at attention against the door opposite the bed. He turned his head to one side and covered his eyes, in an almost delicate manner. Strange in a man with a neck as thick as a bull's and straining with muscles, and a head as big and smooth as a marble basketball, with one ear missing.

Tana Dabra ran her hand across her chest and breasts. She was naked. She pulled the sheet and the white cashmere blanket up to cover her nudity. She tried to ask him where she was, in French, English and Italian. No response. But he did look back at her and bow his head subserviently. When he looked at her again he had a broad, sweet smile that made him look even uglier. He raised his hand as if he were giving her a signal to wait. Then he turned around, unlocked the bedroom door and left the room, locking it behind him.

The room was impressively large. But she couldn't take it in for the moment. She was too thirsty to think of anything but liquid. It was there waiting for her: a carafe of spring water, two glasses and a pitcher of fresh peach juice. She drank all the water and three quarters of the Baccarat jug of juice before she sat back and looked at the room.

Of course, it had to be Rashid's. It was all different shades and textures of white: raw and gossamer silk, taffeta and damask from the handlooms of Lyons. Masculine and attractive, the Biedermeier furniture was of museum quality. But what dazzled and enchanted her were the early eighteenth-century Qajar paintings, portraits of Persian princes, dark and rich in jewel-like colours.

She found the bathroom, which was no less magnificent, even in the details of toothbrushes, pastes and bath oils, perfumes and soaps. An exquisite robe of ivory-coloured silk velvet embroidered all over with flowers of rose cut diamonds, the elegant wide sleeves cuffed in rows of moonstones, was laid out for her use. Two diminutive maids appeared to help her into the marble bath. They bathed and massaged her with oil of bluebell and jasmine. She tried to speak to them, but they said nothing. When she stood up and they showered her with clear, fresh rose water, she found their hands searching and trained to excite. Oh yes, only Rashid's handiwork could have produced such a bath place.

332

She took her time at the dressing table and arranged her hair in a coronet on top of her head. The maids, delighted with what they saw, produced tiny diamond birds on springs that trembled on the end of pins, and arranged them in her hair. She found her jewels in a case in one of the dressing-table drawers and clasped her now famous ruby around her neck.

He was waiting for her at the bottom of the staircase. She looked down into the large, oval-shaped white marble hall, at the ancient statue of the god Apollo poised on a pedestal of black volcanic rock. She waited for Rashid to say something. He didn't. Not until she was half way down the curved staircase.

'You look especially lovely this afternoon. I knew you would grace this house as no other woman ever has.'

'Then why not invite me instead of kidnapping me? What demon put it into your head to do such a stupid thing. Am I going to want to marry a man capable of such erratic behaviour?'

'Of course you will. So stop playing that kind of "I will-I won't" game.'

They were standing face to face now. Tana Dabra felt her anger growing stronger with each exchange. There was a glint of hardness and an arrogance in his eye that infuriated her even further. His handsomeness seemed to draw her to him in spite of her anger. She found him unbearably sexy. The sequence of erotic sensations his very presence set off in her only added to her anger, because it confirmed what they both knew: he could do what he wanted with her and she would have to forgive him; they were already each a part of the other's being. Wanting to reach out and touch him, wanting him to take her in his arms as she did, it called for great strength to stand her ground and slap him across the face. Without a moment's hesitation he slapped her back, smart and hard. He caught her off balance. She began to fall. He grabbed her in his arms and kissed her with a ferocity so intense it and the violence she felt in his slap frightened her. She struggled to tear herself away from him.

His strength seemed to double. He wrestled her down and pinned her onto the marble floor with his body, his hands fixing her outstretched arms by the wrists, pressing, always pressing his kisses upon her until she could resist no longer. Against her will, her body obeyed his passion for her and she relaxed into his kisses. Then the moment came that he was waiting for, from lying limply and submissively underneath him, she slowly came to life. She kissed him lovingly, before her passion and anger, for what he had done and for her unquenchable attraction to him, took hold of her once again. Tears of anger and frustration at her weakness for him filled her eyes as her body gave in, and gave in again, revelling in sensual delight. She tensed her body, her heart and her whole being under him. Then, for several seconds, she was lost somewhere in another world, and ecstasy flowed for her.

He listened to her whimper and whisper, 'Ohhh, yes, yes, dear God. God, yes, yes,' and whimper again from the sheer pain of such tremendous pleasure. Rashid placed his cheek against hers. Her face was hot, she was burning under dusky-coloured skin.

'I feel as if crucified by your strength and your passion for me. Why are you doing this to me?' she asked, barely above a whisper.

'Why are we doing it to each other?'

334

'Fear of love?'

'And commitment. It has to stop and now, right now, this fear of ours. Yes, ours. Yes, I am just as frightened as you are, but my fear is of losing you. That's why I kidnapped you, to show you how desperate I am. To prove to you that what we feel for each other is irreplaceable. Neither one of us is stupid. We aren't going to look a miracle in the face and run away from it. Because that's what our meeting was. Try and think what your life would revert to if I suddenly disappeared from it. Maybe you could bear it. Whether I could or not is questionable. And irrelevant, because I don't intend to. Nor do I intend that you will ever leave me. I will make you accept what we truly are to each other, and you will be my wife. Now, you can get up.'

He then very cautiously released the pressure on her wrists. Rising to his feet he pulled her up with him, and then thoughtfully rubbed her wrists to bring the circulation back into them. He helped her to rearrange her robe.

She had not said a word. What was there to say? He had stated his case. And the fact of the matter was that she believed he was being totally honest with her.

They gazed into each other's eyes and both were taken aback by the emotion they saw there. The moment of truth was strangely embarrassing to them. Tana Dabra made that small, swift movement with her chin and her nose and her eyes that transformed her into the royal being she was. His empress. He closed his eyes for one minute and took a deep breath, trying to still the excitement he felt. He readied himself for what he was certain fate had in store for him.

335

'Rashid, I would like us to marry as soon as we can, please. Maybe in no more than five days time, if that suits you?'

A smile crept across his lips and then spread over his face. 'Tana Dabra Ras Magdala Makoum, you're looking at an awfully happy man.'

She smiled back at him and said, 'I know, Rashid. I'm pretty happy myself.'

'We'll make a good life together, I promise you that.'

'Yes, I know, I have no doubt that we will.'

He began to laugh and, slipping his arm through hers, he kissed her. A lover's kiss. 'Where, when, how shall we do it?' He led her to the Queen Anne sofa against one of the walls.

Suddenly Tana Dabra was aware of the marble Apollo. The monumental beauty of it awed her. It distracted her from Rashid's question. 'That is the most beautiful sculpture I have ever seen. It surpasses Michelangelo's David in Florence and the Praxiteles Hermes at Olympia.'

She studied it for a minute or two in silence, and then she spoke, 'After I saw the Apollo in the centre of the west pediment of the Temple of Olympian Zeus, I dreamed that one day I would have a man such as that in marble or in flesh, and then my life would soar into the realms of greatness. What is he? Who is he? Where am I?'

Rashid was delighted by her reaction to the piece, the treasure of his collection, and answered her proudly, 'He is another Greek Olympian masterpiece and dates from the same period as that temple pediment, sometime around 460, created by one of the unknown masters of that time. He is Apollo. And where are you? In my house in Istanbul, soon to be our house in Istanbul.'

'Istanbul! You really did kidnap me! I mean, I knew it when I woke up. But, good heavens, Rashid, what a risk you took. I think the reality is just hitting me.'

'Oh, but I did take some precautions. If you remember, the last morning we were together in the Carlisle, I brought you a cup of tea and I asked you to answer two questions, and whatever your answers were, to remember them, no matter what happened between us. The questions were, "Do you love me enough to forgive me anything? and are you courageous enough to follow the dictates of your heart?" '

'And I answered both with a yes. You really ensnared me.'

'No, I merely protected our future life together.'

Tana Dabra rose from the settee and walked closer to view the statue, and then walked slowly around it, absorbing the beauty of Apollo. Rashid followed a few steps behind her. 'The Apollo in Olympia that I loved so much was watching a legendary battle between two neighbours. The battle is said to have started among the guests at the wedding of one king to the daughter of another. The drunken centaurs (horses with human upper parts) tried to ravish the Lapith women. What battles has your Apollo been witness to? Was ours his first? Will it be his last? I somehow doubt it.'

They were standing once more in front of the nearly life-size piece. Tana Dabra studied the face of the sculpture for a few minutes, silently, thoughtfully. Rashid understood well the thrill and power of such remarkable beauty, and it was a joy to share it with her. She turned to him and pondered his face, ran her finger along the bridge of his nose, touched his chin, traced his lips with it, and said, 'I think my dream was a prophetic one, and it's come true twice over. I have two Apollos, one of marble, the other of flesh and blood. I am twice blessed.'

'Then you love me?'

'Oh, yes. I love you. It may have taken a kidnapping to make me face that, but I have. Tell me, do you feed your former kidnap victims? I'm starved.'

'What do you mean "former"?' he asked.

'What do *you* mean, "what do you mean 'former'?"' she asked, more puzzled than worried.

'I mean, until we are wed for all the world to see, you will be my prisoner. After that, we will be as one, so there will be no need for such drastic measures.'

'You're not serious.'

'I'm serious.'

She gazed at him until, unable to hold back, she burst out laughing. 'What a man. Well, I had better get on with plans for our wedding. It might be fun to be your prisoner for a few days. But more, I doubt it.'

'I repeat,' he said, all smiles, and kissing her affectionately on the cheek and then the lips, slipping his hand inside her robe and caressing her breasts, 'When, where, how shall we do it?'

He took Tana Dabra's hand and, while walking together from the hall to his library, she said, 'Rashid, let me tell you what I would like most in the world to do about a wedding and afterwards. And please, if you hate the idea, say so, and I will understand, and we don't have to. But it is what would make me a most happy bride.'

In the library she took his hands in hers and she turned to speak to him face to face. 'I, as you know, am a Copt. You are a Muslim. I want to be married in

Ethiopia, by a Coptic priest. It will have to be in secret and we will have to sneak in and out of the country before the authorities find out we have been there. That won't be too difficult, if we pretend until the last minute we are just jet-set lovers. I know exactly how we can do it. We will go in through the Sudan at a remote and relatively safe place. We will pitch camp on Sudanese territory, where it would be illegal for the regime to skip over the border to snatch me, even if they did discover I was there. We'll marry either in the desert or, if we can, one of the rock churches in Gondar. We'll know better once I start making calls to arrange it.

'I know it's not what you envisaged for a wedding, but I promise I will make it up to you. Once we are married, we'll return to the Sudan, and then fly out to Mecca. You can make a pilgrimage to your holy shrine at this very sacred time of our life. I will wait for you, as close as I am allowed as a supposed infidel. And then you choose where we shall have a Muslim ceremony.'

'You appear to have it all worked out.'

'Actually, I don't. I'm thinking it all out as I go along. It's just that I want it to be very much our betrothal. Not for the newspapers and magazines. Can I go on and tell you the rest of what I would like to do for our wedding?'

He nodded his assent and she continued. 'Okay, we take off for a wedding holiday and we hop around the world to places we have always wanted to visit. For four months, we spoil and pamper ourselves and let the whole world know we are married and allow our loved ones and friends to share in it, wherever we may be. What do you say to that? Do you hate it, my plan?'

Rashid's images of them walking down the aisle of St Paul's, standing among the ruins of Ephesus, at the Madeleine in Paris, St Peter's in Rome, the amphitheatre in Aspendos, their vows under a full moon in Cappadocia, all vanished. What could he say? He wanted this to be the happiest time of her life, and what made her happy would make him happy. So he said, 'What would you like for a wedding present? And then I'll have the whole picture.'

He watched her carefully and could almost hear her mind clicking away. Then she clapped her hands together just once and said, 'Anything?'

'Yes,' he said, unable to imagine what she might ask for.

'Guarantee me a credit line for three hundred and fifty million dollars to form an international trading company, the bulk share of whose profits will be invested in my country for the good of the people.'

'No,' he said, shocked and giving her a tremendous shock. Then added, 'But I will, however, give you two hundred million dollars as a wedding gift, deposited in a Swiss bank of your choice, and will look forward to seeing what you can do with it.'

'Rashid?' exclaimed an overwhelmed Tana Dabra.

Rashid walked away from her to her desk, and wrote something on a piece of paper. Then he walked around the desk back to her and handed the telephone to her.

'Place your calls. It's a direct and open line to the international operator. You can call anywhere in the world without delay on this end. If you cannot complete a transaction, give them the number I've written on this piece of paper. That is where we will be. When your plans start coming together, then just tell me what you want me to do.'

She made three phone calls and left three messages as to where she could be reached, and then she went to Rashid.

'It's important for me that you believe that, up until now, I had no real understanding of how wealthy and powerful a man you are. It had begun to sink in in Paris, but then, not really. In New York it was really – with reservations. You see, I kept falling in love with you, the gigolo you, the erotic, libertine you, and now the super-rich you, and all the other you's you are. I'm marrying all of them, and for no other reason than the thrill of a life with you, the excitement of sharing what we can with each other.'

'You needn't have said any of that to me. Remember we don't complain, and we don't explain. I think that's a good rule to live by, for two fast-lane lovers and mates, who want to remain their own masters in a tight and loving togetherness.'

'And the very intelligent you,' she said, and then added, 'Now, are you going to feed me? I'm famished.'

Rashid walked over to a chair and picked up a full-length, white fox cape. He slipped it over Tana Dabra's shoulders and said, 'Feed you? I am about to feed you as never before. Come on, we'll have to hurry. I have something to show you at exactly midnight, a few minutes from now.'

Not many people really knew the extent of Rashid's power in Turkey, especially in Istanbul. He was very secretive about it, for personal and political reasons. It was some of that power that allowed him to give Tana Dabra her first view of Istanbul as few other women had seen it.

The night was bright with stars and the crescent moon that had shown for him and Mirella the night before did not fail him this night either. From the house they went by car to a waiting speedboat, and crossed from the shore to Rashid's ocean-going cruiser which lay at anchor at the mouth of the Bosporus, with the Sea of Marmara on one side and the Golden Horn on the other.

From there they had a sight that for centuries had dazzled the world. They stood at the prow of the ship in the chilly night air, arms around each other, and looked across the water at the hills and shore of Istanbul, and rode the waves between Europe and Asia Minor. A twinkle of lights was spattered like so many still-glowing fallen stars, a mirror image of the night sky above. And then, as if by magic, every light in Istanbul was extinguished, as if blown out by one gigantic breath from some invisible god in the heavens, or serpent surging up from the depths of the sea expressly for that purpose.

Twentieth-century Istanbul vanished. Two minutes later, Ottoman Istanbul appeared, as every building and monument of that period or before sprang to life with light. Nothing else shone in the blackness of the night, just the domes and minarets of Islam and Byzantium and the palace of Topkapi, lit from within and without. An entire modern city banished to darkness for the pleasure of one man and his love. Rashid could behave as a latter-day sultan of Turkey, with the same flair, decadence and selfishness they had possessed, and with something of the love, beauty and grandeur that they had wallowed in and which had finally crushed them. His self-indulgences overwhelmed Tana Dabra, but before the night was over she understood that Rashid without them would have been no Rashid at all.

The yacht sped forward to the triangle of land between the Bosporus and the Sea of Marmara where Topkapi Sarayi waited for them, mysterious and inviting. Once again the speedboat carried them from the yacht to the shore. A dozen small boys awaited them, and Rashid put flame to each of their torches. They lit a path from the water's edge up through the trees to the palace and kiosks above by rotating their positions as they climbed. One boy ran in front of them illuminating the stones under their feet.

In the marble courtyard a pair of black horses, decorated in gold, silver and diamonds, and a splendid carriage awaited them. Rashid chose for the moment to give Tana Dabra only an architectural view from outside the palace, with a promise of many returns to see the inside. The gates of Topkapi Sarayi were opened. The boys ran with their torches through the narrow, twisting streets of the old city in front of the carriage all the way to the Grand Bazaar. All around were people with candles and gaslights, chattering in the streets about what might have caused the blackout.

They alighted from the carriage only to be surrounded by several of Rashid's bodyguards. They walked swiftly through the darkened bazaar and all its stalls and shops and tea houses. Tana Dabra was enthralled, but no more than were the people of the streets, who had seen the carriage and a dusky woman, like a black queen, robed in white, white, furs. And others would speak of a black goddess draped in soft white animal skins from her neck to the ground, surrounded by men as she walked swiftly, seemingly glided, through the bazaar, only to vanish suddenly behind some secret door in the centre of the old Bedesten, the five-century-old domed hall at the very centre of the Grand Bazaar.

Rashid lifted a white silk gauze curtain and said. 'This is the House of Oda Lala. And now I will feed my hungry lady.'

It was not difficult for Tana Dabra to abase herself to her own and Rashid's sexual perversities. It was easy, thrilling and mesmerising at the house of Oda Lala. It was also sensuous and elegant and imaginative. It meant flirting with, but never sinking to, what was base or vulgar. Potentially depraved sexual acts were clothed in erotica, and tinged with sublimity. Rough and common excesses acquired their own beauty.

Before sensual delights, Rashid and she dined with Humayun, who was, if anything, yet more seductive and beautiful than she had been those days and nights in Dominica. Barefooted and apparently naked except for a narrow chain, whose links were inlaid with diamonds, draped loosely around her waist and huge diamonds on her ears, her red-gold hair worn long and loose, yet she wore a transparent silk coat of a silver colour with no more weight to it than a spider's web. Open all the way down the front it appeared to float around her like a veil of sensual smoke. Her every movement with her hands, her exquisite slender fingers tipped in red nail varnish, seduced, spoke volumes. Every nuance of her body, the way she sat, disposed her legs or arranged her thighs, exposing a fleshy crevice, a crack, a slit or the lips beyond, was a masterly posture that tantalised.

Nothing was measured, yet everything was right; nothing was planned, but the spontaneity amounted to perfection. They dined on Turkish cuisine, as varied as it was delicious. They drank French wines blessed by the gods. They saw among the clientele of Oda Lala's exotic sexual sights that fed their own fires burning within. Tana Dabra slipped into place as a part of the House of Oda Lala as if she had always belonged. Through her Rashid felt he had augmented his life. As Humayun and the House of Oda Lala were part of his life, so would they be part of Tana Dabra's.

They remained there for two days. Sexual self-indulgence took on a new meaning for Tana Dabra.

Sometimes a bond can be sealed between two people without words or explanations. Wordless, unexplained, such a bond was set between Tana Dabra and Humayun. Paradoxically Tana Dabra felt it form even as she watched Humayun sexually seduce Rashid away from her. The excitement and mystery, the ethereal quality of what was passing between Rashid and Humayun, worked on her senses, and kept her riveted. When she saw Rashid assume command and take Humayun with such abandoned, imaginative expertise, Tana Dabra lay down next to Humayun so that he might take them both alternately in the same way.

Rashid, on the other hand, thought he first saw it happening not here in Istanbul but back in Dominica. So it came as no surprise to him when Tana Dabra told him she thought she had met her first friend in Istanbul. Only to Humayun did they tell their secret wedding plans. Neither bride nor groom doubted Humayun's reaction to the news. They were both aware of her love for Rashid, and that really she wanted only one thing in life, to remain his sexual slave. With Tana Dabra as Rashid's wife, Humayun knew her position was safe. Her relationship with Rashid would remain as stable as ever. They were all three happy.

Just as they were about to take their leave of Oda Lala's and Humayun, Rashid placed his arm around Humayun and said, 'I want to give you a present, anything you like. Name it and it's yours.'

Humayun was truly filled with joy for Rashid. How could she have envisaged doubling that joyous feeling? But it happened, with his offer of a gift. It was perfect timing for Humayun. His generosity solved a dilemma that had been causing her much anxiety.

'Are you sure, anything, Rashid? There is something that I would like,' she answered in her most enchanting and coquettish manner.

'It's yours, you have my word. Now, what is it?'

'A holiday. I would like to take a holiday, all by myself. Well, with my maid. For four months. Just the time you and Tana Dabra plan to be away. I will make sure I am here waiting for you on your return. I'd like a holiday, just here in Istanbul. And maybe going to stay in one or two of my village houses. I will always leave word where I can be reached. I would like that so much.'

Rashid didn't think her request particularly odd, although she had never asked him for such a gift before. During their years together they had often been separated for months at a time. But she had always been on call, or he had lent her to someone, a man besotted with her, to a man like Christos, or to several friends of his on a cruise, to keep them erotically amused. Once he had even lent her to the Princess Eirene, to accompany her as an erotic play-mate while the Princess was the guest of an Arab ruler and in residence at his palace.

'Then you shall have it. Draw whatever money you require from my secretary. Use her to make your travel plans. I will just insist that you take not only your maid but your bodyguard.'

The three kissed goodbye. Then, as an afterthought, Rashid turned around to have a last look at his magnificent sexual slave. He surprised them both with his final inquiry, 'And Moses? That is under control?'

'Yes,' she answered, 'under control.'

Walking through the Grand Bazaar, dressed in street wear that had been sent from Rashid's residence on the hills of Perama on the other side of the Galata bridge, Tana Dabra asked, 'Who's Moses?'

'Moses? Well, he's all sorts of things. But he's also a problem that I hope has been solved for Humayun.'

And now Rashid felt as if it were he who had been kidnapped. Rashid and Tana Dabra travelled with two Turkish bodyguards, thirty pieces of luggage, and Serge Orloffsky, the pilot who was about to land them on a flat strip of Sudanese desert floor on the shores of the Red Sea, just inside Sudanese territory. Before they set the plane down, they flew five miles along the coastline into Ethiopian airspace towards Massawa, too low for radar to pick them up, and close enough to note the absence of border patrols. In their place, half a mile apart, were ten or twenty men. Tana Dabra recognised some as her own loyal helpers in what she was trying to accomplish for her country and others, devoted highlanders, who had come down from the mountains to see her wedded in her homeland.

A new intensity in Tana Dabra as she smiled and waved from the cabin windows was a feature noted by

Rashid in the woman he was about to marry. He was not unhappy with this new vision of her, but he did admit that this sort of brave adventure stuff was more up Adam's street than his own. She laughed joyously, kissed him, and assured him she would protect him. Not that she expected any problems. Friends had arranged for her and Rashid's safety for the short time she would be there. They would be wed and gone before the regime even heard they had arrived.

The plane banked sharply out over the Red Sea, still ducking the radar, and landed on the strip of Sudanese desert they had chosen. The beauty of the desert sand drifting into the sapphire blue of the Red Sea, empty and silent under a burning white sun, was not lost on Rashid.

They stepped out from the plane and the heat smacked them breathless before their feet touched the hot sand.

'Look, there they are.' Tana Dabra pointed to an Arab dhow under full sail, the one they had seen from the air making towards them. On board were friends who had come to help and to attend the wedding.

It wasn't going to happen in one of the rock churches in Lalibela as she had wanted. Too many people, too many tourists, and an excess of soldiery for them to handle prevented it. But she was going to be married a mile down the coast in Ethiopia, on the sands, with the waters of the Red Sea lapping the shore, some time in the next few hours, as soon as she could ready herself. A brace of bishops was reportedly en route, one from Gondar where he was on a pilgrimage, the other from Addis Ababa. Three priests and sundry deacons of the Coptic church had already arrived in the area from Imrahanna Kristos, the eight-hundred-year church, a remote shrine built in the back of a cave under a mountain on the western slopes of Abuna Joseph.

Tana Dabra boarded the dhow with her entourage of fifteen men: Amharas and Tigreans, highlanders, tall, slender and handsome with their proud, black semitic features and long, dark, curled and shiny hair, dressed in their best for the occasion. The less educated, more pagan and primitive of them, who considered her a living goddess, dropped to their knees and kissed the hem of her dress. Four of them, Cambridge, Harvard, Cairo and NY university graduates, were dressed not as highlanders but as university men. Incongruous in their wrinkled and worn suits of white cotton poplin or seersucker, they were no less respectful. They bowed their heads and kissed her hand.

So this had been her life before he met her. So these had been her lovers. He was certain of it. Had she perhaps led them a merry sexual dance? Were there many broken hearts among them? He tried to put the erotic Tana Dabra out of his mind, at least until sunset, when they would be away from this wild and primitive, yet stirring and mysterious place. But it was difficult. Every glance in his direction was sensual and declared that, above and beyond all this, she was his alone, and that was what this journey was about.

They took with them fifteen of the cases packed with food and gifts and necessaries for the wedding. Rashid would follow them, with Serge and two Turkish bodyguards, in one of the two fast motor launches, speeding across the Red Sea to them from a Saudi Arabian yacht belonging to the royal family. Rashid was not without rich and powerful friends who were eager to help implement the couple's plans.

'Don't be late for the wedding,' she shouted from the prow of the fat wooden dhow, and waved farewell to him.

'And don't change your mind and disappear, and leave me stranded here,' he called back as he walked along the water's edge. The dhow moved swiftly away from the shore, on the hot breeze, as it slipped into the current.

One of the Amharas, a staunch supporter of hers who had arrived from Addis Ababa, remained behind with Rashid while waiting for the Saudi launches to arrive. The man, once an ambassador to the UN in New York, sat with Rashid and Serge under the wing of the plane. There was no other shade under which to savour the champagne, chilled when they took it from the plane, warm before they were able to empty their glasses.

From this man Rashid was able to learn more about how important Tana Dabra's work was for her country, how dependent they were upon her, if the current regime was ever to be supplanted. Day by day it drifted further from the solutions needed for their country.

Rashid stood under a makeshift canopy made of blankets, scarves and odd shaped pieces of fabric, stretched and tied on wooden staves shoved in the sand, some taller, some shorter, a melange of colours, bright and jewel-like. Red and yellow and green and white mixed in patchwork with dull greys and browns and black. Silks stretched next to wool, cotton and nylon, some new, other pieces old, shabby and torn. The sea lay behind him in this strip of desert beach sheltered by small sand dunes undulating smoothly one after another, shimmering in the heat. Only the men he brought with him in the launch were there.

He watched the former ambassador climb over a dune and disappear. He assured Rashid he was going to get the bride. Fifteen minutes later the faint sound of chanting, of tinkling bells and cymbals and other strange instruments off in the distance, broke the silence of the desert and the Red Sea lapping the shore. As it grew louder, a kind of excitement such as Rashid had never experienced before came over him. There appeared on top of the dunes an untidy procession of bishops, priests and deacons, carrying brightly coloured velvet umbrellas embroidered with gold and silver and glass beads and semi-precious stones, dressed in flowing robes and carrying Coptic symbols and crosses. It slowly zigzagged down the sand dune to the beach and the shelter, where Rashid was waiting, in a swirl of wailing and chanting and wild swinging of golden, bowl-shaped incense burners from long chains. The smoke and scent transformed the place and atmosphere into a pungently religious moment, a timeless moment to be remembered always.

Then he saw her dressed in the traditional white cotton, trimmed in coloured embroidery, and worn in the traditional manner draped over her head. An ancient silver Coptic cross, large and beautiful, hung from a silver chain around her neck. She walked alone, an attendant carrying behind her a white silk velvet umbrella, encrusted with gold-threaded embroidery, so that it sloped high above Tana Dabra's head. Surrounded by her trusted men, a dozen or more of the clergy and musicians preceded her, leading the

351

procession, with a similar number behind.

Rashid never knew quite what it was, the heat, the incense, the champagne or the chanting. But by the time she was standing by his side and a ceremony half-pagan, half-Christian, its detail coloured yet more by traditional Coptic ceremony, was in full flood, he was as if hypnotised by the event. As the priests and deacons crowded under the wedding canopy, their makeshift church, with their holy waters and oils and ointments, and they pressed the word of the God of Abyssinia of old and Ethiopia of today, upon them, Rashid felt himself and Tana Dabra as if absorbed by some strange and pagan god, whose name might yet have been Jesus.

And then suddenly, it was as if something snapped, and it all stopped. It was over. Rashid came out of his daze. He saw the devout Ethiopian priests and their elaborate sanctity as fossilised. He was ready to believe Tana Dabra when she told him later that there was less parade among them of moral virtues. Although they were a social fixture, it was unfortunate that the highland priesthood usually attracted the worst kind of highlander, something you could not change easily in a priesthood that was mainly hereditary. Rashid was not a particularly devout muslim, but he was loyal to Mohammed and Islam and had a moment of wondering about his own Hadj to Mecca the following day. How would that and their muslim wedding affect him?

But, if the ceremony was one kind of culture shock for Rashid, what was to happen next was another. As the holy crew dispersed, Rashid and Tana Dabra were able to see, one by one, perhaps two at a time but never more, other kinds of people slowly beginning to appear across the desert, as if from nowhere. Dressed in rags worn proudly as if they were robes of gold, often with a wooden staff across their back, their arms draped over it to hold it in place, helping them to walk tall and ram-rod straight, these were the peasants of Ethiopia. They carried nothing with them but a thin, worn blanket, usually slung over the wooden staff, a skin for water strapped across their chests by a string, and a small leather pouch holding scraps of food. They had covered huge distances to pay their respects to Tana Dabra. These people of the land knew who she was by her near-legendary works. They saw her as their only hope of saving their traditional way of life, threatened as it was by the military regime. They were a poor and wretched people, who had sheltered her and kept her safe when she was working under cover in the country.

All afternoon they came. Rashid and Tana Dabra sat under the canopy on a thin, woven rush mat laid over the sand. They were offered food and drink from the stores that Rashid and Tana Dabra had brought with them, roasted pigeon and wine, fresh fruit and hundreds of sweet cakes. The feast was supplemented by traditional Ethiopian fare arranged by her helpers. Rashid and Tana Dabra had their coterie of Tana Dabra's close associates sitting around them, the clergy behind. As in the tradition of the Coptic church in Ethiopia, by which a man will never go any closer to the centre of the church than he feels worthy, so it was with the wedding guests. Only those who felt worthy sat under the shelter. The rest sat out under the blazing sun, under makeshift shelters of umbrellas and draped cloths and blankets, or in most cases just their turbans, in a large semi-circle facing the wedding party and the Red Sea. By late afternoon it was obvious, by the wide area the people were arriving from, that word of Tana Dabra's wedding had spread swiftly through the country. Rashid took over after speaking with Tana Dabra's associates.

He and Tana Dabra and the two Turkish body-guards slipped away as unobtrusively as possible, in one of the motor launches, to the Saudi Arabian yacht awaiting their arrival. They would spend their wedding night on board, sailing to the port of Jiddah. Tana Dabra's associates, at Rashid's request, and with her approval, kept the party going by inviting those there to stay. Rashid deployed Serge in the other launch to return to the plane and fly directly to Jiddah and ferry back food and drink for the wedding party which he would arrange for from the yacht.

Tana Dabra and Rashid stood silently at the stern of the launch. Happy but pensive, they waved goodbye to those on shore and watched their wedding party – appearing from the water more like a ramshackle, colourful festival of some sort than the wedding of two powerful international celebrities – recede from them, grow smaller and smaller until it was no more than a patch of colour on the horizon.

'I know this may seem odd to you, Rashid, but I loved my wedding.'

'Now why should I find that odd? I loved my wedding too. I may not have understood it, but love it I did.'

They turned to face each other and they kissed. And then, leaning into his arms, she said. 'I never expected so many people, Rashid. It was generous to send them more food and wine to keep the party going. You have style.'

'They came such distances. They had a lot of natural dignity. Impressive. They love and respect you. It was a fabulous wedding. I want it to go on for three days. Nice to think of them camped there still celebrating, while we are at our muslim wedding and feast.'

They watched the red-hot fireball of the sun drop swiftly in the sky and set, seemingly under the waters of the Red Sea. It all made Rashid feel as biblical as he was ever likely to.

Chapter 16

'What if it rains all the time they are here? I'll die.'

'It won't rain *all* the time.'

'Oh, what a relief.'

'Well, it might.'

'Oh, my God. I can't bear it. Then why did you say it wasn't going to?'

'To make you feel better, to stop you from making a Greek drama out of the weather.'

'What you really mean is a Jewish drama.'

'I said Greek.'

'You thought Jewish.'

'What are we fighting about, Deena?'

'The weather.'

'Oh, that's alright then, everyone gets ratty about the weather.'

'Oh, hell, Brindley, now you think I'm ratty.'

'Nervous. I should have said nervous.'

'Yes, you should have.'

'Well, I didn't.'

'Why didn't you?'

'Because, my dear, you were being bloody ratty and turning a Greek drama into a Jewish drama, over the possibility of a little rain. Now try to make something out of that.'

Deena raised her chin a little higher, stared her husband in the eye and said, 'You're quite right. Only you needn't be so rude about it, Brindley.'

'Oh, I give up,' he said, and gave up.

'Me too,' she added, and then they burst into laughter.

A small plane traced a noisy and meaningful circle above the house. Deena and Brindley rushed out of the study and into the courtyard of the Tudor manor house. The plane circled a second time. Deena looked up and waved, crossing her arms over themselves in front of her, beaming with excitement. Then she and Brindley drove off towards the farm and airfield at a reckless speed in Deena's BMW convertible. Behind them, the assistant gardener-cum-chauffeur drove Brindley's father's 1931 black and tan Rolls. Behind him followed two farm hands in one of the pickup trucks for the luggage. They sped down the avenue of lopsidedly pruned lime trees through the parkland towards the entrance to Lyttleton Park. It was a race with the plane to the field.

The plane returned, flew in low and buzzed them from the rear. They saw Adam in the cockpit, and then Mirella and the Princess Eirene waving through the windows. Deena waved wildly back at them. But they were gone.

'Oh God, it's a perfect spring, a perfect show of flowers. The best springtime your mother says she has seen at Lyttleton Park for twenty years. Everything's out, just everything is bursting into blossom at once. They are going to see it at its very best. Oh, Brind, I want it to be perfect for them, because it's the loveliest place in the world, when the sun is out.'

Brindley still felt responsible for the sun and its

358

absences. He was British. He shot her a look. She recouped.

'A slip of the tongue? Okay, I won't mention the sun for a bit. Or the rain. It's just that I love Lyttleton Park so much, and our friends have all made such efforts to come this one week when the gardens are at their best. I want it to be a week to remember. They lead such jet-setting lives, who knows when we will be able to get them all here like this again?'

They whizzed past the Folly and the Grotto that Deena had just had restored as a birthday present for Lady Margaret, Brindley's mother. For a quarter of a century Lady Margaret had wanted it done. But somehow there just hadn't been a moment. Deena caught a glimpse of a white swan gliding, trailed by a black one and five black cygnets, from the water in the grotto onto the edge of the lake. Nearby three more white swans majestically sunned themselves as they made their tour.

'At least the swans are on show. So far, so good.'

Brindley began to laugh. 'So far, so good? They haven't even arrived yet,' he said. He swung off the avenue of trees a hundred yards before the massive iron gates and onto the dirt road that led to the farm buildings and the working farm beyond. There lay the new landing strip of bright green grass, a swathe through two vast fields bright with yellow rape seed in full bloom.

Suddenly Deena grabbed his arm, 'Oh, Brinn, I have had the most terrible thought. What if the runway is too short and they don't clear the wood at the far end before they come in for the landing? What if they overshoot it on this end and go smack into the dairy? How do we know the field is safe? What if they crash? What if they're killed?' she asked, her face filled with terror.

Brindley gave her a look that said, 'You're being very feminine.' He accelerated through the farm and planted £24,000 of car and themselves squarely at the end of the runway. He switched off and put the ignition key in his pocket. He appeared to be proving something. He looked at her and they both looked embarrassed.

The plane appeared, came at them head on, dead centre over the field. From below, any descent would have seemed too fast. It cleared the wood by just a few feet. Deena's eyes were riveted to the wheels, she was frightened silent. The wheels bounced inelegantly on the grass before settling smoothly. Adam's expertise had asserted itself. He noted the challenge presented by the car. The white aeroplane with silver-tipped wings rolled towards it with apparent abandon. Adam braked and the motors eased off without a jolt. The plane roared, creating its own wind storm. Adam let it slide to within about thirty yards of the BMW, then stopped.

Thumbs up from the pilot. Brindley opened the car door for Deena. Her knees seemed reluctant to undertake a stroll. 'Okay,' she said, 'but don't you dare tell them I was frightened. Let them guess.' Her arm managed to imitate a wave towards the plane. Brindley slipped his arm around her shoulder and answered, 'How could they?'

The plane door opened automatically from the inside. The first one out was Mirella. The two women hugged each other, all smiles, and began chattering and laughing all at once, delighted to see each other. Mirella was followed immediately by one of the Princess Eirene's aged Sudanese eunuchs, her constant attendants.

Dressed in a black suit he looked, even at nearly seven feet tall, fairly conventional, except for his bulky but soft-looking, hairless physique and odd facial features, and his black silk turban. If anything, he was too grand for a servant. Deena watched him turn to help the Princess Eirene down the stairs. She was far from reassured to note that, although conventional by oriental norms, Hyacinth looked no less exotic than usual. There was going to be talk among the locals about two men called Hyacinth and Narcissus who had dropped in on Lyttleton Park. Their unusual condition, readily discernible in their strangely bland features and high-pitched feminine voices trapped in the bodies of men, would be just a bit too freakily foreign for the village. With the pair of them sleeping on the floor across the entrance to the guest bedroom where the Princess would sleep, the sense of propriety of the manor house staff was in for an upset. Deena sighed. One thing was sure about the Gloucestershire locals: they didn't mind asking a question or two and certainly liked a good gossip.

The diminutive, delicate-looking Princess Eirene, dressed impeccably though simply in beige and black, stepped onto the airfield. She looked, for all her years, as beautiful and coquettish as ever. She was followed by Narcissus carrying a large black alligator jewellery case. It was for Deena one of her proudest moments. She was so delighted that the Princess, who travelled very little now, saw fit to accept Deena's and Brindley's invitation. Deena and the Princess greeted each other with a kiss on each cheek. Never one to hold back for long, Deena whispered, 'Eirene, you wear those two old boys like a pair of exotic earrings scooped off the harem floor.' The Princess laughed and touched Deena's cheek with her hand affectionately. 'I love the English gardens. They refresh me. But no more than your teasing wit.' Deena went pink with delight.

Muhsine looked as sweet and pretty as ever. She wore western dress instead of her usual *salvar*. She came down the stairs of the plane next and was greeted by both Brindley and Deena. Rashid took the stairs quickly and swung Deena up off the ground in a hug.

'I don't know how you've done it, but you have got us all here, and we are thrilled about it. If the English weather holds and we have a few days like this, it will be a great treat.'

Deena turned to Brindley and sensed he was again assuming his seigneurial responsibility for the climate. She raised an eyebrow and gave him a smug smile, as if to say, 'You see the weather is a factor rather than a fact of life in the English countryside.'

'Deena, I believe neither you nor Brindley have met my wife.' With that Rashid raised his hand to help Tana Dabra down the few stairs to the ground. Deena, so completely excited by this time, had imagined Rashid's wife might be a low point if there was going to be one in her house party. She turned to welcome Tana Dabra, anxious to see what kind of woman was able to, as she liked to put it, 'nail that smoothy to the boards', never expecting that she could ever be a friend to any woman willing to take on Rashid full time. The moment she saw Tana Dabra step into the midday Gloucestershire sunshine and clasped her hand in greeting, she knew she had been wrong.

In years to come Brindley would remember that

arrival, and Deena's happiness, if only in contrast to another arrival that took place during that house party. He wondered whence Mirella and Rashid gathered the aplomb to remain close friends despite their bitter battle over the ownership of the Oujie lands and holdings. He shook Rashid's hand and made him welcome.

Brindley was introduced to Tana Dabra. Even his English reserve was duly impressed. Ever since the announcement of their secret wedding ceremonies and the photographs that flashed around the world of them, with others of their four-month-long, round-the-world wedding holiday, Brindley had felt increasing distaste for the fuss made over what he considered to be just another wedding.

But now, meeting Rashid's wife for the first time, he understood what the fuss was about. Weak-kneed, stern old romantic that he was, he fell instantly under the spell of her dusky aristocratic beauty. The majestic sensuality he saw in her face, in every movement of her long, slender limbs, was something to behold. But it was the remarkable courage he sensed in her, the clever mind, the mystery of soul that shone brightly in her face, that captured his heart. He could take comfort that Rashid had been similarly captivated. And, by the look on Adam's face and the intimate way he rested his hand on her shoulder as he stood on the top step to the plane, Adam had gone the same way, too.

Adam hopped sideways off the top step on to the ground and walked around them all to kiss Deena hello.

'Did you think I was going to skim the top layer off your fairy-tale castle?' he teased, 'and ruin your house party?'

'Never,' she lied.

'Take out a few trees, the barn, or the dairy?'

'Or nothing. I had every faith in you. Even handsome devils know how to use their wings to fly.'

She let him laugh at her. And as he greeted Brindley, she stood and listened to their chatter about the smoothness of the flight and what a nice little airfield Lyttleton Park could turn itself into. It was a gift from Mirella to Brindley, so that he could spend more time in the country with Deena, instead of jostling in airport terminals while jetting the world on behalf of Mirella and the Oujie estate.

Deena was always just a little in awe of Adam, and his handsome, sexy looks. That rugged American-dream look he had, and the exotic life he lived, were never lost on her. Since she had met him, he had become one of the richest, most powerful men in the world. Still there was a touch of hayseed, mid-west, all-American football about him, which she found so attractive. She liked to think, even as she stood now with him and her best friend, Mirella, that the very private sexual world the couple indulged in was just a phase that would peter out. Although in her heart of hearts she knew differently.

Mirella, only weeks ago, had confessed to her that she was still as sexually involved with Rashid as ever, and that Tana Dabra, like Adam, accepted and never discussed it with him. That is, if Tana Dabra knew. Rashid assured Mirella he had never told her and never would. Deena took one last look around her house party and had to admit to herself that it still shocked her that she was not the sexually wild woman she had always thought she was. Here were the true libertines, who practised what they loved, sexual freedom. They indulged their most erotic of fantasies without guilt or self-recrimination. Brindley and she were bumpkins when it came to sex in the big league as these guys practised it. Here they were still on the airfield, and Deena was already getting turned on sexually by their very presence. If he asked, could she say no to anyone as sexy as Adam? Maybe the question was, would she ever say yes?

'You coward, you fink, Deena,' she thought, and then remembered what Brindley once said to her, 'You and I, we were so lucky to meet Mirella and Adam and Rashid, and watch them change with the love they found in their unusual relationship. They and their boldness maybe catalysed our own frustrated sexual desires, and we were there at the right time and in the right place to come together, throw out those frustrations, and set ourselves sexually free with each other. We owe them a great deal. But it's not a bad idea to remember we are no less free because we choose to live a more staid and conventional life than they do. That's just the way it is, we aren't all cut of the same cloth.'

On an impulse she reached up and put her arms around Adam and, before she kissed him, she said, 'Give me a kiss, soldier,' in her best Marlene Dietrich voice. He gave her one while everyone laughed. She felt sensual stirrings within and was relieved that what she really wanted was her husband. She glanced over to him and saw a smile in his eyes. She pulled herself away from Adam, and now wanted only what she had had the first crazy, erotic night with Brindley after they had watched Humayun. Her thoughts flashed back in time to Humayun and the night of Mirella's wedding when she had seen her in a sexual orgy. Suddenly Deena snapped to and realised that Moses was missing. She was upset. Part of the fun of this week was to have Moses there to see her new home and her new life. The house party was planned as a four-day affair for the guests now standing around the plane, plus Moses, nanny and baby. After the Princess Eirene and her attendants and Rashid and Tana Dabra left it was going to be a more intimate house party. A 'for-old-times-sake party' as Deena had called it, when discussing it with Brindley. Now, before they had even left the airfield, something had gone wrong.

'Moses, where is Moses, Mirella?' she asked, hoping he would surprise her and pop his head out of the plane.

'Oh, Moses will be coming in a day or two. Something came up to delay him. I'll explain it all later. And the baby and the nanny will come with them. Don't worry, he wouldn't miss this for the world.'

Deena sighed, and smiled at everyone as she placed her hand, fingers splayed, over her chest. With the sigh she said, 'Oh, that's all right, then. It would have been so sad for him not to have come. He has been so good to me for so many years I should like to share a really lovely English spring with him.'

The cargo hold was opened and the two farm boys started loading the luggage into the pickup. Brindley supervised who went in which car, and at last they were off to the manor house.

'It's one of the great mysteries of the world, the English countryside,' said Tana Dabra. 'The English garden. English country life. In my first year at Oxford, I used to think it candy box pretty, frivolous and unreal. What else would you think, coming from

Addis Ababa? In my second year at Oxford, I began to understand that it is one of the most powerful, privileged experiences on earth. A greater Don Juan even than my husband. So seductive, all those bluebells, wild daffodils, narcissi – peppering the greenest of grass, for miles on end – and thousands of tulips. Deena, this drive is poetry and every giant Dutch elm a key word. Thank you so much for asking us.'

Deena could almost feel herself preening her feathers, so proud was she. Not because it was hers, because she never considered it that – she considered herself the latest in a long line of custodians to come to Lyttleton Park – but because she had something unique to offer her friends, a few days in time for them to romp through a paradise on earth.

Tana Dabra had been right, of course. The English countryside, and in this case the gardens and the house, worked their magic spell upon the guests. The land absorbed the strong-minded group into itself. The house party took off just as Deena had wanted it to. The sun stayed out for the four days that Rashid and Tana Dabra and the Princess were there. Brindley dared it to hide its face. It afforded them the good fortune of being able to spend most of their time wandering over the nine-hundred acre estate.

There were sumptuously Edwardian picnics in the orchards under fruit trees in full bloom, in the Folly and the Grotto, and on the island in the lake. Delicious English teas were served on the lawn: scones with Cornish double cream and blobs of jam thick with fruit, shortbreads, cakes of every kind which came second only to mouthwatering cucumber sandwiches, Scottish smoked salmon on buttered brown bread thin and shapely as a fifty-pence piece, potted shrimps, and an endless stream of excellent English country fare, all made proudly in the kitchen by cook and extra village women brought in to help for the occasion.

They went on long walks through the gardens, ten acres of them, bursting with glory, and rambles over the Capability Brown landscape or through the fields of wild flowers. Then there were visits to the greenhouse and the kitchen gardens, where they all helped pick the vegetables for their dinner, and the walled garden where they thought they had stepped back in time, and visits to the Lyttleton Park stud, Deena's new business venture.

They amused themselves with fishing in the trout stream, riding over the estate, punting on the lake, clay pigeon shooting over a field. Playing croquet or boules on the lawn became more amusing than competitive. The tennis was definitely competitive. The cricket game, assembled with some of the local lads, was a disaster, for the house team. They discovered cricket was not a game you could successfully avoid practising for – too skilled and deadly.

At night they dressed for dinner, and every evening some of Brindley's friends came to join them. Memorable food and vintage wines grew more welcome as they were anticipated each evening. The forty-two-room house was alive with laughter and people coming and going. The atmosphere seemed to spill over to the farm and the staff that was running the house party, inevitably perhaps, since Rashid, of course, had charmed every man, woman and child on the estate by the end of his second day there. This ensured a laid-back, casual atmosphere that allowed both guests and staff to wander through the rooms at will and at ease as if in their own home.

Both the men and the women spent a great deal of time in appreciative exploration of the architecture, the interiors and their furnishings. They noted the cosiness-cum-splendour of the English country manor house, of which Lyttleton Park was an excellent example, with its four oriel windows, and its hundreds of years of beeswax and woodsmoke, and collections of beautiful, if not modestly scaled objects acquired by its owners on the 'grand tour'. They were all aware that Lyttleton Park was not a stately home in the great English tradition. But they considered it more than that: it was a grandly modest house.

It was Mirella who generously remarked, 'It takes more than Colefax and Fowler – and don't get me wrong, England has a great deal to thank those decorators for. However, it takes more than them, or any decorator for that matter, to create the so-called "English Room", "English House" or "English Look". It actually needs the English aristocracy, all their heritage, and hundreds of years to mellow in, just like this house has had. Democracy is not good for houses.'

Deena felt grateful for those words from Mirella, because, first of all, Mirella should know: she had been brought up in the New England version of Lyttleton Park. And, second, because Lady Margaret, Brindley's mother, was in the room when Mirella spoke. Lady Margaret, who had worked her hands and her heart out for Lyttleton Park, its gardens and the house, deserved some praise, of which the era she was growing old in stinted her.

The house and gardens even took over Hyacinth and Narcissus. Not that they looked or sounded less odd, but it was as if, like some rare object bought on a tour of Asia, they had a place there too. Deena's several encounters with them left her with memorable vignettes: Hyacinth in the kitchen, mixing a home-made face cream for cook's too red complexion and smearing it all over her face, while cook wrote out in an ill-formed scribble a recipe for treacle tart that Hyacinth had to have. Another day, she saw him starching and pressing aprons for two extra girls from the village who were waiting at table. He was teaching them how to put accordion pleats in them so they were more attractive. The girls were churning fresh almond and honey ice cream for him. Two other girls were there as well, looking in hand mirrors at Narcissus as he instructed them how to curl their hair with a hot tong. They giggled and nudged each other while trying to keep under their blouses a pair of pure white farm kittens they were giving the 'two flowers of Asia Minor' (so gardener had christened them, and all the staff had picked it up).

But if there was one thing about the odd couple that Deena would never forget, it was when she saw their giant, bulky forms walking down the hill towards the lake at sunset. They were giggling and chattering like schoolgirls while gathering small bunches of wild flowers. At one moment they stopped and pointed to the bright pink, sinking sun, and then they turned to face each other. Although she was a good distance away, Deena was still able to see a sweet but twisted smile cross their pasty, ugly faces. Then they bent forward and, bodies still apart, pressed their lips together in a sweet, passionless kiss. Deena thought her heart would break. She slumped down where she was standing in the tall grass, not wanting to impinge upon that personal moment, and wept tears for them, but didn't understand why. When she parted the tall grass, they were gone.

At night, after the house had gone quiet and everyone was in bed, Brindley and Deena made not love but great sex. The house guests during that stay had the ability to shatter the reserve of both the Ribblesdales. It was a kind of reversal of roles. Every day that went by the guests became more English and less flamboyant, while the host and hostess seemed to imbibe something exotic from their visitors.

But there were odd moments when they all had to perk up and accept visitors from the outside world. Times when several people called to ask if they could come by to visit the Princess Eirene, who had declined all invitations to visit them. Times that gratified whatever of the snob lurked in Deena. They brought a Duke, an Earl, even two Royals, in the span of four days, to Lyttleton Park. Deena looked set to be the most sought-after hostess of the season, and the season had hardly begun.

In between all the fun, Deena and Mirella managed a few long gossip sessions. The first chance Deena had, she asked why Moses had not come with them.

'Moses will come, Deena. But he couldn't now, not with Rashid here. He has confided in me, and now I am going to confide in you. A few days before Rashid eloped with Tana Dabra, he was in Istanbul. She was there with Rashid, but locked away in his house, supposedly under the weather. That was the time Adam left for that now famous dig of his in Anatolia. I spent the next two nights and a day with Rashid. First at the love kiosk, and then later at that place I told you about, the house of Oda Lala. It was a crucial time for us. And I had just turned the legal guns on his attempted rape and pillage of my holdings. He had to be told, and I wanted to be the one to tell him. I did, but not until the second night we were together.

'Deena, I know you don't approve, but the magic is still there. We knew it within five minutes of being alone together. I'll never be able to explain it to you, this being in love with two men. But that is the way it is, and it will never change, no matter what we do to each other. He transports me to another kind of dark and depraved world I play in, which has become almost as much a part of my life as his. Humayun joined us, of course. Moses was never mentioned. He was not even on our minds. But a few hours after Rashid took me home, I thought of Humayun and the sexual experiences we had shared with Rashid. I knew then, with some fright, that she could never live without Rashid. Of course, that is no problem, because she doesn't have to. Rashid will never leave Humayun. Not for me, nor for a wife. Not for anything. They have a very special relationship.

'Now, I know, since that long heart-to-heart we all had in Easthampton, Moses has worked out his relationship with Humayun. He never lets on about his unhappiness over her not wanting to marry him anymore. He has accepted that all he is going to get is the odd night of sex and love. Or so I think. He has not spoken to me about it. Rashid has. Otherwise I would know nothing. Rashid got it from Humayun.'

'Something's wrong. I get a bad feeling about what you're telling me, Mirella.'

'I don't think we have too much to worry about. But let me go on to tell you the rest of it. As you well know, Rashid calls me every day from wherever he is. The morning after our reunion, and the following morning, he called from Oda Lala's. He was there introducing Tana Dabra to its sexual delights. We met again in our love kiosk, and there he told me he was eloping with Tana Dabra. She knew about and accepted Humayun and Oda Lala's as part of his life. We both agreed he would say nothing to her about our affair.

'We had a terrible row, just hideous, about my determination to fight him for all that was my great-grandmother's. But, of course, the sex took over, and we parted as we always do, trapped in an erotic love affair. One of the last things he told me was that he and his bride would be away on a four-month honeymoon, but of course he would be in touch every day. He then casually added that he had given Humayun the same length of time for a holiday as well, and that she was going away.

'I never mentioned that to Moses. Then, when the news of Rashid and Tana Dabra's wedding broke a few days after they had left Istanbul, I noticed an odd change in Moses. But, frankly, I was having a great deal of trouble emotionally at that time coming to terms with Tana Dabra. I have resolved that, by the way. Although, as you can see, while we are civil, even like each other, we are certainly not friends.'

Deena rose from the worn, over-stuffed, glazed chintz chair she was sitting in. She walked to the oriel window and looked out to the Japanese cherry trees in full bloom, across the gravel courtyard and down the avenue of trees and the blanket of daffodils and tulips that spread into the distance. She said, without turning back to look at Mirella, 'I don't like what I hear. I want him here. Pick up that phone and call him. If he saw all this,' she turned back to Mirella now and gestured at what she saw through the window with a sweep of her hand, 'he would love it.'

'They'll be here tomorrow, in time for lunch. There is no use calling for the moment, they are calling us tonight. Please, though, let me finish, put you in the whole picture. A few weeks went by, and I was feeling better about Rashid's marriage. He had been no less attentive than usual, and I flew out twice to meet him for erotic afternoons. A month more went by, and Moses came to me to ask for time off. Humayun had disappeared, and he was going to try to find her. He was certain this was the time for her to leave Rashid, if not to marry him, at least to be free and begin a new life. I was appalled at his determination that she must be free. In the end, I had to call Adam in to help. He managed to calm Moses down with reasoning, once Adam had proof that she was happy and safe in Central Anatolia, and that she would call him on her return.

'He was like our old Moses. Better than I have seen him in years. We all returned to New York. He was deeply involved with his Harlem kids and the gym, and taking care of our affairs. Her name was not mentioned again. Then they returned three weeks ago, Tana Dabra and Rashid. I don't know how it got back to him, but he heard Humayun was back and had been for weeks. He had news that she was well and happy, more beautiful than ever and spending a great deal of time with Tana Dabra. They had become friends. I knew that to be true because Rashid let it slip once when we were alone. He was rather rude about me still playing on the fringe of depravity without ever really submitting to it for love of him, as his wife and Humayun did. Then one day – I have no idea what

374

possessed her – Humayun called Moses, and they spent a day and a night together. That was three days before we came here. The day before we were to leave, Moses told me he wanted one last chance to speak quietly and alone to Humayun. He gave me his word that, if she didn't want to give up Rashid, he would never see her again. It would be over. That's it. The whole story. She's unable to leave Rashid, so it's over.'

Kadin arrived with her nanny, flown in on Rashid's plane, the same plane that would fly him and the others out the following day. But there was no Moses on board. Mirella was on the telephone to him as soon as she had read the note he sent. He assured her all was well and he would fly in the day after Rashid's departure, on the plane that was to remain at Lyttleton Park. That, he promised, was the final change of plans. The women weren't happy. This constant changing of plans: it was so unlike Moses. But, chided by the men for making a drama where one did not exist, they forced thoughts about Moses and his unhappy love affair out of their minds.

They had one grand evening. A Ball. The first Lyttleton Park Ball since its new master had taken over. Brindley had dreaded that night. He was certain that Deena would work herself up to a frenzy. But he need not have worried. She was unflappable, and behaved as if nothing could go wrong, and it didn't. For years to come the aristocracy of Wiltshire and Gloucestershire, and the Princess Eirene's admirers (who begged invitations for no other reason than to be able to spend time with her) would speak about the dazzlingly simple but glamorous party. The home counties had never seen such a receiving line. The women were resplendent in haute couture and jewels that dazzled the eyes of every guest. The men, handsome and charming, won the local ladies' hearts much too easily.

Deena saw her friends as heroes and heroines, high jumpers in life, who played for big stakes in work and play. But there was something more in them, she realised, during their stay with her. They were not just high fliers, big livers. They *liked* living, had a real passion for all kinds of life, and made strong their bond with all mankind. She savoured the ease with which they added laughter and merriment, and their own brand of humanity, to Lyttleton Park.

Long after Mirella, Muhsine, Deena, Adam and Brindley waved the other guests off as their plane soared into the air, the aura of their presence lingered on in the seventeenth-century, oak-panelled rooms and among the Turners and the Sargents, the Charles II silver, the Queen Anne furniture and the Georgian pieces, and with those of the houseparty who remained.

She would never again take tea in the sitting room without remembering the Princess Eirene lost in an over-stuffed chair of beige, peach and aquamarine roses on cream-coloured, glazed chintz, playing charades. Behind her loomed Hyacinth and Narcissus, like a pair of oversized bookends. Or Rashid playing with Kadin on the old leopard rug in front of the fire. Or Tana Dabra and Mirella chatting to each other by the huge leaded window, crisscrossed with stone mullions, the evening sunset casting a golden light behind them. Mirella at the ball, looking more beautiful than Deena had ever seen her, her raven hair and violet eyes outshining every other woman there. Tana Dabra, like an Ethiopian empress in a league all her own. And Adam, with that special all-American look of his, emanating power and success. He had fussed with Muhsine, who was sweet and quiet, submissive and shy, trying to teach her how to play croquet on a lawn squared off with thousands of white tulips. There were so many images of their days together that would never fade.

Deena was getting quite blasé about this aeroplane thing, as she called it. Not so the farm hands and the house staff. They remained thrilled by it all, stopping everything to see who was arriving and who leaving, fascinated by the touchdowns and the take-offs. Another plane had just buzzed the house.

The remaining house guests joined Deena and Brindley to welcome the newcomer. 'Moses,' thought Deena. She beamed at Brindley, slipped her arm through his, and smiled broadly at the others. 'Dear old Mose. You're going to love it here. Wait till you see what I've landed myself in. Heaven, heaven on earth. And I'll make it clear that you are always welcome here whenever you want to come. You can have one of the little old cottages in memory of all the kindness, tolerance and friendship you've shown me.' As the plane taxied slowly to a halt, she looked up at the sky, and then said, 'Is the weather going to hold, Brinn?'

'The sun is out, Deena.'

'I know that. But is it going to hold?'

'You're doing it again, Deena.'

'What?'

'The weather.'

'Sorry about that. Forgot myself. And besides, I'm

too happy to worry about the weather.' She gave her husband a friendly poke in the arm.

And then he was there, framed in the open door of the plane, looking big, handsome and kind, and controlled as always. He hurried down the steps and greeted everyone, apologising for his delayed arrival.

Deena didn't know what she expected, or what to make of the latest news of his unfortunate love affair. But the moment she saw that calm, almost ethereal look that always lingered in the back of his eyes, she was reassured that all was fine with him.

'Boy, am I glad to see you, Mose! Actually, I'm furious you've missed out on these last four glorious days. Brinn has laid on the most wonderful weather.' Everyone interrupted her with elaborate groans. She had the good nature to laugh at herself and wave them off. She continued as she pulled him along to one of the waiting cars, 'You've missed the ball. It was fantastic, Mose. But never mind. The gardens are even better than four days ago, so I have a whole heap of horticulture to show off to you that you won't believe. Kitchen gardens you'll be mad about. The lot. And I have a lovely guest room ready for you with a fine view over the orchard and . . .'

'Hey, woa, woa, girl. Slow down,' Adam interrupted. 'I think you've brought something for Deena, Moses? I'll just go fetch them from the plane.'

'No, I'll do that, Adam,' Moses said, a little too sharply. Something strange in the way Moses looked at him made Adam declare emphatically, 'We'll go get them together.' None of the others appeared to register whatever passed between the two men.

From the doorway, the pilot greeted Adam and asked, 'Ready for the cargo?' Adam made an effort to step forward, prepared to mount the few stairs. Moses put a hand firmly on Adam's arm. This time Adam understood the look in Moses's eye: he was telling him something was wrong.

Moses said, 'Why don't you wait here, Adam, at the bottom of the stairs? I'll hand them down to you, one at a time.' Adam's shrugged consent confirmed that he had absorbed Moses's message. Moses mounted the steps, and Adam said, 'Deena, Brindley. Here, from your house guests, is a small present. Small is the operative word here.'

One by one, Moses handed down six top-of-the-breed miniature horses, the largest of which was twenty-seven inches high. Absolutely perfect, full grown miniatures. One pair was white, another chestnut, and the other black. They whinnied and kicked up their heels, enchanted and distracted everyone. They supplied Adam and Moses with a chance to have a word on the side, away from everyone.

'I need your help, Adam.'

'You have it.'

'Humayun is inside the plane. She's run away from Rashid. That's maybe not quite right. We have run away, together, from Rashid and the life she has lived with him. I thought for the moment – until he cools down – this would be the safest place for us. I don't want to compromise you or the Ribblesdales. But we had no place else to go.'

'Moses, I don't care about being compromised. That doesn't even come into it. But have you any idea what damage you may have done to yourselves with this piece of rashness? Of course you were right to come here. You know both Mirella and Deena feel you are family. And, yes, we'll help and make you welcome. Is Humayun all right?'

'Yes, I think so. She was fine when we made our plans two days ago. But then she was with Rashid on his return yesterday, and I think that upset her. She hasn't spoken about it. She asked to be left quietly for a day or two before we sprang ourselves upon you all. I need help to find a quiet place for her, just until I break the news to everyone, and they get used to the idea and till things calm down with Rashid.'

'Look, we can't talk now. Leave it with me. Tell her to stay where she is until we return. I'll taxi the plane over to the hanger. Let her know she's welcome.'

The discussion was brief. Moses was being nagged to hurry by Deena. The last thing he wanted was for her to climb into the plane and discover Humayun.

Adam had never met Humayun. He was quite overwhelmed now by her extraordinarily sensuous beauty and the degree of elegant chic about her. She was dressed in an icy grey silk that flattered her skin and her luscious hair. Her jewels were superb: art-deco diamonds and emeralds. She was out of Moses's league. She had the unmistakable mark of Rashid on her. How could they have made such a disastrous mistake?

He knew. She saw it in his eyes, sensed it when, after he had moved the plane to where no one would disturb it, he returned to her, sat down facing her, taking her hand in his, kissed it.

'I have made the most dreadful mistake in my life,' she said, her voice scarcely a whisper.

'Yes, I think you may have,' Adam said sadly. 'We'll find a solution for you. But first I will find somewhere comfortable and private for you to stay for a few days.

I'll be back. I'm sure we can do what we have to to make it right.'

'I don't want to hurt anyone.'

Adam had no answer for that. He stood up and stroked her hair, laid his hand on her shoulder, and she placed hers over it. He looked into the seductive green eyes of the stunning voluptuary. He understood how easy it was for a man to be possessed by her. Moses, he thought, is it poor devil, or lucky devil? He pressed his lips together and sighed again in sadness. Whichever it was, for Moses it had to end in 'poor devil'.

Moses came to her in the dead of night. It had been impossible until then to get away from Deena's enveloping hospitality. He was much relieved to see that Adam and Brindley, in whom Adam had to confide, had done Humayun proud. They had put her in the newly restored, eighteenth-century Folly situated on a small hill just above the Grotto.

He saw her through the panes of glass in the door, lovely in a peach chiffon dressing gown over a semi-transparent yellow night-dress. He had never seen her look lovelier than she did then in the candle-light of the one-room Folly, with its walls and ceiling draped in bright yellow silk.

He closed the door and took Humayun in his arms, kissing her passionately. She let the book she had been reading fall from her hand to the carpet soundlessly. He slid her night-clothes from her shoulders and let them drop to the floor where they were standing. Then he took her in his arms again and kissed her.

They walked to the Napoleonic day bed, leaving a trail of his clothes as they went. Humayun was filled with potent sexual desire. She could feel herself coming as he took her naked in his arms, just from the touch of their skins, the depth of their kisses.

'Take me, please take me. I want to come and never stop coming.'

They were tender with each other, and then wild and passionate. The more she came, the more he wanted her to come. He, too, never wanted her to stop. Sustained ecstasy for them both. They were as far out sexually as it was possible for two people to go.

He revelled in her wetness and, if he could, he would have crawled all the way inside her. He would have been happy to drown in her orgasms. For hours they kissed and made love that way. They made love that was as pure and as light as a white down feather. They worked themselves through passions as base and perverse as were imaginable. Until dawn, when he left her with a kiss and saw the ecstasy in her face as she came once more.

It was Adam who found her in the Grotto below the Folly, naked, floating face upward, her red-gold hair spread out like a great fan around her, her peach chiffon dressing gown still on her shoulders and billowing like a soft pink cloud over the water. Her hands were tied loosely behind her with her yellow nightdress. It had been torn in three pieces. A second strand was tied the same way around her ankles. She had been gagged with the remaining piece of the once sensuous silk.

A water lily was caught in her hair. A white swan was gliding over the mirror-bright-surface of the water not far from her body. She looked no less sensuous and remarkably beautiful, at peace with herself. He waded through clumps of iris and the water lilies and swam to her. He touched the beautiful arabesque designs tatooed around the nimbus of her breasts, and covered those over her pubic mound with the wet chiffon of her gown. Then he gathered her in his arms and carried her from the pebbled and shelled grotto up through the wild daffodils and bluebells, to the Folly. There he sat down with her on the day bed and rocked her in his arms, so sad he thought his heart would never lift again. Then he rose and laid her on the day bed and covered her with a blanket.

Chapter 17

Rashid stopped at a flower stall. He bought masses of flowers and one of the old worn white plastic buckets that the vendors kept their flowers in. He filled it with fresh water from a tap in the street, plunged the flowers into it and carried them to his waiting taxi. They drove to the cemetery on the edge of town. En route he had the driver stop at the old stonemason he remembered and, after renewing their acquaintance, he purchased an urn, simple, almost archaic in its beauty. That too was put in the taxi.

When they arrived, the driver helped him take these objects to Humayun's grave. He placed the urn where Rashid directed, and then he left.

It was a clear sunny day. Hot, but with that delicious heat that comes to Crete after a long, cold, wet winter. Alone in the cemetery, with the driver gone, he felt what seemed to be the ultimate in loneliness around him. There was something desolate and pitiable about Humayun's grave, much more so than the others he had walked by, or even the ones close to hers. A small stone had been placed at the head of the plot. It was of white marble, the marble of Paros, and it had simply carved on it HUMAYUN.

He looked around the cemetery and saw green grass

in some places, a few trees, flowers and wreaths. But around Humayun there was nothing. Only the marble headstone surrounded by dead, dry earth, some old leaves that had blown there, a few pieces of crumpled brown paper and a broken purple plastic fork. Even the weeds were dead, brownish and ugly.

He looked at the stone again and he thought of his Humayun. He imagined her head carved of the same white marble, and holding it in his hands, he carried it, not knowing, even in his imagination, where to put it down. It exhausted him. His imaginings since her death were like bad dreams. They were something he had to accept, because she was gone, while he was alive still to happiness. How could he make her understand that dead, she remained a part of him as she had been alive? They were as one, even now in her death, and so could never again be separated.

He refused to think of her body decomposing in the ground, but tried to see her as she was alive. Instead, all he could conjure was a vision of the skull beneath the skin: eyes not open, not closed, because they were no longer there; a mouth without lips, that could not speak; only bones broken through the skin that had once been caressable cheeks.

Rashid looked at his perfect hands, but in his mind they were mutilated because they could no longer touch her. His horrid vision of his Humayun mercifully disappeared, but took his strength with it.

If only there were a word, just a sign of some sort, as to why she did this terrible thing.

He looked into the plastic bucket of flowers and the myriad colours sparkled like jewels in the dead atmosphere. There were tears in his eyes as he gave a painful sigh, knowing how much the fresh blooms would have pleased her. He lifted the flowers out and laid them on the unyielding earth. The quick flow of water from bucket to urn sparkled with life. The ground was hard under his knees as he arranged the flowers in the urn. Afterwards he crawled over the plot picking up the rubbish, dusting off bits of gravel, lumps of dirt and dried weeds with the sides of his hands as he went.

There were birds singing somewhere in the trees in spite of the heat. He stood up and walked around the back of the white marble headstone and cleaned that as well. He had been bending over, pulling at a weed, when suddenly he heard someone calling. He straightened up and looked all around, but saw no one. He was certain someone was calling. There it was again: 'Help me, help me.'

He quickly walked to the edge of the cemetery that overlooked the sea far below. Again the sound. He ran between the gravestones seeking the person in distress. Once more the cry came, but this time from another direction, and it was not 'Help me,' as he had thought, but 'Help him, help him'.

There was no one. Rashid was quite alone. He walked slowly back to Humayun's resting-place and, picking up the bucket, let what was left of the water stream down upon the barren earth that lay over her bones.

He was feeling nervy, disturbed by the voice he was sure he had heard, and saddened to the depths of his soul. He picked up the empty bucket and put it a few feet away. Then he walked back to the foot of the grave. He straightened his jacket and smoothed his hair.

With tears slowly lining his cheeks, he spoke to her,

'I remembered this was where you wanted your final resting-place. That last time we were here in Crete together, I said I thought I would never return, and you answered me "Maybe not together, and not in our bodies, but I know I shall. My soul will wander under the sun . . ." ' Rashid was unable to continue. Finally he composed himself and went on, 'What does it matter now what you said? It's what you wanted, to be here in Crete where we first met, to be near the love and passion and complete happiness you once found here with me. I too, my dear Humayun, found it with you here and always. You are here under this simple stone because you wanted your heart and soul to roam under the sun in this old port of Khania, in the house where we were so happy, and to haunt the sea lapping the shores of our beloved Crete. I have come to tell you my heart and soul will roam here with you, even though I am alive.

'I should have come sooner, I should have placed you in the earth myself. I couldn't. I was desolate, your death was an incalculable loss to me. But to have died as you did . . . why, why, my dear heart? I am sorry, so sorry for you, Humayun. I will come whenever I can. It won't be often, but know that you are not forgotten. Every day, wherever I am in the world, and no matter with whom, I am always with you. In Istanbul I am building you a small mosque on a hill where the Black Sea flows into the Bosporus. In the light of a full white moon it will stand out as a place of worship and great beauty. A jewel upon the earth, as I know now, too late, you were for me in life. And, in the garden of my house, a magnificent fountain that will flow always with sweet water for you. Every morning fresh gardenias are placed there by your maid, whom I have taken into my household.' He broke down and sobbed. He was a man.

Some considerable time later he wiped his tears away, raised his bowed head to take a last look at the flowers that half covered Humayun's inscription. Then he turned around, picked up the old white bucket and left.

He passed a row of cypress trees at the edge of the cemetery and was starting down the hill to the village when he met an old man dressed in shabby clothes. He wore some of the bits and pieces of the traditional costume of Crete, a wide sash wrapped around his waist; a worn, but magnificent black embroidered waistcoat, and a black scarf tied around his head, over which there was a battered Panama hat. He was a handsome man of considerable age, with a huge white moustache, yellow at the edges, and a white stubbly beard. He was dark-tanned, with a face and neck expressively wrinkled by time. He was leaning on a broken rake that had been tied together with a piece of heavy hemp rope, lighting a cigarette.

Rashid went to him and said in Greek, 'Good afternoon, are you the caretaker here?'

'No. The gardener. For forty years.'

'Are you in charge?'

'But of course I am in charge. You are a Greek American come to visit a relative?'

'No,' Rashid answered. 'Not a Greek American. I came to visit the grave of an old friend.'

'If you are not a Greek American, and you speak Greek as well as I do, are you a Greek?'

'No, I am a Turk, from Istanbul.'

'Oh,' said the gardener. 'From Istanbul. I do not welcome your background, but your Greek is to wonder at. I have not seen you here before. Who have you come to see?'

'I have come to visit the grave of Humayun.'

'The foreigner.' With that the old gardener made the sign against the evil eye, spat twice into the dusty road and crossed himself three times.

Rashid looked coldly at the old man, rage and grief at war within him. 'It is not good to dishonour those who are dead,' he said simply.

The old man eyed him, then put his hand on his shoulder, and said, 'Sir, it is truly something to hear a foreigner speak my language so good as you do.' Rashid shifted irritably. The old man removed his hand from Rashid's shoulder, but then put it right back again and said, 'Please, sir, remember that you do not know everything. There is no rest here for the lady. You saw, nothing will grow there, where your friend is buried.'

'What do you mean, there is no peace? Why do you not care for the plot? I see that you care for the other plots. There are flowers, shrubs, wreaths brought by friends and relatives. But I also see green grass and planted blossoming bushes. Why have you not done that for her, even if she has no relatives to come?'

'You are right. No one comes. Since Mr Mavrodakis brought her and we buried her, no one. Maybe one person, a black man once. He cried for long time, and he gave me money to plant bulbs. But the grave is cursed, nothing grows. Whatever I plant dies at once.' His mouth spread in an impassive smile not reflected in his eyes. He crossed himself three times again, but did not spit.

'It is impossible that nothing will grow there. If I

390

give you money, can you think of something hardy enough to grow?'

'Come,' said the gardener.

He took Rashid to the end of a row of cypresses, where there was a crooked wooden bench, two legs shorter at one end. The two men sat down on a slope. The old man offered Rashid a cigarette, then lit one for himself. He said, 'I can speak to you about this problem. Do you think I like having a cursed grave in my cemetery? I wish they would come and take her away to another country. I am over forty years in this cemetery, and I have never had anything so strange happen here. There have been times while I am up there working alone that I hear something. At first I thought it was the wind playing jokes on me. It was not the wind.

'One day there was a Greek lady from Athens, she came to see her father's grave on his name-day. I stand there talking with her for a long time. Then we hear the sound, but I say nothing. I pretend I do not hear it. The lady, she say, "There is something wrong, I hear someone calling for help. Do you not hear it?" I say, "Yes, I hear something but I do not understand it. I hear it many times." She tells me that the sound we hear is not the wind but someone calling two words. Turkish words. It is someone calling for help.'

He formed the words, imitating the whine. The very sound that Rashid had heard only a few minutes before.

'Sir, you are unhappy about your friend. I am sorry for you, but I do not want to be near the grave. That lady is not at rest. From the first it is a bad story.' And again the old man made the sign against the evil eye. He crossed himself three times and was about to spit into the dirt, but hesitated under Rashid's gaze.

Rashid sat there with the old man and told him he too had heard someone calling, but that it had to be the wind; that the lady from Athens and he were wrong, although in his heart Rashid knew they were not.

'No, sir, it is not the wind. The lady from Athens heard the same words we do, and she should know the meaning because she is a Greek born in Izmir. That is in Turkey. It is the soul, the soul that will not rest. I am not frightened of the soul calling. It is that I do not like to think of a soul that will not rest, one that is destined to wander endlessly. It is an evil thing, that.'

Rashid spoke with the gardener further about the problem of the wandering soul. Was there something they could do to give the restless spirit more care? He worked hard on the old man and charmed him into helping, finding it impossible to leave Humayun's grave unattended and as shabby as he had come upon it. Together they decided to plant a crescent of cypresses around the back of the headstone. They would buy them as large as possible in the hope that mature trees might survive where nothing else had.

'They will be like sentinels shielding the grave from nothingness,' Rashid said, 'and make up for the people who do not go to visit her. Maybe she will understand when there are tall, beautiful trees watching over her, keeping her company, and she will rest.'

How could Rashid tell the old man that he believed all would be well now because Rashid had come to Humayun and assured her they were as one? Rashid wanted a sign of some sort from the spirit world that she understood. He was saddened that he had received none, but his faith in Humayun was strong enough to convince him that she would give it in time. He believed in these things as his mother and father had, as the Princess Eirene did. It was part of their culture to believe.

The gardener said, 'Sir, forgive me for speaking so frankly, but I think you are a dreamer, and it will not be. But I tell you the truth, I am willing to try because who needs such bad spirits around?'

Rashid gave him the money for the trees and for fresh flowers to be placed in the urn every day, and said he would send a friend, Christos Mavrodakis, to see that it was done and how it looked.

'Are you leaving Khania soon?' the old man asked.

'Yes,' and the moment Rashid said the word, he knew he would never return to this place. The two men shook hands. The gardener kept pumping Rashid's hand and said, 'I am happy for all you are doing. Who knows, maybe she was only waiting for you to come and take care of her. Maybe the trees will grow for the dead woman and for you.'

Under a blazing, cloudless sky Rashid walked down the hill with the empty white bucket swinging in his hand.

Then, suddenly, upon a further thought, he turned and ran back up the hill. The gardener was nowhere to be seen. Rashid walked swiftly, weaving between the crosses, headstones, and plangent marble sculptures until he stood in front of the tiny desert that was Humayun's grave. He was breathless and closed his eyes, emitting deep sighs and taking in gulps of air. He called out to her in his pain and anguish. 'I asked you. I ordered you. I begged you to let Moses go from you. One mistake, just one mistake in our sexual game, and we pay for it, all three of us, with the loss of your life.

Always you listened to me and I kept you safe. While the others speculate about what happened, only I really know the truth. You committed suicide. And it was because although you ran away with Moses, you found it impossible in the end to leave him . . . or me. What was it, then, that forced you to make a decision to abandon me? Our lives could have gone on as they had been. Surely you must have known what pain you cost us by this violent act of yours? What made you inflict such pressure upon yourself or even try to change your life? We both know you were happy in it until you thought to leave it. What choice do I have but to forgive you, because unless I do I can never forgive myself? And after all, am I not one with you?'

He could hear the bells of a small domed and whitewashed church down the cliff behind the cemetery, a hundred feet above the sea.

As if in answer, bells sounded now not only from the church below, but from another on the other side of town. Then another and another. The Greeks ring the bells when someone has died, and bells in many little white chapels and churches around Khania were ringing now for someone. Rashid had his sign.

At last he was able to mourn the death of Humayun. In the taxi all the way back to Rethimnon where his sleek, black yacht, the *Aziz* lay at anchor offshore, memories of their years together became vivid in his mind once again. All good memories.

For the first time since her death a terrible blackness that had settled over him now began to lift. The deep emotional depression that had dragged him down into a lonely pit he had never known before, where no one and nothing could reach him, began to dissolve. Life was flowing back. The very air that he breathed once again had a scent to it. The glare of light returned to the sun, and he was able to feel its heat. He was aware of his limbs. He lifted his hand and squeezed it, and felt the bones under the skin. He realised how anaesthetised he had been since that horrible night when he had claimed Humayun's body from Adam in Istanbul.

The driver was leaning on the horn, blasting everyone off the road, as Greek taxi drivers are prone to do. He actually heard the horn. It grated on his nerves and he smiled, happy that he was feeling and reacting to his senses and the world once again.

He boarded the *Aziz* and they set sail at once from Crete. Rashid watched the big island recede until it was no more than a dot on the skyline. His self-doubt about his role in Humayun's life vanished. The weeks of torment since her death were over. The pilgrimage to her grave had set them both free.

His mind was clear, unfettered from shock and grief. Events that occurred one after the other, suddenly, like pieces of a puzzle seemed to fit together and make a picture.

On his return from Lyttleton Park, he had spent the night with Humayun, just the two of them. Tana Dabra had flown on to Switzerland. They had had a glorious erotic idyll. He remembered now, for the first time, their last words to each other.

'Some would say I am addicted to you, Rashid. What would you say?'

'We love each other and the erotic life we have made together. We're not tired of it or each other. If that's an addiction, we are both hooked.' Then he had kissed her goodbye and was gone.

Two days later she was dead. Adam had secretly removed the body from Lyttleton Park, trying to avoid a scandal and to keep the tragedy from Mirella and Deena. A coroner had been called in and an autopsy performed in Istanbul. Cause of death was water in the lungs. But their verdict hovered between murder and suicide. Adam, with the help of the Princess Eirene, returned the body to Humayun's home, a remarkably beautiful and romantic two-hundred-year-old Ottoman town-house, painstakingly restored to its original splendour, in the Old City not far from Topkapi. Rashid did not believe that she had run away with Moses or that she was dead, until Adam took him to the house. In the enclosed courtyard he had stopped next to the marble fountain, dipped his hands in the water and held them to his face. It was at that moment that he knew it was true: the spirit of the place was gone. When he saw the body he had completely lost his senses. He refused to leave her body. Periodically he would come back to life for a few minutes and make rational decisions. That was how she had come to be buried where she wanted, near Khania. Christos was called in to help.

Rashid felt cold and left the deck of the *Aziz*. In the saloon he poured himself a glass of champagne. The picture became even clearer.

Adam confirmed to Rashid that the first thing she had said to him was, 'I have made the worst mistake of my life,' and the second, 'I don't want to hurt anyone.'

He believed Adam. Of course, that piece, too, fitted into the picture Rashid was constructing. For some reason which for the moment Rashid could not work out, Humayun was unable to stay away from Moses. For argument's sake he would call it love of a good man, because, if nothing else, Moses was a very good man. What reason could there have been strong enough to force her to make the decision to abandon Rashid? It still escaped him. He knew the exclusivity of her love for him was unquestionable.

For whatever reason, Humayun had run off with Moses to Lyttleton Park, and knew at once it had been a mistake. The lines of the picture were defined even more. Once there, Humayun was thrust into a foreign world. She realised that even Moses's love could not redeem her from her need to be sexually enslaved by Rashid. Her years of debauchery had become an addiction which she desired even more than love and affection, security and freedom with her black American lover. She discovered that she was incapable of hurting Moses by rejecting a life with him, or of leaving one steeped in sexual depravity and erotic love with Rashid. Perhaps there mingled in her the fear that age and time were no longer on her side at just the moment when Tana Dabra had become very much a part of their lives. Could she be sure that Rashid would forgive her mistake? Humayun chose the only way out she thought would redeem her.

Or was murdered. Unlikely.

Rashid poured himself another glass of champagne. After slipping into a heavy-knit jacket, he walked out on deck, glass in hand. The air felt good to him. He drank half a glass of the chilled wine in one swallow. He looked out onto the black sea, and then up at a white, nearly full moon. He knew in his heart she had taken her own life. So he needed only to know the one thing that had pushed her over the edge.

A great dark cloud slipped over the moon just then. He watched and waited till the white moon reappeared. He guessed the person who would have that knowledge – the Princess Eirene. She had spent some months a few years back with Humayun when, at the Princess Eirene's request, Rashid had lent Humayun to her as an erotic companion on a world cruise with friends. After Rashid himself, Eirene knew her best of anyone. He would go to see her at once upon his return to Istanbul.

Rashid walked the deck for some time. He was feeling his old self again, yet not unaware of the debt that he owed Adam. And indeed owed Brindley, who, more than anyone, had been compromised by this tragedy. Adam had been clever enough not to let Brindley know what had happened until he had removed the body from Lyttleton Park. He had had no choice. As a solicitor, Brindley could not have allowed the body to be touched before the police were called in. The ensuing scandal would have been ruinous for the Ribblesdales and the Park. For a friendly enemy, a competitor in the love stakes, on the tennis court, and often in business, Adam had proved himself forever a friend. Rashid would never forget it. Most of all, he would never forget the kindness Adam had shown to Rashid's beloved sexual slave Humayun in the hours before and, indeed, after her death.

And Christos. He would not forget, ever, the passive cool look on Christos's face when he viewed the body of Humayun. Nor the look of sadness in his eyes when he clasped Rashid to him and ordered him to pull himself together. Nor his wise refusal to allow Rashid to accompany the body to Crete. Christos had seen he was in no state to conduct himself with dignity in front of the islanders so inured to tragedy, so scornful of weakness in bearing it.

Eirene of course had saved his sanity by taking over. Her staff and Humayun's had seen that the corpse of

398

Humayun was dressed and cared for, and laid out to look no less beautiful and sensuous in death than she had in life. It was Eirene who arranged religious and traditional ceremonies for the dead in the house, had prayers said in mosques all over the city, had pilgrimages made, with flowers and offerings, to Eyyup and other sacred shrines.

The house that Humayun treasured was only one of several Rashid had given her over the years. Her village house in central Anatolia, a wooden *yali* on one of the Princes Islands, another on the shores of the Mediterranean between Side and Urfa, were all opened and filled with flowers and food to receive those who wanted to pay their last respects.

And it was Eirene who had had Humayun's period *caique* filled with flowers and sailed to the Black Sea. On its return voyage down the Bosporus to the Sea of Marmara and the Golden Horn, flowers were cast into the waters leaving a trail of blossoms in her memory.

It was also the Princess who had taken over the practical side of things for Rashid. She sent the obituaries to the Istanbul newspapers as well as those in other capital cities, brought letters and cables, flowers and charitable donations in Humayun's name from men who had known her, friends of Rashid's who understood his loss. Rashid in his few moments of clarity during that period was impressed by the people from all walks of life who trooped through the house and wept for Humayun. Princess Eirene had arranged obsequies befitting a great courtesan of Topkapi's Harem. Only now, restored to his own self, could Rashid understand how important that had been for them all.

He sat in a deckchair and watched the stars shine

brightly, and the white moon glow over the water. Moses. He had not spoken to Moses. Nor had Moses approached him. Every day Moses had come to the Ottoman house with fresh flowers, lilies of the valley, which he had placed in her hands. He had sat there for an hour, never taking his eyes from the casket and then he would leave. Rashid had never seen a tear, heard a sob, nor glimpsed an agony such as he himself was suffering in Moses's face. There was strength there, a superior kind of strength that was sustaining him through a loss no less devastating to him than to Rashid. Rashid thought about those times he had seen Moses there. He recognised that now, on his return to Istanbul, he was ready to speak to Moses.

Still shattered by her loss, a kind of madness still clung to Rashid, although he was lucid for longer periods of time than he had been. He went into a period where he did little but lose himself in a world of erotic pleasure, either with Mirella in her love kiosk on the hill, or in the arms of Tana Dabra and others in the house of Oda Lala.

Tana Dabra, his wife. Only she had been strong enough to penetrate his grief during this tragic time in his life. Only she truly understood her husband's depraved relationship with the dead woman and what it meant to him, and her understanding touched him deeply. He had chosen well when he chose this Abyssinian of royal blood whose remarkable courage had sustained him during these terrible weeks. He wished she were with him right now to seduce him as she always did, by playing off her apparent aloofness against the fire that burned within her. He loved all those traits in her that had made her his wife. He knew they would eventually make her the mother of his children as successfully as she had made herself the new keeper of his sexual depravity and his darker nature.

Rashid rose from the deckchair, his heart beginning to feel glad once more. Only two pieces of the puzzle to put together. One he would acquire from Princess Eirene. The other he had to work out himself. What did those two words borne on the wind at the cemetery mean? 'Help him? Help him?' Who? Was she asking the gods to help Rashid? Or was she asking Rashid to help Moses?

Rashid arrived at the Princess Eirene's *yali* a few minutes before five. It was for Rashid still the most beautiful *yali* on the Bosporus. Much of that had to do with its colour, that lovely, faded oxblood red, pinkish in the sunlight. And, of course the quality of time standing still. One of the servants came to help him tie up the speedboat he had driven himself. He was dressed in black tie at Eirene's request. She explained she was giving a little dinner attended by the clan, the Coreys, and the Lala Mustaphas. He had been delighted because it would be an undemanding reintroduction to the life he must continue to lead despite Humayun's death.

The invitation had been made when he called her from on board the *Aziz* two days before to tell her that he wished a word in private when convenient. There had been something in her voice, a kind of enthusiasm that he knew always meant surprise. Now, as he walked up the stairs to the *yali*, he felt a boyish anticipation.

She was coming down the staircase when he entered the hall, so beautiful still, he stood stock still admiring her. She was wearing silver lamé in a dress whose top was simplicity itself, with its high, round neck and long, tight-fitting sleeves. Around her waist she wore a belt of gold and rubies, a treasure. From under it, the long skirt was accordion-pleated and rustled as she walked. Diamonds of unimaginable beauty and size were on her ears and in dazzling bracelets on her wrists. She looked splendid. Behind her, muttering, were Hyacinth and Narcissus. In this house it was always as if the Ottoman Empire retained a mute domination still.

They kissed and went into the drawing-room overlooking the Bosporus and sat together near the window. From his inside pocket Rashid withdrew a slender, black velvet box. He opened it and slid a magnificent diamond bracelet from it.

'I had a selection of these sent down from Paris this morning. This was the finest among them. A bauble that can hardly say thank you for all that you did for Humayun and myself. But something I would like you to have nevertheless.' He clasped it around her wrist.

'My dear Rashid, it's wonderful to see you so much recovered. How lovely, I am delighted with it. You always spoil me and I adore it. It has been my life to be spoiled by men. There is nothing better for a woman, no matter what they may tell you.'

'Eirene, I have to ask you something. I sense that only you will know the answer to this. This tragedy, Humayun – was it self-inflicted?'

'Yes, I am certain of that.'

'Why?'

'It was not uncommon for the women of the Harem who could no longer go on to drown themselves. There is a history of it. Not only did they do it themselves, in the way that Humayun did, but sometimes, because of violent intrigues at court, they were thrust into sacks weighted with stones and thrown into the water from the cliffs below Topkapi. There were even mass drownings, once as many as three hundred at one time. Humayun would have known all that. She would have seen it as an honourable way out of her dilemma.'

The Princess rose and went to a table in the middle of the room. She adjusted a long-stemmed rose that was out of place and offended her eye, one of five dozen white ones in a rock crystal vase with an ormolu rim and elegant feet. The gesture gave Rashid a moment to recover. She returned to Rashid and sat down.

'Eirene, there has to have been *something* that forced her to make that decision to leave me. My heart tells me you know what it is.'

'Your heart tells you right.'

Rashid closed his eyes in relief. The Princess Eirene studied his handsome face, the sensual lips. There had not been many men in her life, even among those she had met casually, who had such unbridled love of the erotic that it stood out physically upon them like a second skin, rousing the dormant sexuality in those they encountered. Rashid had it. He opened his eyes, and she smiled at him and said. 'Not something, Rashid. Someone.'

That seemed to shock Rashid. She clapped her hands and Hyacinth answered her command. She crooked her finger and signalled for him to lean down so that she could whisper to him. He left the room. Then she turned back to Rashid.

'A few days ago, a woman came to see me. A Scottish woman. She brought me a note. It seems the woman had instructions from Humayun that if she, a Miss Stirling, did not see or hear from Humayun over a period of one month, she was to come at once to me with the note.'

'Who is this Miss Stirling?'

'I'll explain about her in a moment. The note introduced me to Miss Stirling. It further entrusted me to tell you that, whatever happens, you are to have everything that belonged to Humayun, to do with as you see fit. She trusted you implicitly. There was something else. A note for you.'

The Princess reached into an inlaid mother-of-pearl box on the table and withdrew an envelope and handed it to Rashid. He recognised Humayun's handwriting and the lavender ink she always used. The Princess handed him a letter-opener. He was about to slide it through the lip of the envelope when there was a knock at the door. It opened, and a woman walked in. He could only assume she was Miss Stirling. She held in one arm a sleeping baby dressed in white cotton and lace. With her other hand she held the hand of a little boy, so handsome as to be beautiful, dressed in a sailor's suit with short pants, and trailing on a long string a wooden Donald Duck on wheels.

Rashid gasped as he looked at the little boy.

'Here are your someones, Rashid. Humayun ultimately could not choose between the fathers of her children. She tried to choose and knew at once that she had made a mistake.'

Rashid and the Princess Eirene spent some time with the children. Moses's son's name was Aaron. He was only a few weeks old, a beautiful and happy, dusky-skinned image of his father.

'I never even guessed,' said Rashid after Miss Stirling had taken them away. 'How did she do it, manage it, I mean, without my knowing about it?'

'The first time, with me, when we were supposedly on a cruise. The second time, when you gave her a four-month holiday while you were away with Tana Dabra. The first time was planned. The second was lucky timing.'

'Why didn't she tell me I had a son? A handsome and clever son. Why didn't you tell me?'

'Humayun knew that a son was not part of the life you lived together. She feared it might displease you and change things between you. She had planned to tell you when he was older, and she thought you would want him in your life.'

The door opened and little Rashid ran back into the room to ask, very politely if he could sit with his father. One hour later Rashid had fallen in love with his son.

From the Princess Eirene's *yali* Rashid made his phone call to Moses. He asked to see him. It was seven in the evening when he arrived. The other guests were due at half-past eight. That gave the men a chance to talk.

They said surprisingly little to each other. But such restraint itself helped to bury the hurt they might have felt against each other in the loss of their beloved Humayun. It was Rashid who gave Moses his son.

Placing him in Moses's arms, he said, 'I would like to keep him as my own, if you should not want him. But I know that's impossible. What man does not want the son of a woman he loved as much as you did Humayun?'

When Tana Dabra arrived, Rashid went out to meet

her. They walked through the lovely gardens and he told her what had happened. The Princess watched them from the window, called for nanny Stirling, and sent her out to Rashid and Tana Dabra with his little boy. Mirella and Adam already knew what was happening at the *yali* before they arrived. The Princess had confided in them because, as she said, 'Your lives are indissolubly linked by a deep and lasting friendship.'

It was not often that anyone realised how powerful a woman the Princess Eirene was. So subtle and persuasive, seductive and wise, she rarely showed her strength. But only a few minutes before they were to go into the yellow dining room for dinner, Joshua and Zhara, Adam's eldest children from his first wife, arrived, having flown in from New York for this dinner. They felt Princess Eirene's matriarchal force even as they foregathered as a family. Maybe she would watch over them still, the Corey and the Lala Mustapha, and yes, even the Moses Jefferson family. When they teased her about this, she answered them well.

'Family. Family indeed. I think you should ask yourselves when a family stops being a mere family and becomes a dynasty. We dine tonight together in my house to celebrate three dynasties – the Coreys, the Lala Mustaphas, and that of Moses which is now beginning. And let us not forget the most ancient of all, the Oujie dynasty. That after all, has brought us all together. We may never be any closer than we are tonight. And may we never be any further apart. But you are rich and powerful families, young for dynasties. Who knows where you will go, what you will do, how you will make your marks in this world? For me I have my own vision of you all as the kind of people who make kings and princes, presidents and premiers, scholars, discoverers, industrialists. Your money and power can shape the world. And now, ladies and gentlemen, let us gather at my table and celebrate life!'

A dozen times during the sumptuous dinner served that evening, Mirella marvelled at the dazzling array of people and jewels and magnificent gowns, the bursting of life and gaiety all around her. This was her life, her family now. She was a part of two dynasties, and she loved every glittering minute of it. Not once but many times she saw Rashid look her way. She recognised the want in his eyes for her. Her heart raced to think a part of him was hers too. And Adam, this extraordinary man who knew that to share her was to hold her forever.

After dinner Mirella, her husband, and her lover, gravitated towards the window overlooking the Bosporus. They were mesmerised by the white moon dancing lightly on the black sea. Mirella slid her arm through Rashid's. She pulled Adam closer to her and passed her arm through his. Thus linked, both men looked at Mirella. Passion, erotic yearnings, untainted love was throbbing within her for them. She caught the selfsame feelings issuing from them.

She whispered in a soft and sensuous voice, 'Let me be the one to say it just once. I shall break the rule this one time, then never again. What I have with you both is stronger than life itself: an endless love.'

A selection of bestsellers
from Headline

THE LADYKILLER	Martina Cole	£5.99	☐
JESSICA'S GIRL	Josephine Cox	£5.99	☐
NICE GIRLS	Claudia Crawford	£4.99	☐
HER HUNGRY HEART	Roberta Latow	£5.99	☐
FLOOD WATER	Peter Ling	£4.99	☐
THE OTHER MOTHER	Seth Margolis	£4.99	☐
ACT OF PASSION	Rosalind Miles	£4.99	☐
A NEST OF SINGING BIRDS	Elizabeth Murphy	£5.99	☐
THE COCKNEY GIRL	Gilda O'Neill	£4.99	☐
FORBIDDEN FEELINGS	Una-Mary Parker	£5.99	☐
OUR STREET	Victor Pemberton	£5.99	☐
GREEN GROW THE RUSHES	Harriet Smart	£5.99	☐
BLUE DRESS GIRL	E V Thompson	£5.99	☐
DAYDREAMS	Elizabeth Walker	£5.99	☐

All Headline books are available at your local bookshop or newsagent, or can be ordered direct from the publisher. Just tick the titles you want and fill in the form below. Prices and availability subject to change without notice.

Headline Book Publishing PLC, Cash Sales Department, Bookpoint, 39 Milton Park, Abingdon, OXON, OX14 4TD, UK. If you have a credit card you may order by telephone – 0235 831700.

Please enclose a cheque or postal order made payable to Bookpoint Ltd to the value of the cover price and allow the following for postage and packing:
UK & BFPO: £1.00 for the first book, 50p for the second book and 30p for each additional book ordered up to a maximum charge of £3.00.
OVERSEAS & EIRE: £2.00 for the first book, £1.00 for the second book and 50p for each additional book.

Name ....

Address ....

....

....

If you would prefer to pay by credit card, please complete:
Please debit my Visa/Access/Diner's Card/American Express (delete as applicable) card no:

Signature .... Expiry Date ....